Stories of the World's Great Operas

STORIES
of the
WORLD'S GREAT
OPERAS

BY THOMAS MATTHEWS

ILLUSTRATED BY ROBERT SHORE

Golden Press · New York

ACKNOWLEDGMENTS

THE years that have gone into this book about the world of opera have been filled with so many artists and friends that it is quite possible, although genuinely unintentional, to overlook some devotee or some helpful person. *All* those lovers of opera are immediately thanked here and now.

Specifically, there are important and helpful people that cannot be forgotten. I am grateful to Göta Ljungberg. This silver-voiced soprano dedicated her life to music, and she taught me that the young must be paid attention to . . . Thomas Scherman, who has spent years of devotion and tireless energy in the pursuit of the "unexplored opera" . . . Sophie Stasiun, one of those rare souls who loves music almost as much as she loves humanity. Her professional and personal knowledge of the young readers of our time has been invaluable in the reconstruction of these opera stories. . . . Dale Edward Fern, whose assistance in the early days of this book cannot be calculated . . . Coe Glade, the supreme Carmen, and Regina Resnik have given me of their wealth of ideas and experience concerning this volatile gypsy . . .

Stephen Lloyd, whose cooperation, as a singer and a perfectionist concerning accurate opera detail, will never be overlooked—not to mention his endless hours typing the manuscript . . . Patricia Read and Marge Ternes, two sophisticated ladies of the publishing world, who urged me to finish this project and afforded me every cooperation known to see it through . . . John Coveney, that learned man of opera and Angel Records, who first read these stories and encouraged me. He also allowed me the privilege of access to his illustrious company's unique catalogue of artists and records . . . Herbert Weinstock, whose mind and imagination are a Gibraltar of the opera world . . . Victor Gollancz, whose book *Journey Towards Music* is a never-ending inspiration. And last we come to that all-important part of any book, the editor. Mine is Ann Reit. She is lovely, talented, and understanding. And I am grateful.

T. M.
New York City
April 17, 1968

*The most important arias, duets, trios, etc., in each opera
are identified as they occur.*

FOR
ISABELLA AND NICOLAS VERTÉS,
WHO HAVE THE WORLD OF OPERA BEFORE THEM,
AND FOR THEIR PARENTS,
WHO HAVE MADE THIS WORLD A BETTER PLACE
WITH THEIR BELIEF IN THE DIGNITY OF
MAN AND MUSIC

CONTENTS

INTRODUCTION

WHEN I was just seven years old, my sister and I were taken, as a special holiday treat, to a matinee performance of Rimsky-Korsakov's *Coq d'Or* at the Metropolitan Opera House. Imagine the excitement of two small children sitting on the stairs of the aisle of the Family Circle. (My mother told me, years later, that the tickets had been mislaid, but the usher, seeing two bright-eyed children faced with the closed door, had had pity and allowed the three of us to enter and sit, against fire regulations, in the aisle!) We first soaked up the grandeur of the theatre itself, the stunning chandelier, the gorgeously dressed people in the boxes so far below and, more than anything, the mystery and beauty of that famous gold curtain. Then, as the lights lowered, how we must have held our breath with anticipation when we saw, seemingly miles away, a tiny man walk into the cavity between the stage and the audience. For the first time, we noticed that there were dozens of men and women tuning up and noodling on their musical instruments. We both knew about violins because we were taking lessons at the time; but much more exciting to us, we could just see in the corner the beautiful woman strumming on the harp.

When that tiny man turned and bowed to the audience in acknowledgment of the applause, I asked my mother who he was.

"That's the conductor."

Since I only knew about streetcar conductors at the time, I didn't pursue the question further. I wouldn't have had time to, anyway, as just then those magic curtains opened and the colorful fairy tale began. My sister and I were both transported into a completely different world.

I am describing this incident in such detail because it has, I feel, a great bearing on this present volume which Mr. Matthews has written for just

such anticipatory young listeners. Let me go on with the reaction of those two unsophisticated but receptive children, sitting in the aisle of the Family Circle of the Metropolitan Opera House on that afternoon.

The chorus and principal singers sat on raised tiers in a semi-circle around the stage, dressed in dark red, almost purple, dominoes. The action was danced and mimed by ballet dancers in the wide area in front. If I remember correctly, the scenery, although brilliantly colored to suggest the quasi-Oriental atmosphere, was not realistic; it was probably made of linen.

My sister and I were both highly involved in the story and carried away by that fairy-tale atmosphere. We had been well briefed on the plot beforehand by our mother, but it came as a complete surprise to us when, after the opera was over and the curtain closed, the first bows were taken by a man and a woman dressed in dominoes.

"Who are they and why are they bowing?" we asked.

"Those are the singers; that is Galli-Curci, who was the Queen, and the great Didur, who was the King."

"But those aren't the King and Queen! There they are!" We clapped gleefully as we saw the dancers in costume come forward and take a bow.

We were, as any children would be, much more interested in the dancer-actors, because at that age they embodied for us the representation of the story. We were not, of course, unaware of the music—it grasped us and undoubtedly put its spell on us, adding its own glamor to the whole magical afternoon. But at most it can be said we did not consciously absorb the great score of Rimsky-Korsakov. The important thing to us was the *story* and the *color*.

Let me now skip to my next encounter with opera, also at the Metropolitan, but this time in the evening, a big event for a thirteen-year-old boy. It was *Tannhäuser,* by Wagner. In the years between the two events, I had grown much more sophisticated musically. By 1930 I knew the *Tannhäuser* overture and the "Entrance of the Guests" from records, as well as one aria—although I had no idea what the latter was all about.

So my reaction to *Tannhäuser* was on a considerably different plane from my reaction to *Coq d'Or* six years before. Although I had read the story carefully, even going so far as groping desperately with the bad Victorian translations of Wagner's flowery poetry, I was equally anticipating the music. I now knew who a conductor was and clapped long and loud as he made his appearance. I listened very attentively to the overture, and was very pleased when I heard familiar strains from it in the ballet that opens the opera and Tannhäuser's first outburst to Venus. Even though I must admit I was surprised and disappointed that the ample figure of the soprano did not look like my idea of Venus, I *was* excited enough by her singing to allow my imagination full play, and substitute in my mind's eye whatever visions a thirteen-year-old boy would conjure up of that goddess.

For the three long acts I was equally enthralled by the music *and* the story, allowing one or the other of them to take precedence in my attention during the three and a half hours. There were, I am sure, many things I did not understand, and perhaps places where my mind wandered, but I was not bored or restless for a second.

When Tom Matthews showed me the manuscript of *Stories of the World's Great Operas,* my mind immediately leaped to those two experiences. I realized that had I read a similar book in 1923 or 1930, it would have added tenfold to my enjoyment and appreciation of those two fascinating theatrical experiences. For Mr. Matthews in these skillfully written stories of the opera devotes himself primarily to the plot—the drama, which is, of course, the first thing which grasps the attention of a young person at the opera, or any musical show for that matter. Mr. Matthews does this ingeniously by devising vivid word-pictures which conjure up exciting colors and fascinating flesh-and-blood people.

Places and characters so described can only intrigue and remain vividly with the reader—and demand that he or she read on and on.

But what of the music? Mr. Matthews very cleverly tells the reader what the actors are singing about, by paraphrasing the arias.

When the reader hears the singers either on records or at the opera house, the music will have taken on a new dimension, because it has become an integral part of a very real story.

One thing that was an eye opener to me about Mr. Matthews' approach in some of the stories is that he has obviously gone to source material other than the libretto itself to round out his presentation.

The stories abound in little sidelights which add immeasurably to the enjoyment, such as the fact that Baron Scarpia, Tosca's enemy, lived in a formidable palace which was designed by Michelangelo. Or that *Aïda* took place in the days of the Old Kingdom, about 3998–3335 B.C., when Egypt was called the Gift of the Nile and her capital was Memphis.

And so I could go on about Thomas Matthews' invaluable book, but I think it is much better able to speak for itself. All I wish to urge you to do is to read it, for the magic world of opera will then have gained another faithful participant. Once you have experienced a thrill similar to those which I experienced in 1923 and 1930, a future listener is sure to be born.

THOMAS SCHERMAN
New York

What Is Opera?

A SIMPLE misunderstanding of what an opera really is deprives many young people of a vital and important experience—an experience that could grow and live in their memories.

Mary Costa, the gifted young soprano who left a career as one of television's highest paid commercial singers to become a *prima donna* at the world-famous Metropolitan Opera House, said, "Opera is show biz." What she meant was that opera is colorful and exciting entertainment. Well, it is that and more than that.

When did it all begin? Opera started in Florence, Italy, about 1580. A group of musicians under the patronage of Count Giovanni Bardi decided that they were going to write a new type of music—one that was simpler and more dramatic than the complicated church music of the time. Opera is a completely original Italian musical form. The word *opera* means "a work." These musicians wanted to create a work in which the music projected the drama and life of the words, specifically those of the Greek drama.

The first successful opera known to us is *Dafne,* which was performed in 1597. It was adapted from Ottavio Rinuccini's work by Jacopo Peri. After the première Peri joined forces with another composer of note, Giulio Caccini. They made an excellent team. Peri still clung to some of his simple musical ideas, but Caccini, the father of a famous singer, wrote with more flair. He knew that singers liked to show off their special talents, and he composed music for that purpose.

Peri and Caccini's collaborations pleased many people, both listeners and performers. Though this florid style of singing grew popular and threatened to get out of control, the greatest composers seriously attempted to heighten the power of the words with their music.

Many other Italian composers were attracted to this new world of opera: Claudio Monteverdi was one. Monteverdi was a much-respected composer of madrigals. His first opera, *Orfeo,* was composed when he was forty years old. At its opening night in Mantua, in 1607, it was a great success. Monteverdi was actually the first composer to use the orchestra as a solid base for the drama of the score. *Orfeo* was called an *opera seria,* which means a serious work. Like most of the operas of his time, it used a legend or a myth as its libretto, or text.

In the fifty years that followed, opera became the captive of the singers of the day, and sopranos became more important than composers. They were the "stars" of their time. Operas grew to be display pieces for the voices and temperaments of the favorite singers. However, this did serve a purpose: opera was lifted out of the hands of the nobility, and given to the people. Audiences wanted to hear their pet stars singing more arias, which are melodies sung by a single person. This led to duets, and then to bigger and bigger ensembles.

Jean Baptiste Lully was the first important man in French opera. Up until the appearance of his gracefully melodic works, the only operas produced in Paris had been Italian. In 1672, his *Les Fêtes de l'Amour et de Bacchus* was produced. This was a noteworthy step in the history of opera.

By 1700, Alessandro Scarlatti was a leading figure in the music world. At twenty he wrote his first opera, and it attracted the attention of Queen Christina of Sweden. He excelled in the art of writing intricate, highly ornate operas; by his death in 1725, he was considered a master of the form.

Audiences in 1733 were becoming a little bored with the *opera seria.* Giovanni Battista Pergolesi then presented the public with a real comedy, *La Serva Padrona* ("The Maid as Mistress," 1733). *Op-*

era buffa, or comic opera, was born. This high-spirited farce, along with Cimarosa's *Il Matrimonio Segreto* ("The Secret Marriage," 1792), started a new trend. But even these composers were not able to break down the system that forced composers and librettists to write as they were directed to by the great singers.

Christoph Willibald Gluck, about 1762, approached this predicament from a very personal angle. Gluck was concerned with the importance of words and their relationship to music. His *Orfeo ed Euridice* (1762) was free of unnecessary vocal displays and concentrated on music that fit into the dramatic structure of the opera.

When Gluck died in 1782, one of the supreme operatic composers of all time, Mozart, was just beginning his career. Mozart was a fountain of musical genius. He wrote about contemporary people instead of Greek figures, and was the creator of *singspiel*—opera in German, containing spoken dialogue. Mozart's *The Marriage of Figaro* (1786), *Don Giovanni* (1787), *Così fan tutte* (1790), and *The Magic Flute* (1791) overflow with beautiful melodies and thrilling dramatic writing. Wolfgang Amadeus Mozart's writings were the beginning of a whole new world of German opera. This world of romanticism produced Beethoven and von Weber. *Fidelio* (1805) and *Der Freischütz* (1821) are two masterpieces of that period and they are still performed in major opera houses.

In 1810, Gioacchino Rossini was dazzling the entire opera world. Rossini, Donizetti, and Bellini wrote melodious additions to melodramatic opera. *The Barber of Seville* was Rossini's first major success. The Romans of 1816 loved it. Rossini had the great talent of being able to transfer his love of laughter and fun into music His last opera, *William Tell* (1829), is one of his serious works. It, too, is full of the Italian love of living.

In the 1830's, Vincenzo Bellini contributed *Norma* (1831), *La Somnambula* (1831), and *I Puritani* (1835) to the opera stage. Gaetano Donizetti added *Lucia di Lammermoor* in 1835. French composers were also being heard. Cherubini wrote his magnificent *Medée* (1797), and Hector Berlioz wrote *The Damnation of Faust* (1893). But it was Giacomo Meyerbeer who put the word "grand" into opera. His productions for the Paris Opera were overwhelmingly sumptuous and difficult to sing. He and the Parisians loved great casts of singers, hundreds of dancers, and violent plots. His *L'Africaine* (1865) and *Les Huguenots* (1836) fulfilled these requirements.

In Russia, the spirit of nationalism was expressed in *A Life for the Tsar* (1836) by Michail Glinka, *Ivan the Terrible* (1873) by Nikolai Rimsky-Korsakov, *Boris Godunov* (1874) by Modest Moussorgsky, *Eugene Onegin* (1879) by Peter Ilyitch Tchai-

kovsky, and *Prince Igor* (1890) by Alexander Borodin.

In 1842, a young German composer, Richard Wagner, began to attract attention. He was in agreement with the French idea of the grandiose, but he wanted to lift opera into the bigger-than-life vistas of "music drama." These longings fascinated King Ludwig of Bavaria, and the king made it possible for Wagner to build his own theater in Bayreuth. This great theater was designed for the presentation of Wagner's works only. Today this magnificent house still pays homage to the master with performances of all his operas.

Wagner wrote most of his own librettos. Eventually he cut away the popular use of the aria. His music dramas are surging symphonic dramas that use the singers as instruments of the orchestra. Wagner used the idea of having each character identified with his own theme of music. These themes appear each time the character does and they are woven and rewoven into the score. His *Tristan and Isolde* (1865), *Die Meistersinger* (1868), and *Ring of the Nibelungen* (1869–1876), are gigantic musical monuments that audiences demand to hear year after year.

A disciple of Wagner's, Engelbert Humperdinck, is the composer of *Hansel and Gretel* (1846). It is remembered best for its lovely "Children's Prayer" and the tour-de-force role of the evil Witch.

Wagner was born in 1813; that same year witnessed the birth of Giuseppe Verdi. Verdi worked slowly as a composer, and he worked to please the public. His spectacular and gripping operas like *Il Trovatore* (1853), *La Traviata* (1853), and *Aïda* (1871) were filled with great arias, and his audiences loved them all. Verdi's beautiful songs thrilled the singers, too, for he knew how to write for the human voice. Reality and the emotions of real people appealed to Verdi and he was not against blood and thunder. These same things attracted Leoncavallo and Mascagni. With them—and *Cavalleria Rusticana* (1890) and *Pagliacci* (1892)—the word *verismo* entered the opera vocabulary. The word means realism. Ponchielli also wrote in this realistic style. His *La Gioconda* (1876) is full of melodramatic villains and heroines.

In 1859, Charles Gounod's *Faust* was presented. 1875 saw the first production of Georges Bizet's *Carmen*. This story of the life and death of a wicked Spanish gypsy was not a success at its première, but it was performed twenty-seven times in its first season. Although he was French, Bizet had a most extraordinary feeling for the sunlight and shadow that lurked in the music of Spain.

Drawing closer to our own times is the appearance of Giacomo Puccini. This remarkable Italian had a marvelous flair for melody and a seventh sense about the theater. For a long time he had great difficulty in finding the right librettos for his musical ideas. *La Bohème* (1896) was the first work he wrote to touch the hearts of audiences; after its appearance, the public clamored for more. Listeners loved his characters as much as they loved his music, and they responded with equal enthusiasm to *Tosca* (1900), *Madame Butterfly* (1904), and *Turandot* (1926).

The twentieth century brought the genius of Richard Strauss into focus. This colorful German composer enlarged the orchestra for all of his operas until it seemed that not another man could fit into the orchestra pit. His *Salome* (1905) and *Elektra* (1909) shocked their first hearers. The fabric of sound from the instruments was so strong that it demanded tremendous effort on the part of the singers to be heard. Singers, however, met the challenge and survived. Strauss also wrote the delightful *Der Rosenkavalier* (1911).

In France, Jules Massenet was writing *Manon* (1884), and Charpentier wrote *Louise* (1900). One of the great operas of this century, *Pelléas et Mélisande,* by Claude Debussy, was produced in 1902. Another master work is Alban Berg's tragedy *Wozzek* (1925).

England's Benjamin Britten has also contributed greatly to contemporary opera with *Peter Grimes* (1945) and *Billy Budd* (1951).

American composers did not, until very recently, offer any real or serious competition to the European operatic writers. The atmosphere of creating music for the opera stage was foreign to them. Even the popular Victor Herbert's talent for writing touching melodies failed him when he wrote *Natoma* (1911).

Deems Taylor's *The King's Henchman* (1927) and *Peter Ibbetson* (1931) are melodic and forceful music dramas, and they have been performed many times. George Gershwin's *Porgy and Bess* (1935) has been a triumph for its composer. In 1937, Fritz Reiner conducted a performance of an *opera buffa* by an Italian-American, Gian-Carlo Menotti. It was called *Amelia Goes to the Ball,* and it was an instantaneous success. The composer followed this with *The Medium* (1946), *The Consul* (1950), *Amahl and the Night Visitors* (1951), and *The Saint of Bleecker Street* (1954).

Kurt Weill's contributions to American opera are *Street Scene* (1947) and *Lost in the Stars* (1949); Marc Blitzstein gave us *Regina* in 1949. Recently we have had Douglas Moore's nostalgic *The Ballad of Baby Doe* (1956). Samuel Barber's strangely Gothic *Vanessa* (1958) has held a justified place in the Metropolitan's repertory, and Lee Hoiby's *Natalia Petrovna* (1964), originally produced by the New York City Center, reached its full stature during its almost immediate "revival" in Washington.

The elusive road that leads to the hearts and minds of the opera world is still a winding one for American composers, but they, too, will find the right way.

Such is the basic history of opera.

AÏDA

BY

GIUSEPPE VERDI

(1813–1901)

···· ◄─►─ ····

LIBRETTO BY ANTONIO GHISLANZONI

BASED ON A SKETCH BY MARIETTE BEY

···· ◄─►─ ····

CHARACTERS

AMNERIS	*Mezzo-soprano*	RADAMES	*Tenor*
THE KING OF EGYPT	*Bass*	RAMFIS	*Bass*
AÏDA	*Soprano*	AMONASRO	*Baritone*

···· ◄─►─ ····

TIME: ANCIENT EGYPT DURING THE REIGN OF THE PHARAOHS

PLACE: MEMPHIS AND THEBES

FIRST PERFORMANCE:

Cairo Opera House, Cairo, Egypt;

December 24, 1871

Verdi had actually decided to retire professionally when the great Khedive of Egypt, Ismail Pasha, asked him to write a special opera in celebration of the opening of the Suez Canal in 1869. However, due to the Franco-Prussian War, Aïda was not performed until 1871. The Khedive's opera house afforded Aïda a magnificent setting. With its walls of ivory and gold and its foyer of brilliant mirrors, it was a fitting place for this spectacle in the grand style. Aïda was an instantaneous success. Its first performance at the Metropolitan Opera House was on November 12, 1886.

ACT I

EGYPT was a mighty, feared country during the days of the Old Kingdom. Those years—3998 to about 3335 B.C.—were her greatest. She was called the Gift of the Nile. The capital of Egypt was Memphis, a wealthy, golden city that was protected by the great white Pyramids.

Farther up the muddy Nile was Thebes. This city's magnificent Avenue of Sphinxes and her temple of Khonsu, the god of the moon, were being threatened by the warriors of Ethiopia. The possibility that Thebes might be conquered was of great concern to the Egyptians and to Ramfis, their high priest. He stood silhouetted against the entranceway to the main hall of the royal palace in Memphis, focusing his steely eyes on a distant pyramid. Ramfis was the spokesman for the goddess Isis to whom all Egyptians turned for advice in times of strife. Even the King of Egypt listened when Ramfis spoke.

The sun reflected its rays on the massive bronze doors and the gold-painted timbers of the walls. Bold shafts of light shot back and forth from one of the alabaster vases to the red and green, painted statues that lined the hallway. Ramfis turned to Radames, a young captain of the army, who stood next to him.

"It is more than a rumor that Ethiopia is threatening Thebes again. A messenger should bring us the news shortly."

"Have you consulted holy Isis today?" asked Radames.

Ramfis nodded. "Yes. She has already named the supreme commander of the Egyptian armies." A shaft of light from one of the tiny windows high in the wall illumined Radames' face, and his dark eyes spoke silent words of ambition and pride.

"What a fortunate man!"

"Yes," said Ramfis, never taking his eyes from Radames'. "He is very young and very brave. I will leave you now and tell the King of the god's decree." He slowly left the hall.

Radames thought of how he wished that *he* might be the great warrior who would save his people and return in glorious triumph! He would bring back the spoils of war and victory, not just for the people of Egypt but for Aïda. "Beautiful Aïda," he said to himself, "you are the splendor of my life. The victor's laurels would be a garland for your hair and I would place you on a golden throne for all the world to see. Even the blazing sun would smile down on you!" (Aria "Celeste Aïda.")

He looked thoughtfully at the winged sun over the great doors, then saw the doors opening. Amneris, the Princess of Egypt, walked in and spoke.

"Joy is written across your face, Radames, and an enormous pride shines in your eyes today. I am envious of any woman whose face could kindle such a light in you." Her black eyes smoldered in their nest of blue eye paint and the thin, dark lines that shaped them like almonds.

Radames smiled. "I was lost in daydreaming. Today the goddess Isis has named the warrior who will lead the Egyptian armies into battle. If I were chosen for such an honor——"

The Princess interrupted him. "Perhaps it was some greater dream? Have you no hopes or desires right here in Memphis?" She had long suspected that he was in love with her slave Aïda, and she could not always control her jealousy.

Looking past Amneris, Radames could see Aïda coming down the long hall, and the Princess could tell from the look on his face that her suspicions were probably true. She smiled coldly and spoke to the slave girl. "Come to us, Aïda. You are neither slave nor handmaiden here. Do I not call you sister in this palace? Tell us why you are weeping."

"I have heard the sounds of war in the city and I am afraid for my country. I am afraid for all of us." She looked quietly away from Radames and Amneris and stared at the red brick floor.

"Are you sure that nothing else disturbs you?" Amneris asked. Like a cat, she moved closer to her. Radames could see the anger in her eyes, and feared what might happen should Amneris ever find out that they were in love. But then the big doors swung wide and the King and his retinue entered the hall.

The King walked toward Radames and commanded an officer to bring in the messenger they were all expecting. The hot and perspiring messenger knelt before the King and told of the invasion of Egypt by the Ethiopians. "Our fields of wheat and tobacco have all been destroyed—not even a cactus blossom remains in the desert. At this very minute the troops of Ethiopia, led by Amonasro, are marching on Thebes!"

Aïda trembled at the name "Amonasro," for he was the King of Ethiopia. But he was also her father! This had been her well-guarded secret since the day she had been captured, and no one at the court at Memphis knew it.

"Then war and death will be our battle cry," the King said as he turned to Radames. "The goddess Isis has named the leader of our legions, and it is you, Radames!"

"Praise to the great Isis," Radames said, bowing before the King. "All of my prayers have been answered."

"You must go now to the Temple of Vulcan," the King said to the proud young man, "and put on the sacred armor. I know you will lead our people to victory!"

"Return victorious, Radames," Amneris said arrogantly, and her words were echoed by all the priests and the followers of the King.

"Return victorious! Return victorious!" rang through the great hall as everyone left to escort their new commander to the Temple of Vulcan. The words circled about Aïda like the oppressive heat of high noon. She leaned against the great doors as they closed and the words throbbed in her ears.

"'Return victorious!' Even I have spoken those traitorous words," she thought. "Victory over my father? He who has taken up arms for me! To give me back my country and my great name. I would rather the gods destroyed all the legions of Egypt. All of them! They were the ones who conquered us. But how can I ask for death for Radames? I love him." (Aria "Ritorna vincitor!")

(SCENE 2) In the incense laden Temple of Vulcan, Ramfis stood before the center altar and called upon the mighty god Phtha. A mysterious shaft of light seeped through the murky blue shadows above the altar. The soft voices of the priestesses combined with the scent of sandalwood. Radames watched the priestesses in their soft white veils, swaying as they performed the sacred dance to Phtha, and he felt the coolness of the silver veil that was being placed over his head by the priests.

Ramfis spoke to him in solemn tones. "Radames, you are the beloved of the gods. You hold in trust the destiny of Egypt." The High Priest pointed to the sacred sword that blazed on the altar. "This sword has been forged by our gods. In your hands it will bring death and terror to our enemy!" The sword was placed in the young captain's hand, and he raised it high above his head in a salute to Isis and Phtha and all the gods.

The light from the sacred flame danced on the walls and the monotonous chants grew louder. "O, mighty Phtha! O, mighty Phtha!" The invocations soared up with the smoke from the altar out of the temple and resounded over all of Memphis.

And Radames went to war.

ACT II

As THE gods had ordained, Egypt and Radames were victorious. Thebes and the Valley of the Kings were saved, and Radames made preparations for his triumphal victory march that would include his presentation of hundreds of prisoners to the King.

Amneris, too, was preparing for a victory celebration. In her apartment, surrounded by her Moorish slaves, she reclined on her couch, luxuriating in the soft breeze from the ostrich fans that her handmaidens moved above her. She dreamily thought of Radames. She would wear her favorite amulet for the celebration . . . the one with the glowing red stone whose color gave force to its magic charms. Radames would love her, even if he did not now. He was the one who would bring joy and excitement into her life, although she was still plagued with jealousy when she thought of Aïda. (Aria "Vieni, amor mio.")

Aïda entered and the princess motioned to her servants to leave. Amneris spoke to her slave with

mocking tenderness. "Poor Aïda. The fortunes of war have gone against your people." The Ethiopian girl stood silent. "But do not be afraid. I understand your unhappiness, and I will give you anything you wish. I want you to be happy."

"How can I be happy? I have heard no news of my father or my brothers," Aïda replied.

Amneris rose from her couch and embraced Aïda. "I can weep with you, Aïda. But this is only an earthly sorrow which the gods control. It will pass and you will be happy. You will fall in love." She watched the play of the words on Aïda's face. "Trust in me, Aïda, and tell me what really disturbs you. Perhaps there was someone you loved among the soldiers of our army?"

Aïda looked up. She felt the blood rising in her cheeks. "What do you mean?"

"I mean," Amneris lied, "that our leader was killed by your people! He lies dead on the battlefield!"

The tears welled up in Aïda's eyes and she threw herself at her mistress' feet. "The gods have always been against me. Now I shall weep forever."

"She really does love him," Amneris thought as she cupped Aïda's face in her jeweled hands. "Look into my eyes, Aïda. I have lied to you. Radames is alive."

"The gods be praised," Aïda cried, trying to control her joy.

"So, you do love him!" Amneris screamed as she pushed her slave to the ground. "So be it! But do not forget that your rival is the daughter of the Pharaohs, and I am the one who controls your fate."

The music of the harps and tambourines in the palace was silenced by exultant blasts from the golden trumpets on the rooftops and the distant voices of the soldiers. Amneris smiled and ran to the window. She could see the troops and the curling Nile, weaving their way through the golden-brown sand. Everyone was heading for the triumphal celebration. She, too, would be triumphant.

"Remember, Aïda, you are the slave," Amneris said. "We shall see if you can do battle with me."

Aïda extended her hand to Amneris. "Have some pity, royal princess. Have pity."

A cloud drifted across the sun and the room was suddenly gray and cool. Amneris looked straight into Aïda's eyes, then she strode from the room. Aïda shuddered.

(SCENE 2) People were everywhere. The populace of the Valley of the Kings was determined to show its gratitude to Radames and his army for having saved them from the hordes of Ethiopians. The Avenue of Sphinxes was a sea of men, women, and children waving palm branches and carrying gifts for the victors. Near the Temple of Ammon, the sun god, the thrones of the King and his daughter had been set up. Encrusted with gold and precious jewels, they blazed in the sun. The streets were strewn with laurel and lotus blossoms and even the fields of cotton were empty of slaves. Everyone was prepared to welcome the triumphant Radames. The priests gave thanks for the great victory.

As the golden trumpets blared, all the pageant of a victorious Egypt unfolded before the ecstatic people. There were chariots of bronze and silver; dancing girls; the treasures won from the enemy; the prisoners, dirty and bloody from battle and chained together; and finally Radames. Borne aloft on a golden litter carried by twelve captains he stood before them, radiant and glowing in his triumph. ("Triumphal March.")

The King came down from his throne and embraced the conqueror of the Ethiopians. "I salute you, Radames. Come, my daughter will give you the victor's wreath."

The daughter of the Pharaohs smiled as she placed the laurel on the young officer's head. The King continued, "By my sacred oath, Radames, you shall have whatever you wish. No gift shall be refused you."

Radames bowed before his King. "Before I give my answer, let the prisoners be brought before you."

Aïda was shocked to see her father among the tired, defeated Ethiopians. Ignoring the guards, Aïda ran to her father and lovingly threw her arms about him. "Do not betray me," he whispered, pointing to his uniform. He could tell from the look on her face that she was wondering why her father, the King of Ethiopia, should be dressed as an officer and dragged about with the mass of prisoners.

The King of Egypt spoke to Amonasro: "And who are you?"

"I am this girl's father. As you can see by my uniform, I have attempted to defend my King and my country. If love of one's country is guilt, then I am ready to die!"

Aïda remained at her father's side and together they beseeched the proud and victorious King of Egypt to release the prisoners.

"The gods have spoken!" Ramfis roared. "They must die!" But the Egyptians were in a grateful and benevolent mood. This was meant to be a day of joyous celebration, and they also asked the King to show mercy. Radames watched Aïda's sad and weeping figure and he knew that he loved her more than he had months ago. Bowing again before the King, he asked, "As my wish to be fulfilled, I ask that all the prisoners be set free."

"All of them?" questioned Amneris.

Ramfis pushed his way in front of Radames to talk with the King. "If we free them, they will only seek revenge and strike again. The gods have decreed that they all must die!"

"They cannot strike again," Radames said; "Amonasro, their King, is dead. He was slain in battle."

Angrily, Ramfis continued, "At least, as a pledge of truce, make Aïda and her father stay with us."

"I yield to your wise counsel, Ramfis," the King replied. "And you, Radames, shall have the hand of my daughter as your reward. One day, you will both rule Egypt together!"

"Glory to Isis and to Egypt!" the crowd roared in approval, and the King and Amneris raised their hands in salute to Radames.

In the midst of the shouting and the storm of flowers that was being thrown at him, Radames felt as though he had been struck by the lightning blow of some enemy god. It was not worth even the throne of Egypt to lose Aïda. Swept up onto the shoulders of the delirious throng, he gazed at the green palm trees that rose into the sky and at the towering statue of Ammon the sun god at the top of the temple.

ACT III

THE days and the nights moved on, and soon it was the eve of Amneris' wedding. The velvet-black night looked down on the Temple of Isis and the muddy waters of the Nile that flowed near its entrance. The temple was almost hidden by the palm trees and the granite rocks near its main gate, but as the boat carrying the Princess drew near the shore, the full moon crept out from a network of clouds and illumined the white columns and the golden doors. Everything was quiet except for some birds in the rushes and the haunting cry of the locust. The ground beneath Amneris' jeweled sandals was cool and wet near the river, and she drew her white veils around her tightly.

"I shall stay with you while you pray," Ramfis said. "It is only right that you pray to Isis on this night before your wedding. Every mystery of life is known to her and she will guide you."

Amneris smiled. "I shall pray that Radames will love me as I love him."

As the gods would have it, Aïda had come to the same place to talk with Radames. Leaning against a tall coconut palm, she looked across the river and wondered what he would say to her. "The river is no longer muddy," she thought. "It is black like a tomb . . . my tomb perhaps." Tired of the hot, dry days in Egypt where, suddenly, the rains could be phenomenal, Aïda longed for her homeland. "My homeland," she mused, "I will never see you again." In her mind's eye the darkness that surrounded the temple lifted and she could see the blue skies of Ethiopia. She could feel the caressing breezes as they cooled the green valleys and rolling hills. The streams there were fresh and cool, nothing like the murky Nile. "My homeland, my hopes—everything is gone now." (Aria "O patria mia.")

The sound of footsteps and the rustling among the rushes awakened her from her dreaming. She saw her father standing before her. His figure against the white columns of the temple looked ominous and frightening. Before he spoke he looked about, motioning for her to be quiet. "I have watched you, Aïda, and it is easy to see that your love for Radames is destroying you. I can see that he loves you, too. But you must not forget that the daughter of the Pharaohs is your rival. However, if you wanted to, you could defeat her and return to the country of your birth. You, too, could have a kingdom and a throne!"

Aïda smiled sadly and thought of her happy days as a child.

"You forget too easily, Aïda, that the Egyptians were the ones who defiled our temples and carried off our young into slavery." Amonasro paced back and forth in the shadows. "Our people, your people, are ready again for battle. If only I knew what route the enemy would take this time."

"But who could find out?" Aïda asked innocently.

Her father looked at her. "You could! I know that you are waiting for Radames. He could tell you."

"I could never do that," Aïda answered. She was frightened, and the moonlight seemed to be enveloping her father like some blazing flame about a ferocious and menacing statue.

"Then the soldiers of Egypt will sack our cities again and terrorize our people. You call yourself my daughter? I can see the red blood swirling over our cities and all the dead rising up, pointing at you. I can hear their voices screaming, 'It is because of you that we died!' I can even see your mother cursing you."

Aïda screamed in terror and ran to her father. "Do not curse me, Father. I will be worthy of my country and of you. You will see."

"Be brave, Aïda, for I can hear Radames coming. Be brave and wipe your tears. Remember that all our people are waiting to rise to glory again—through you!" He disappeared into the shadows of the palm trees.

Radames came up the path from the river. Aïda turned away from him. "Why don't you go away? What do you want from me?"

"I came here to be with you. I love you, Aïda," Radames said.

The Ethiopian Princess turned and spoke calmly but with a hint of anger in her voice. "You are to be married to Amneris tomorrow."

"The gods of Egypt are my witness, Aïda. You are the one I love."

"If you really love me, there is an escape," Aïda said.

"And what is that?"

"We could run away . . . from Egypt and Amneris."

"Run away?" Radames asked, hardly believing Aïda's words.

"Yes. Run away to my country." Radames was stunned. How could he possibly leave Egypt and his gods and the land of his triumph?

"Go, then," said Aïda. "Go to Amneris! She is in the temple, beside the altar. If we stay, my father and I will be slain."

Radames looked first at Aïda and then at the temple. Across the desert was freedom and here was nothing but misfortune. He knew that he loved Aïda, and with her he would be happy. He drew her close to him.

"If we are to escape," Aïda asked, "how will we avoid the Egyptian legions?"

"We will go by the pass of Napata. It will be free until tomorrow."

"Napata!" shouted Amonasro from the shadows. "My men will be there!"

"Who has heard us?" Radames asked, looking into the darkness.

"Aïda's father, the King of Ethiopia!" said Amonasro, coming out into the moonlight. Radames stepped back dumbfounded. "You . . . Amonasro? You are the King?"

Aïda looked toward the temple, afraid they had been overheard. "Be calm and trust in me."

"But I have betrayed my country," said Radames in torment.

"You are not guilty," Amonasro assured him. "It is the will of the gods. Aïda's love for you will build you a new throne! Come, the two of you. My men are waiting across the Nile. We will all be free."

Radames' moment of indecision allowed time for the temple doors to swing wide. They were confronted by Amneris and Ramfis with their guards. Amneris pointed her jeweled fingers at Radames in rage and screamed, "You traitor!" Amonasro lunged at her with his dagger, but Radames rushed between them and threw the King's weapon to the ground. The moon was behind a bank of clouds, and Amonasro took Aïda by the hand and drew her into the night. As the guards raced after them, Radames humbly gave his sword to Ramfis.

"I am your prisoner," he said as Amneris swept past him, past the palm trees and the river, past the pyramids into the dark.

ACT IV

No ONE heard of Aïda and Amonasro from that night on. Radames was imprisoned to await his trial as a traitor. Amneris intermittently sulked or raged in her apartment, and roamed the great, quiet halls of the palace in moods of deep melancholy. One day, she walked through the halls silently, speaking to no one. She paused for a moment before the heavy doors that led to the judgment chambers, trying to put some order to her confused thoughts. Aïda, her rival, had escaped. Radames was surely to be punished by the priests. She hated them both! Hadn't he meant to run away? "But since I love him," she thought, "I should try to save him." She called to the guard and demanded that Radames be brought to her. While she waited for him she hoped that he would still find her beautiful, although her eyes were red from weeping.

Radames emerged from the darkness of the passageway and Amneris observed that he was no longer the gleaming hero of that triumphal day in Thebes, but in spite of that she knew that she still loved him.

"Even now, Radames, the priests are deciding your fate," Amneris said. "But if you clear yourself with me, I could intervene with the priests, and you would have your pardon and your life."

The young captain's eyes smarted in the brightness of the corridor and he raised his hands to shield them. Through his fingers he could see Amneris' eyes, pleading and angry. "The judges will never hear me, Amneris. Before al! my gods and before all men, I do not feel that I am a traitor. I revealed a secret, that is true, but I do not feel guilty."

"Then save yourself or you will die."

"No. I wish to die," said Radames.

"My throne—my life, I would give them all up for you," cried Amneris.

"I know," Radames replied. "I gave up my country for her."

"Do not mention her name!" Amneris said angrily.

"You ask me to live?" asked Radames as he breathed in the fresh air of the hallway. It was sweet and invigorating after the stifling days in his cell. "Everything is dead, Amneris. Perhaps even Aïda is dead because of you."

Amneris laughed. "Aïda dead? No, she is alive. Only her father was killed in the escape. She has disappeared. But I can save you!" she said, touching his arm. "Only swear that you will never see her again."

"I cannot."

"You can live, Radames, if you do."

"I do not wish to live without Aïda," Radames said, and he walked back into the passageway that led to his prison.

Amneris cried out to him, "I have done this! Now who can save him?" (Aria "Ohimè! morir mi sento.")

Amneris heard the voices of the priests from the judgment chamber. Their cries of "Traitor!" rang out from all the walls. Radames was silent, never defending himself.

Amneris' pleas to the gods echoed up and down the corridors. The once-victorious captain was being sentenced. He was to be entombed—alive!

The Princess waited on the steps for the priests to appear. When they did, even her personal pleas to Ramfis were ignored, and they filed out of the hallway chanting, "Traitor, Traitor! He must die."

As the last white garment disappeared through the gold doorway, Amneris hurled herself against the great bronze handles, sobbing in rage and fear. "My curse is on you! The gods will strike you down, you infamous priests! My curse is on you!" and she fell weeping to the floor.

(SCENE 2) Radames was condemned to die. He had been led through the elaborate passages of the tombs beneath the Temple of Vulcan, from which no human could escape. He was alone now in the tiny vault where he was to end his life. He sat calmly, listening to the sound of the priests' hammers as they put the last sealing stone in place. There was nothing to do now but pray to his gods and wait for the goddess Hathor to come to seek him out. The patron of the dead would surely find him. He thought of Aïda and hoped that she was safe.

In the darkness a figure moved. Aïda was with him! She smiled and knelt at his feet. "I came into the tomb secretly. I want to die with you, Radames."

"By loving you I have killed you," Radames said, brushing her black hair from her eyes.

The air was growing close and Aïda reached out for Radames, who was desperately trying to move the final stone that closed the vault. "It is useless, beloved. All life on earth is useless now. Our wandering souls will be safe now. We will be escorted by Hathor to a world of happiness." (Duet "O terra, addio.")

Above them, in the main part of the temple, Amneris knelt to pray. Behind her the incense curled up, blue and green against the white fluted columns of the temple.

"I call on you, Isis, to forgive him. Open the doors of heaven to him and bring him peace. Bring them both peace."

THE
BARBER
OF
SEVILLE

IL BARBIERE DI SIVIGLIA

by

GIOACCHINO (ANTONIO) ROSSINI

(1792–1868)

LIBRETTO BY CESARE STERBINI

Based on the play

Le Barbier de Séville

by Beaumarchais

FIORELLO Bass	ROSINA Soprano
COUNT ALMAVIVA Tenor	DR. BARTOLO Bass
FIGARO Baritone	DON BASILIO Bass
BERTHA Soprano	

Time: 1600's   *Place:* SEVILLE, SPAIN
First performance: TEATRO ARGENTINA, ROME;
February 5, 1816

Rossini wrote *The Barber of Seville* in the phenomenal time of only thirteen days. This caused Verdi to comment that Rossini must have had the music in his head for a long time. Giovanni Paisello had previously written an opera called *The Barber of Seville* (1776), but Rossini decided to redo the same plot and use it for his opera. There are conflicting opinions as to whether Rossini ever wrote to Paisello asking his permission to use the plot. However, Rossini's actions infuriated Paisello's followers, and at the first performance of Rossini's *The Barber of Seville* they created a bedlam of catcalls, yells, and shrieks. At this performance Rossini tried to lead the orchestra, which no one in the audience could hear. At the second performance Rossini stayed home, but this time his opera was well received by the spectators, and it has been ever since.

ACT I

THERE is an old proverb that says, "He who has not seen Seville has never seen a miracle." And rightly so, for Seville, particularly in the seventeenth century, was a joyful, young city full of bubbling fountains, graceful balconies, and jasmine-scented patios where beautiful dark-eyed ladies danced alegrias with their suitors. There was beauty everywhere.

The house of the old and pompous Dr. Bartolo had its patio and balcony, too. Stained-glass windows opened onto his balcony. It was dawn, and soon Rosina, Dr. Bartolo's beautiful ward, would be stepping out on the balcony to greet the morning.

Count Almaviva and his servant, Fiorello, cautiously crept into the square. The Count held his dark-brown cape tightly about himself. He was in disguise. He pulled the black brim of his hat down over his eyes and warned Fiorello and the men with him to be very quiet. "Come now, gather around me, but without a word."

Fiorello looked up at the balcony. "No one is near to disturb our singing," he said. Count Almaviva smiled. He and the musicians he had brought along were about to serenade Rosina, but since his song was intended only for her ears he did not wish to awaken the entire neighborhood.

The Count's serenade was a delicate romantic song, for he was truly in love with Rosina. (Aria "Ecco ridente in cielo.")

"Can you see her?" Almaviva asked Fiorello.

"No, my lord. And it is almost morning."

Almaviva sighed. "Everything is in vain. Well, my friends, I have no more need of your music." He tossed the men a purse of gold coins and Fiorello bid the musicians good night.

The square was silent for a few minutes, but not for long. The sound of a happy voice drew closer and closer. The robust "La, la, la's" were indeed the expression of a man who was very pleased with himself this morning. "Who is that coming now?" Almaviva asked. "We'd better hide in this archway and see what happens." He and Fiorello hid themselves just in time, for in seconds the new arrival was directly in front of them.

What a happy man he was! His black eyes sparkled and laughed. He wore a white satin waistcoat and breeches. His silver buttons glistened in the sunlight, and his red sash and garters bounced as he walked. A brilliant pink coat was his crowning glory.

As he strummed his guitar he gaily sang of his life as the favorite barber in Seville. He was ready for everything! Everyone of quality called on him for a shave or for a wig. Even the famous ladies were enthralled by his charm and his skill with the scissors and comb. It was a shame that there was only one Figaro! What a life! "I am happy," he sang, "for I can truthfully say without boasting that I am of service to everyone!" (Aria "Largo al factotum della citta.")

"I must be mistaken," the Count said, loud enough to be heard. "It can't be . . ."

"Who is that?" asked Figaro as he strummed the last chord of his song.

"Figaro?" the Count asked.

"Your excellency!"

"Sh, sh! I am not known here nor do I wish to be, for the best of reasons."

Figaro smiled. "I understand. I shall be on my way."

"No," said the nobleman, slapping the barber amiably on the back. "Stay awhile."

"Why are you in Seville?" asked Figaro.

"I saw a beautiful girl on the Prado. She is the daughter of some silly old doctor who recently moved here. Since I am in love with her, I left my home to be near her. I come here every day and every night just to watch this balcony."

"*That* balcony? In that house I am barber, sur-

geon, botanist, apothecary . . . in other words, I do everything," said Figaro.

"What good luck!" Almaviva replied.

"But that is not all. The young girl is only Bartolo's ward. She's not his real daughter."

"That's a consolation," said Almaviva happily.

"Sh! The window of the balcony is opening." Figaro pulled the Count back into the shadow of the portico where now they could see and hear Dr. Bartolo at the door.

He explained to his servants that he would be gone only a few moments, and if Don Basilio came to call he should be asked to wait. Before he closed the door he said, "I want to hasten my marriage to Rosina. Yes, today I am going to conclude the whole affair."

The Count could hardly wait for the old man to cross the square before he blurted out, "Conclude his marriage with Rosina! That old fool! Tell me, Figaro, who is this Don Basilio?"

"He's a famous matchmaker. A good-for-nothing hypocrite with never a penny in his pockets. He has lately turned music teacher and Rosina is his pupil."

Figaro laughed and whispered to Almaviva, "You could explain everything to Rosina in a pretty song, you know. Here is my guitar."

The Count was eager to try anything that might win him Rosina's hand, so he began to sing:

> If you want to know my name
> Listen to the song I sing.
> I am called Lindoro.

Rosina appeared on the balcony. Her jet-black hair and lashes perfectly matched her luminous black eyes which looked searchingly out over her pink fan. "Continue to sing," she urged, looking down into the square.

The Count continued singing and Rosina answered:

> Sincere and enamored Rosina,
> Her heart to Lin . . .

With a shriek she ran from the balcony.

"I imagine someone entered her room," Figaro remarked, trying to see into her window.

"I must see her and talk with her," Almaviva said. "I must! If you will help me, you will be rewarded."

"Lots of gold?" asked Figaro.

"In abundance. Now let's plan it."

The thought of shining gold coins triggered Figaro's imagination, and together they decided on a clever plan. A regiment of soldiers was due that very day in Seville and the Count would come to Rosina's house disguised as a soldier and pretending to be drunk. He would carry a letter from his friend the Colonel in command, ordering Bartolo to give him lodging during the regiment's tour of duty.

"I will meet you at my shop in a few minutes," Figaro said. "You can't miss it. It's down the street there, number fifteen. You'll see five wigs in the window and on the placard, 'Pomade Divine.'" They laughed and shook hands to seal their ingenious plan. The Count waved good-by, and Figaro boldly walked into Bartolo's house with the sound of gold coins already clinking in his brain.

(SCENE 2) Rosina was standing at the window and she could see Figaro as he entered the house. She tapped the letter she was holding against her chin and smiled. The sound of the serenade she had just heard was fresh in her memory, and she had already decided that Lindoro was going to be hers.

"The voice I just heard has pierced my heart," she said as she played with the black fringe on the pink curtains. "My guardian will never consent, but I'll sharpen my wits and find a way. I'm really very respectful and obedient but—if I am crossed in love, I can really be a viper!" (Aria "Una voce poco fa.")

She remembered that she was still holding the letter in her hand, and she began to wonder how she would get it to Lindoro. Perhaps Figaro, who was an honest fellow, was the one to help her in her plan.

"Good day, Signorina," Figaro said as he entered the room.

"Good day, Figaro. It's good to see you, for I am dying of boredom."

"I must talk with you," Figaro said.

"Later, Figaro. I can hear my guardian's footsteps in the hall."

"Then I will go," Figaro said as he bowed low before her. Rosina smiled and watched him as he hid himself behind the heavy pink draperies.

"What a rascal! What a scoundrel," roared Bartolo as he walked into the room.

"Always shouting," whispered Rosina behind her fan.

"He has made a hospital of this house. Have you seen him?"

"Yes, I saw him. I even spoke with him. I enjoy talking with him. He's such a handsome man." Looking over her fan, she added, "Choke on that you wicked old man"—but very quietly. Then she turned and left the room.

"How charming," said Bartolo, taking a pinch of snuff. "The more I love her, the more she disdains me. Probably that miserable barber has put her up to this."

Old Don Basilio entered and Bartolo greeted him. "Ah, Basilio, you have come at just the right time. By tomorrow, by force or love, I must marry Rosina. Is that clear?"

Basilio sneezed into his red handkerchief. "You speak wisely. It is for that very reason that I have

THE BARBER OF SEVILLE

come. You must keep this bit of news a secret, though. Count Almaviva is in town. He has just arrived."

"Who? That mysterious lover of Rosina's?"

"The same man!"

"Something must be done," Bartolo said as he flopped down in a huge pink chair.

"Certainly," agreed Basilio, "but very quietly. We must begin by inventing a story about him that will put him in a bad light with the public. I will attend to it. In four days he will be thrown out of Seville!"

"But that is slander," said Bartolo, reaching for his snuff box.

"And what is slander?" laughed old Basilio. "It is only a gentle breeze that lightly whispers here and there. Then it goes gliding and rambling into the ears of the people. It gathers force, little by little, and then with a great roar like thunder it spreads in an explosion. The poor wretch who is its victim is trampled down by the blows of public opinion, and then he is ruined!" (Aria "La calumnia.")

"Well, that may be true," said Bartolo, getting up from the chair, "but we are wasting valuable time. Let's go to my room and prepare the marriage contract."

Figaro laughed as he stepped from behind the curtain, and he almost bumped into Rosina who was just closing the door. Figaro told her, "This fine guardian of yours plans to become your husband tomorrow!"

"Nonsense," said Rosina as she peered through the slats of the venetian blind. "He still has me to deal with. Tell me, Figaro, who was the gentleman I saw you talking with a while ago beneath my balcony?"

"He's my cousin. A fine young student who has recently come here to seek his fortune."

"He'll probably make it," Rosina said, turning around.

"I doubt it. He's dying of love."

Rosina laughed and tapped Figaro lightly on the head with her fan. "Really? He interests me very much. Tell me, does his sweetheart live far away?"

"Oh no! Here, about two steps away. Her name is Ro . . ."

"Rosina!" they both laughed together.

"Yes, Lindoro is madly in love with you," Figaro said, realizing that Rosina was a very clever girl.

"But how will I ever be able to continue to speak with him," the young girl asked as she caressed the petals of one of the pink roses on the table near the window.

"Be patient. Lindoro will come to see you very soon. He is only waiting for some sign of affection from you. You might give me a note and I could take it to him."

"I shouldn't," Rosina said, smiling, "but here."

She took the letter from her bodice and gave it to Figaro.

"She's already written it!" thought the barber. "How clever. Who will ever understand a woman's mind?" Begging Rosina to be patient, Figaro said good-by, and left the room.

"How nice Figaro is," thought Rosina as she was interrupted by Bartolo again.

"What brought Figaro here this morning?" the old man asked.

"Oh, he was telling me of a hundred trifles . . . about the fashions of France and about the health of his daughter Marcellina."

"Indeed? And what is the meaning of your ink-stained finger?"

"Stained? Oh, nothing. I burned myself and used the ink as a medicine."

"The devil you did!" shouted Bartolo as he slapped her hand. "And these sheets of paper . . . there were six and now there are only five!" He rattled the pieces of paper on the desk and then shook them in front of her face.

"You are right." Rosina smiled. "I used one of them to wrap some sweets for Marcellina."

"You'll need better excuses, Rosina. It takes more than that to deceive a doctor of *my* standing." Rosina pouted and pretended to weep behind her fan, but Bartolo only raged on and assured her that she would be locked in her room forever, and huffing and puffing he pulled her into the hallway.

The fever of their conversation brought Berta, a very old servant, into the room. She looked about but saw no one. Now the voices seemed to be coming from the street, and there was more knocking at the door. Opening it, she saw the Count, but, of course, he was in disguise and she did not recognize him. She curtsied just as Bartolo arrived.

"Is no one at home?" roared the Count, acting as if he were drunk.

"What do *you* want?" asked Bartolo.

"Ah, you must be Dr. Balodoro?"

"I am Dr. Bartolo."

"Here, sir, is my certificate that says I will be lodging with you."

"A common soldier in my house!" thought Bartolo.

Rosina tiptoed in behind him as Dr. Bartolo began to pace the floor. The Count moved closer to Rosina and whispered, "I am Lindoro."

Bartolo stopped in his tracks. "Leave this house, my dear soldier. You shall have no lodging here. I am exempt from having to house the military . . . and you, Rosina, leave this room!"

Bartolo lumbered to his desk to search for his exemption papers, which gave the Count a few more seconds to talk to Rosina. "I may not be able to stay. Here, take this note. I will drop it on the floor and you can drop your handkerchief on it. Then you can pick it up."

"Stop! Stop," roared Bartolo, noticing their maneuvers. "Let me see that."

"Oh, it is only the laundry list," said Rosina.

"Come here, you little flirt," ordered Bartolo, as Basilio and Berta entered the room to add to the confusion.

"You . . . you . . . are right," stammered Bartolo, "It *is* only the laundry list."

Rosina was in tears. Berta was frightened by all the noise, and Bartolo and Basilio began to scream back and forth at each other. In the midst of this bedlam, the Count threatened to murder Bartolo, and then Figaro came in to join in the fracas. The shouting and weeping grew to such heights that no one even heard someone else knocking at the door. Before they had time to say "Seville," they were confronted by the police.

"What is the meaning of this disturbance?" asked the officer in charge. Everyone started explaining at once, until silence could only be restored by the announcement that the Count was under arrest.

"Under arrest?" said the Count, with a sweeping gesture of surprise. He called the officer to his side and privately showed him his real papers and his Order of the Grandees of Spain, which he was wearing under his disguise.

The apologetic officer motioned to the soldiers to withdraw immediately, which left Rosina, Basilio, Bartolo, and Berta fixed to the spot with amazement. As they looked from face to face, their confusion grew and their voices rose again in heated argument.

ACT II

DR. BARTOLO paced back and forth in his library, bemoaning his misfortunes and wondering if it were not Count Almaviva who had sent the soldier to his house. There was a knock at the door, and praying that it was no new trouble, he called out, "I'm at home. Can't you hear? Come in."

It was the Count in another disguise. "Peace and happiness be with you," said the Count.

"A thousand thanks," Bartolo said, wondering who this man was. "Do come in." As he spoke he had the strange feeling that he had seen this face before. But where?

Bartolo asked, "Who are you?"

"I am Don Alonzo. A pupil of Don Basilio's. The poor man has taken ill and I am here to give Rosina her singing lesson."

"Taken ill?" said Bartolo in amazement. "I must go to him immediately."

"That will not be necessary," the Count assured

him as he looked around for Rosina. "Actually, I come from Count Almaviva."

"Sh, sh . . . speak quietly. I'm listening."

"Well," said the Count, "I met him in the inn where I am staying, and by chance this note fell into my hands."

"Why, that's Rosina's writing!" said Bartolo.

"Don Basilio," continued the Count, "knows nothing of this paper. But with it . . . one could . . ."

"Could what?" asked Bartolo.

"Well, I could make Rosina believe that it was given to me by a sweetheart of the Count's. It would be proof that he is toying with her affections."

"Ah ha!" laughed Bartolo. "A scandal! You have been well taught by Basilio. I will call the girl right away."

Left alone, the Count realized that now, with this new fabrication, he was involved even more deeply in the plot. How would he explain things to Rosina?

When Rosina was led in by Bartolo, she immediately recognized her beloved "Lindoro."

"Come, sit by my side," said the Count, "and I will give you your music lesson."

Rosina was happy and sang very prettily.

"A beautiful voice," commented the Count.

"Thank you." She smiled.

"Truly a magnificent voice," agreed Bartolo, "but the music is tiresome. Music in my day was quite another thing." He began to sing another aria ("Quando mi sei vicina") and was so engrossed he paid no attention to Figaro's arrival. But as the barber began to imitate the old man, Rosina could not curb her laughter and Bartolo looked up: "Well, you rascal, what are you here for?"

"This is your day to be shaved."

"Most certainly not today," grumbled the old doctor.

"Today you don't want it. Tomorrow I can't come. I shall be busy with all the officers of the new regiment and all the nobility!" said Figaro.

"Less chatter, Figaro," said Bartolo. "I do not want to be shaved today!"

"What can one do?" said Figaro, placing his basin and shaving equipment on the piano. "This place is always a madhouse. Find yourself another barber. I'm going!"

"Oh, well," said Bartolo, giving in, "go into the other room and prepare the towels. No, on second thought, I will go myself." He walked out, taking a bunch of keys from his pocket.

"Tell me, Rosina," Figaro said quickly, "doesn't one of those keys open the balcony window?"

"Yes. It's the newest one," she answered.

Bartolo immediately remembered that he did not intend to leave Figaro in the same room with Rosina, so he quickly came back. "Here, Figaro, take the keys and prepare things yourself. Everything is on the shelf at the end of the corridor."

There was a great crash in the hallway and Bartolo cried, "What was that!" He dashed out of the library to investigate this newest disturbance.

"Now that we are alone, Rosina," the Count said, "are you willing to place your destiny entirely in my hands?"

"Oh yes, Lindoro. It is my only wish."

Figaro and Bartolo were back again and this time the barber dangled the gold key over the doctor's shoulder. The plan would work now.

The elaborate preparations for Bartolo's shave were well under way when Basilio blustered into the room. His great black hat could barely go through the door, and in his haste the scrawny old man almost tripped on the hem of his black cassock. With a flourish he placed his umbrella, which he always carried, rain or shine, on the piano and stared at them all. "At your service," he said, bowing almost to the floor.

"How are you feeling, Don Basilio?" Bartolo asked, as Figaro nervously tried to apply mountains of lather to the doctor's face.

"Shall I shave you or not?" the barber asked.

"How am I feeling?" Basilio asked.

The Count was quick to whisper in Bartolo's ear. "Don Basilio knows nothing of the letter. He *might* expose us."

"You are right," Bartolo agreed as he spit some lather out of his mouth. "I will send him away."

"Good heavens," Figaro said, waving the shaving brush in Basilio's face. "You look ill. You must have scarlet fever."

"Here, dear Basilio," the Count added, "take this money and get some medicine. You must go to bed immediately."

Rosina chirped up, too. "Yes, save yourself. Go right home to bed."

Poor confused Basilio now really believed that he was ill and he bid them all farewell. Figaro intended to pile the old man's face so high with lather that he would not be able to see Rosina and the Count as they talked together. The scheme did not work, however, for the wily old man could hear their conversation. He could hear very clearly as the Count tried to explain his new disguise and his use of Rosina's letter. Realizing that he had been duped

again, and hearing the Count's instructions to Rosina concerning her abduction that night, he jumped up from the chair. Water and soap and curses went in all directions. He stamped and raved and ordered the Count from the house. "You are all scoundrels!" he roared, and Rosina ran weeping from the room. She was followed by Figaro with the old man close behind.

Berta arriving on the scene was in a quandary. "Was love the reason for all this madness?" she thought. "The old man wanted a wife and the young girl wanted a husband. They are all fit to be tied. Love," she decided as she picked up the overturned barber's bowl, "is a mania. But I feel it, too. And I am just an old maid with no hope at all." She threw up her arms in desperation and hobbled out of the room.

As Bartolo and Basilio returned to the library Bartolo said, "The wedding will be tonight. You must hurry and get the lawyer to draw up all the necessary papers."

Basilio replied, "I'll be back quickly."

Bartolo then worked out a scheme to ensnare Rosina further. When she came into the room he shoved the letter Alonzo had given him in front of her. "See," he said, "you have been fooled. Your lover does not really care about you. He is in love with another woman."

Rosina gasped in amazement. "Where did you get my letter?" she cried.

"Alonzo and the barber are scheming together. They are determined to catch you for Count Almaviva."

Rosina, hurt and furious, answered, "I will marry you tonight. But you must know that the barber and Lindoro are coming to get me at midnight. They will use the balcony."

Bartolo then left Rosina and went after the police.

A storm then broke over Seville. With a great gush its torrents fell on all the rooftops and streets. The rivulets of rain raced and bounced about the little balcony of Dr. Bartolo's house. The balcony windows opened and Figaro and the Count stepped into the room.

"What weather," said the Count, brushing the rain from his cloak.

"A perfect night for lovers." Figaro laughed as he set his lantern on the table. In the shadows they could both see Rosina with her black eyes flashing in the dark. The Count opened his arms to her.

"Stand back, you wretch!" Rosina snapped. "I only came here to wipe out the shame of my foolishness and to show you what I really am!"

Neither the Count nor Figaro knew what she was talking about. What had gone wrong? Rosina stepped out into the light of the lantern. "You! You

pretended to love me, Lindoro, only to get me into the clutches of that wicked Count Almaviva!" Bartolo had obviously been talking to her.

The Count smiled. "You have been deceived, Rosina. Please look at me and know that I am the Count Almaviva, *not* Lindoro." Rosina rushed into his arms, delirious with joy, as they declared their love for each other. (Duet "Ah, qual colpo.")

"Some people are at the door below," Figaro said, glancing from the balcony window. "Let's get away. We'll use the ladder from the balcony." As they started to go, they warned each other to hurry. (Trio "Zitti, zitti, piano, piano.") But to the surprise of all three, the ladder had been removed and they were trapped.

"Have courage, Rosina," the Count said as the door flew open and they saw Basilio followed by a notary. Figaro quickly and cleverly greeted them both, and pretended that he thought this was the notary he had requested to come and settle the marriage contract between the Count Almaviva and Figaro's niece! Almaviva was quick to catch Basilio's confusion, and also the threads of a new Figaro plot.

He called Basilio aside and gave him a magnificent gold ring. "This ring is for you."

"But . . . but," stammered Basilio.

"If you offer any opposition, two bullets are waiting for you."

"Dear me," said Basilio, stumbling over his umbrella, "I'll take the ring. Who will sign the marriage papers?"

The Count went on, "Figaro, you and Basilio will be witnesses." Pointing to Rosina, he added, "Here is my bride."

The papers were signed and the doors burst open. The marriage party was surrounded by a police guard and a red-faced Dr. Bartolo. "Arrest them. Arrest them!" he shouted. "They are thieves!"

"Your name, sir," asked the officer, addressing the Count.

"Count Almaviva!"

The officer gave the old doctor a withering glance, and Bartolo knew that he had been defeated. "You betrayed me," he roared at Basilio. "And what a fool I am. I took the ladder away and it only made things easier."

"Ah, my good doctor," Basilio said as he smoothed his long beard, "the Count had good reasons in his pocket that convinced me to sign the papers. I could not argue."

Rosina ran to her husband's arms. She smiled behind her fan as they were congratulated by everyone. She had fallen in love with a humble student, but now she was the wife of a Grandee of Spain! Love and faith would always be in their hearts.

Miracles always happen in Seville.

La Bohème

By Giacomo Puccini (1858—1924)

Libretto by Giuseppe Giacosa and Luigi Illica

Based on the novel

Scènes de la Vie de Bohème

by HENRI MURGER

RUDOLFO	Tenor	MIMI	Soprano
MARCELLO	Baritone	MUSETTA	Soprano
COLLINE	Bass	ALCINDORO	Bass
SCHAUNARD	Baritone	BENOIT	Bass

Time—1830, during the reign of Louis Philippe   **Place—Paris**

FIRST PERFORMANCE:

Teatro Reggio, Turin; February 1, 1896

Henri Murger, the author of the novel on which *La Bohème* was based, spent his youth as a struggling writer, much as Rudolfo in the opera. Puccini, too, as a poor student, lived a Bohemian life. So the characters and scenes in *La Bohème* have an exciting realistic quality, for both composer and author personally knew the people and places they wrote about. In spite of this, the beauty of the music, and the fact that the twenty-eight-year-old Arturo Toscanini was conducting, one music critic wrote after *La Bohème's* première, "*Bohème* . . . will not leave much of a trace in the history of the lyric stage. The composer will do wisely if he writes it off as a momentary mistake."

ACT I

RUDOLFO, a young poet, stood by the window of his attic studio, gazing at the blue smoke rising from the snow-topped chimneys.

"What a way to spend Christmas in Paris," he mused quietly.

His friend, Marcello the painter, laughed. "The freezing waters of my masterpiece, 'The Red Sea,' make me feel cold all over. Why, I feel as though they were running over me. And look at this no-good stove of ours! You'd think that he was the gentleman here. He *never* works. Shall we burn my painting in it?"

"No," Rudolfo said smiling. "Canvas smells terrible. My play will warm us better."

With that they stuffed the pages of his manuscript into the dark face of the little stove, lighted them, and basked in the brief warmth of the fire. Actually, they were accustomed to this state of affairs; the wolf had been at their threshold many times.

With a sudden burst the door behind them flew open. It was Colline, grumbling, "The Apocalypse is surely upon us. Not a single pawnshop is open on Christmas Eve. I can't even sell some of my books so that we can eat!" He stamped his feet and angrily threw his beloved books on the table. He looked at the blobs of melting snow on the floor and sighed.

"You are just in time to see the last of my play go up in flames," Rudolfo said humorously. Then the three of them laughed and applauded as the little fire sputtered. Soon it was only a glow of blue and green and there were cries of "Down with the author! Down with the author!"

Just then the door opened again and two red-faced porters came in carrying bundles of wood and armfuls of food and wine.

"Our holiday feast," said the happy man striding in after them. There was Schaunard, always the friend when one was in need, beaming triumphantly.

With a great flourish he threw a fistful of coins on the floor. "The money is real," he said, catching the look of incredulity on all their faces, "and you will never believe how I came by it."

No explanation was necessary, for already Rudolfo, Marcello, and Colline were busy setting the table and excitedly opening all the packages of food. Their attention was riveted on other things than Schaunard's story: the firewood, for one.

"Musician that I am," said Schaunard, ignoring their inattention, "an English gentleman hired me to play the piano until his bird died. So I was charming, and played for three days. Then, I got the maid to feed the forlorn old bird a sprig of parsley. Voilà, he opened his mouth and died. He was as dead as Socrates!"

"Who was?" asked Colline, completely oblivious to all the conversation.

Schaunard whipped off his scarf with a grand flourish. "Well, my friends, since you will not give me your attention, you may all go to the devil!" He began to remove all the food from the table. "Not tonight, my friends. The delicate bits of food here are for our dark and dismal future. Tonight is Christmas Eve. We dine in the Latin Quarter! But first, a toast." They raised their glasses only to be interrupted by a knock at the door. To the dismay of everyone it was Benoit, the landlord. Funny, fat little Benoit who always wanted the overdue rent at the wrong moment.

"Ah ha, dear Benoit," exclaimed Marcello, "please come in and take a glass of wine with us. Join us in a toast to Christmas."

"Yes, dear young Benoit, do have a glass of wine," said Rudolfo and Schaunard.

"But you promised me the rent," croaked Benoit.

Marcello laughed. "That was certainly a pretty young girl I saw you with in the café last night! Poor Madame Benoit! Is she ill?"

Thoroughly befuddled by the friendliness of his tenants and by the wine (his glass had now been refilled twice), Benoit bubbled forth, "Poor Madame Benoit? She is too skinny and too bad-tempered to be ill . . . that was . . ."

"Poor Madame Benoit!" roared Colline, pretending to be outraged. "We cannot allow ourselves to be in the same room with such a deceitful man! Away with him!"

Now bewildered and reeling from too many glasses of wine, Benoit found himself lifted bodily toward and out the door. The four friends danced about and Marcello threw back his head, roaring, "Well, that takes care of the rent!"

"Remember, good people," said Schaunard, "tonight is a night for merrymaking. We shall divide the money equally and depart for the café."

"I will join you in five minutes when I have finished an article for my magazine," Rudolfo said as he urged his three companions forward. "It must be finished tonight."

As their voices echoed down the hall, Rudolfo set a candle upon the table and started to write. "How can I create?" he wondered. "I am not even in the mood!" Just then, there was a gentle knock at the door. Was it someone, or only his imagination? Rudolfo rose and opened the door. Indeed it was not his imagination! What a beautiful young girl! Even in the darkness of the hallway he could see her shining dark eyes. She stood against the door, coughing.

"These narrow stairs always take my breath away," she said softly, "and my candle has gone out. In the dark I will never be able to use my key in my door." She coughed again, drawing her little blue shawl tightly around her shoulders.

"Please come in," urged Rudolfo.

She hesitated, and then suddenly fainted into Rudolfo's arms. Her white hand relaxed and both the key and the candle fell to the floor.

"How beautiful she is," thought Rudolfo as he carried her to a chair. "She must be very ill." Her dark eyes opened slowly. They seemed to smile from somewhere deep inside.

"May I light my candle?"

"Of course," answered the poet. "I will light it for you." He did, and wished at the same time that he could think of some other words than just "Good night."

The girl walked to the door, stopped, and timidly said, "How stupid of me. I've forgotten my key."

"Not only have you forgotten your key," said Rudolfo, "but the draft in the hallway will blow out your candle again."

It was true, for as he opened the door a sudden swirl of cold night air did just that. In fact, now both their candles were out. The room was plunged into darkness.

Mimi apologized. "I'm so foolish. Please forgive me, but we must search for my key."

Now a shaft of moonlight came through the window. In the shadowy blue darkness Rudolfo could see the little figure, on her knees, vainly trying to find her key.

"Please let me help you," the young man said, and he joined her in her search.

There it was! Close to the door sill. Playfully, Rudolfo reached for the key and pocketed it. As his hand moved back across the floor it touched the girl's tiny fingers. How soft and how cold they were!

"Your hand is frozen. Let's not look any longer for the key. Soon the moonlight will help us find it. Did you know that I am a poet? I write poems and songs of love to earn a living." (Aria "Che gelida manina.")

A smile danced about the girl's face. Rudolfo looked into her eyes. "I am very poor, but when I look at you I am wealthy beyond everything, and yet I don't even know who you are."

"They call me Mimi, but my name is really Lucia. I earn my living by embroidering tiny little roses and lilies. They remind me of love and springtime. I spend most of my time alone, waiting for the spring. I love the sunshine and the flowers that come with the spring. The gentle little flowers that I make have no scent at all. But that is enough of me. I am just your neighbor and I'm disturbing you." (Aria "Mi chiamamo Mimi.")

"Will you join me and my friends at the Café Momus?" Rudolfo asked hopefully. "They are waiting for me and probably wondering where I am."

They were. Their voices could now be heard from the street below. Rudolfo walked to the window and called down, "Reserve a place for two of us. There is someone with me."

Mimi now stood next to him, drenched in the brilliant shafts of moonlight that suddenly flowed through the panes.

"You are very lovely in this light," Rudolfo said. "Now that the moon has joined us perhaps we should stay here for a while."

The little seamstress smiled. "I will stay with you forever." (Duet "O soave fanciulla.") She lowered her eyes, and arm in arm they walked out into the Christmas night.

ACT II

THERE was holiday excitement everywhere. The Café Momus was not far from Rudolfo's and Mimi's little garret, and the winding streets that led one there were filled with shop windows that caught everyone's eye and imagination. As the lovers came into the square they saw Colline, Schaunard, and Marcello.

"There are no tables out here. Come, let us look inside," said Marcello, beckoning to Schaunard and Colline.

Mimi was happier than she had ever been. She was enchanted with the lovely new bonnet Rudolfo had bought for her. Its soft, blue velvet framed her dark eyes and accented the whiteness of her skin which the winter air had now tinged with pink.

"The necklace you admired will be yours one day, too," Rudolfo told her, "if my rich old aunt is good to me." They laughed as they were jostled about by the noisy throng that soon thinned out to follow a boisterous group of vendors and students.

"Our own private dining room!" said Marcello as he and the musician and philosopher emerged from the café, carrying a tiny table.

"I cannot bear rubbing shoulders with the crowds," stated Colline.

"My friends, may we join you? This is Mimi," said Rudolfo, introducing the little seamstress. "She will be the Muse that inspires me to great heights!" (Aria "Questa è Mimi.")

"Ha! Ha!" his friends laughed, cynically. But actually they were delighted with Mimi's quiet charm, and they rose gallantly to salute her.

"Has Rudolfo given you a gift for Christmas?" Marcello asked.

"Oh, yes! This beautiful bonnet that I have admired for a long time. He's extraordinary, you know. It is as though he were able to read my mind."

"He can, undoubtedly," agreed Schaunard, smiling wryly.

"Rudolfo is a great romantic poet," confided Colline, and Mimi smiled, proudly. "I believe you."

"Believe and your most fantastic dreams will come true," added Marcello.

"I believe that love is the highest inspiration," mused Rudolfo.

"Love," reflected Mimi, "is a matter of taste. It is either honey or vinegar." Catching the look of dismay in Rudolfo's eyes, she quickly added, "But I did not mean to offend you."

"Enough of this sentiment," grumbled Marcello. "Let us drink a toast." Suddenly thinking of Musetta, his former sweetheart, he shouted angrily, "I think I'll drink some poison!" Mimi had little time to question his remark, for as if his thoughts had called Musetta to him, there she was! Almost touching them, she was sweeping among the tables, bubbling with gaiety. But the grumpy old man following her certainly was not! The blue silk of her dress rustled, and the green feathers in her hat danced on her golden hair.

"That is Alcindoro, her new admirer," someone was heard to say.

"I must have a table over there!" commanded Musetta, contemptuously snapping her fingers at her companion. She smiled sweetly in Marcello's direction. He, in great fury, turned his back to her. Co-

quette that she was, Musetta was angry at being ignored. She screamed for the waiter, berated the service, picked at the food, and finally, violently broke the plates, throwing them into the street.

"My dear, my dear, you must be more quiet," begged Alcindoro.

"Do not speak to me. You only make me more angry," snapped Musetta. Her blue-green eyes caught Marcello's angry gaze. "People always stop and look at me. My beauty always attracts their attention. Their eyes look at me longingly." She laughed. "I know it and I'm delighted," she went on, mocking Marcello. (Aria "Quando me'n vo' soletta.")

"You, too, once lost your heart to me," she called over to Marcello. "Remember?"

"They must still be in love," said Mimi to Rudolfo, glancing knowingly at the faces of Musetta and Marcello.

"Alcindoro! This shoe is killing me," wailed Musetta. "Go and buy me a new pair immediately! Go! Go!"

The blustering old man obliged her whim. What else could he do? She was so beautiful. As he disappeared down the street Musetta ran into Marcello's arms. She had planned it all that way, and now they were together again!

The waiter was with them, too, hovering over them with the check!

"What shall we do?" lamented Schaunard. "We have no money left!"

"Let me have the bill." Musetta laughed, calling to the waiter, "The gentleman who came in with me will pay for us all!" This seemed to satisfy the waiter, who left the happy friends to themselves. Why not? After all, it was Christmas and everyone should be together on that special day.

"But how can I go with you?" wailed Musetta, looking first at her satin slipper and then at her toes wiggling gaily in her sheer silk stocking. Colline and Marcello swept her up on their shoulders and they all left. And just in time, for there was Alcindoro, scurrying down the street, waving a box of shoes. But he was too late. The happy Bohemians disappeared into a crowd that was following a giant drum major, and the square was empty. The café was empty, too, except for Alcindoro and the bill.

ACT III

THE months that followed brought many happy times and also many times when there was not enough food and certainly not enough firewood for the little garret stove, but somehow they all survived. Mimi's beloved spring came and went, and the soft blue sky of autumn dwindled into the

sharp, azure-blue of winter. Marcello and Musetta were now living in a tavern on the outskirts of Paris, and Rudolfo had left Mimi. Why, she never really knew.

Thinking that perhaps Marcello would know where Rudolfo had gone she went to visit him. The big gate to the city opened and the guard directed Mimi to the tavern. It was surely Marcello's place. His painting of the Red Sea was swinging sadly in the wind over the door. An old woman came out.

"Would you tell the artist Marcello that I wish to see him?" implored Mimi.

He found the seamstress, weeping and coughing. The snowflakes mingled with her tears, making glistening little rivulets on her cheeks. "Dear Mimi," he called, hugging her to him.

"Dear Marcello, oh, dear Marcello," she wept.

"Musetta will be glad to see you, little one. As you can see, I am a sign painter now and Musetta is giving singing lessons. We manage to live. Now, come inside. Rudolfo is there."

"No, dear Marcello, I cannot. But I do need your help. Rudolfo loves me but he has run away from me. He is suspicious and jealous of every glance that comes my way. He accuses me unjustly," she continued, brushing a snowflake from her eye. (Aria "Oh, buon Marcello, aiuto.")

"Perhaps it would be wise to separate for good," advised her old friend. "You must be able to laugh and sing together, not weep and argue."

"You are right, dear Marcello, and you must arrange our parting so that all is understood. Will you?"

"I will go and waken Rudolfo now. You are coughing so badly, little one, you must not remain in this bitter cold."

"Marcello!" The voice from the tavern was Rudolfo's. As he strode from the house, Marcello gently pushed Mimi behind a great tree. "Better they don't talk to each other right now," he thought.

"I must not stay here any longer. I must go back to the city and say good-by to Mimi, forever," Rudolfo said excitedly.

"You are right," Marcello chided him. "When love brings tears, it is no good. Particularly for one as jealous and bad-tempered as you!"

Rudolfo protested. "Mimi is a coquette and she is unfaithful."

"That I do not believe," replied Marcello sharply.

Rudolfo looked up contritely. "Nor do I, if the truth were known. But it is more serious than that. Mimi is very ill—she is doomed. She never complained of the cold or of all the times we had no money and no food. I have never been able to give her what she needs."

No longer concealing herself, Mimi drew her threadbare scarf about her shoulders and sobbed. It was so cold and now everything was over! "Mimi, Mimi," cried Rudolfo, seeing her shivering figure for the first time. "You must come inside."

"No, Rudolfo, I cannot. I must go back to my attic. Will you look in the trunk for my prayer book and my bracelet? I would like to have them. You may keep my bonnet, as a remembrance, if you want it." (Aria "Addio, senza rancor.")

"We cannot part like this," said Rudolfo, and his words were almost drowned out by the sound of crashing pottery and crockery. Musetta was in one of her tempers again—all because Marcello had accused her of flirting.

"We will wait for another spring," said Rudolfo, tenderly taking Mimi in his arms.

"No one is lonely in April," sighed Mimi, "but I wish this winter would last forever." She smiled at Rudolfo. One could not stay unhappy when he was near.

"We will part when the flowers bloom again," they both agreed, "and everything will be as it was." (Duet "Addio, o dolce svegliare.")

ACT IV

TIME, as usual, had its own way of changing things, and before too long Rudolfo and Marcello were alone again. Their little studio was the same, but they were not. Vainly trying to paint and to write, they found their thoughts preoccupied.

"I saw Musetta today," said Rudolfo. "How elegant she looked in her velvet gown."

"I'm delighted to know that she's doing so well," said Marcello, dabbing at his canvas. He laughed.

"You're laughing." Rudolfo smiled. "But you're boiling on the inside."

Marcello interrupted him. "I saw Mimi today, riding in a grand carriage and dressed like a queen."

"I, too, am delighted," said Rudolfo.

"You lie," roared Marcello. What a state to be in. They both agreed that to work without Mimi and Musetta was impossible. Yet life with them also seemed impossible.

Schaunard and Colline suddenly appeared in the doorway.

Soon the dismal little room was changed into a rollicking party of dancing and play. They were in the midst of a brilliant fandango when they saw Musetta standing in the doorway.

"Musetta!" exclaimed Marcello, in genuine surprise. "What brings you here?"

"Mimi is out there. She's trying to climb the stairs but her strength has failed her."

Rudolfo rushed out the door to find her huddled on the last step. Schaunard helped him carry her, frail and shivering, into the garret, and they placed her on the rickety old bed. Mimi's voice was barely audible as she spoke. "Rudolfo, may I stay here with you?"

"For always," he said gently, "but for now you must rest and be quiet."

Musetta drew the anxious friends aside, whispering, "I saw the poor child stumbling along the street. She said that she knew death was near and she wanted to be with Rudolfo again. She begged me to bring her here."

"We have no money and no medicine," lamented Schaunard, "and a doctor is what she needs now."

"We can remedy that," said Musetta. "Here, take my earrings and sell them."

"Also my overcoat," said Colline. "It has served me well and long. Now I can bid it good-by. Come, Schaunard. We have often disagreed about many things, but let us agree to sell my coat together. Also let us leave Rudolfo and Mimi alone." (Aria "Vecchia zemarra, senti.") Schaunard nodded in approval and they left for the pawnshop followed by Marcello, comforting a weeping Musetta.

"Have they gone?" Mimi whispered. Rudolfo nodded. "I wanted to be alone with you," she continued. "I want to tell you that I love you. That you are my life." (Aria "Sono andati.")

"Beautiful Mimi," Rudolfo said, warming her cold hands in his.

"Beautiful . . . like a sunset." She smiled weakly.

Rudolfo took her bonnet from his coat pocket where he had kept it all these months, and placed it in Mimi's hands.

"My little hat, my little hat," she repeated, pressing it to her heart. "Do you remember, Rudolfo, the first time I came here?"

"You were so upset."

"You were so grave and kind."

"Then you lost your key and I helped you look for it," said Rudolfo, laughing.

"It was so dark . . . the shadows were so blue . . ." Mimi tried to continue but was seized by a fit of coughing.

Distraught, Rudolfo called out, "Schaunard!"

"It's all right, Rudolfo," Mimi said weakly, "I'm fine. Please forgive me?"

Soon everyone had returned, secure in the fact that the doctor was on his way.

"And for Mimi I have brought a beautiful muff," said Musetta, placing one decorated with tiny blue ribbons in the seamstress' cold hands.

"How good you are, Musetta," said Mimi. "You and Marcello must promise never to argue again."

Sadly, the young poet turned away to place Musetta's cape across the dirty window. It would shield Mimi's eyes from the first rays of the sun. Musetta was praying when Schaunard, who was standing near the bed, gestured to everyone but Rudolfo, who was gazing at the blue smoke beginning to rise from the chimneys. Then Rudolfo turned around. "What is all this strange moving back and forth, and why the odd expressions on your faces? What is the matter?" he begged.

"You must have courage," said Marcello.

Rudolfo realized the truth now. Mimi was dead. Mimi of the dark eyes and the frivolous blue bonnet.

The young poet wept, and the cold, blue dawn crept into the room and cast cold, blue shadows about the sad Bohemians.

Boris Godunov

BY MODEST PETROVICH MOUSSORGSKY
(1839-1881)

Libretto by the Composer

BASED ON THE PLAY "BORIS GODUNOV"

By Alexander Pushkin

Characters

Prince Shuisky . . . . Tenor
Pimen . . . . Bass
Boris Godunov . . . . Bass
Feodor . . . . Mezzo-soprano
Xenia . . . . Soprano
Gregory . . . . . . *{ later Dimitri the Pretender }* . . . . . . Tenor
Stechelkalov . . . . Baritone
Marina . . . . Mezzo-soprano
Hostess of the Inn . . . . Mezzo-soprano
Varlaam . . . . Bass
Missail . . . . Tenor
Rangoni . . . . Bass
The Idiot . . . . Tenor

Time: 1598-1605

PLACE: RUSSIA; POLAND

First Performance: Marinsky Theater, St. Petersburg; January 24, 1874

Boris Godunov has a history of an incredible number of revisions. Moussorgsky first composed the opera in 1869. However, it was rejected by the St. Petersburg Opera, and in 1872 Moussorgsky rewrote it. In 1874 it was performed, and though the public enjoyed it, the critics did not. In 1896 Rimsky-Korsakov revised the opera thoroughly, including cutting many parts out. He wrote another version in 1908, restoring the previously cut parts. *Boris Godunov* was to have still more versions of it written. In 1928 the Soviet Government published Moussorgsky's two versions, and in 1941 another version was written by the Russian composer Shostakovitch. In 1952 the composer Karol Rathaus wrote still another one. It is the Rimsky-Korsakov 1908 revision that is usually performed today.

ACT I

THE sable-soft branches of the pine and fir trees that surrounded the monastery of Novodievich were heavy with snow. Inside, Boris Godunov's thoughts were heavy with fear, but his ambitious mind was dreaming of the weighty Cap of Monomakh that would one day be held above his head, making him the Tzar. Outside, the courtyard was packed with people who had gathered, by official command, to implore Boris to ascend the throne. Their shoulders were heavy with the centuries of oppression and terror that was the lot of the peasants, and it took only a few blows from a police officer's whip to make them fall on their knees and call out to Boris to save them.

Stechelkalov, the Clerk of the Douma, or Council, which consisted of the ruling boyars who served the Tzar, stepped out into the courtyard. He looked up at the frosty-gray sky and brushed the snowflakes from his great fur coat.

"Great Boris has refused to yield to the prayers of the Douma and the Patriarch," he said, looking into the sea of gaunt faces that stared back at him. "Pray to God that He will send comfort and help to us in this hour of need. Pray that He will enlighten the weary soul of Boris."

The sound of the chanting of pilgrims, carried by the crisp, cold wind, drifted over the walls of the square. Stechelkalov and the people listened. The brown-robed men entered the courtyard and walked among the people, distributing amulets and begging them to take icons and other holy images to the great Boris. The sound of their voices disappeared as silently and coldly as it had come. As they filed into the monastery, the wind wailed and the snow fell like powdered bits of diamonds that refused to melt. It glistened and glittered on the dirty cheeks and rags of the Russian people.

(SCENE 2) In his cell in the Monastery of the Miracle in Chudov, Pimen, an old monk, was writing the last sentences of his book on the history of Russia. "Perhaps," he thought, as he stopped in his labors and put his pen down on the table, "some industrious monk will find my book and take up where I have left off."

The old man picked up his pen only to drop it with a start as Gregory, a young monk who was sleeping on the bed in the cell, woke with a terrified cry.

"I saw myself climbing the stairs of a tower," the young boy said as he wiped the beads of cold perspiration from his forehead. "From the top, Moscow looked like an ant hill. Below me, the square was filled with a seething crowd. They pointed up at me and laughed."

Pimen looked at the boy whose eyes were wild with excitement. The rays of the lamp in the room cast a strange hue on his reddish-brown hair. "As they continued to laugh," the boy said, "I fell from the tower. Then I woke up."

"Cool your young blood," old Pimen said calmly, "with some prayers and fasting. I, too, dream of wild happenings. I always recall the battles and the great feasts of years gone by."

Gregory relaxed and listened to the old monk. "*I knew Ivan the Terrible and was present at his sumptuous banquets. I even fought with him against Lithuania at the walls of Kazan!*" Pimen said proudly.

"I envy you," Gregory replied. "Your life is full of rich experiences and the memories of them . . . my life is empty and futile. I am nothing but a poor monk."

"Do not forget how many great Tzars, who were weary of the world, were willing to give up all the splendors of court life for the peace of the monastery. Ivan himself sat in this very cell. I recall how his son, Feodor, changed the palace into a cloister. But God was angry with Russia and sent her its present Tzar, the man who murdered a Tzar's son!"

Gregory leaned forward. "How old was Tzarevitch Dimitri when he was murdered?"

Pimen looked at him. "Had he lived he would be your age and sitting on the throne!"

Gregory's eyes blazed.

"It is with that sad story that I have closed my history of Russia," Pimen said. "I hope that you will continue it some day for me."

The matin bell began to toll, and Pimen extinguished the light and left the cell. Young Gregory stopped at the door and looked back into the darkened room. "Some day, Boris, you will pay for your crime," he said to himself. "Men will hate you and heaven will punish you!"

From the corridor, the lights of candles fell on his pale face and his crown of reddish hair.

(SCENE 3) The wily Tartar, Boris, had yielded to the entreaties of his people, of course, and he was crowned the Tzar. In the courtyard of the Kremlin, as the kneeling people awaited the arrival of their new ruler, the sun burst forth in a blaze of glory.

Prince Shuisky, the court adviser to Boris, stood on the steps of the Cathedral of the Assumption, watching as the long procession of boyars moved along on their way to pay tribute to Boris. As if by signal, a sound of trumpets echoed across the square and the Prince raised his great fur-gloved hand to the populace. "Long live the Tzar Boris Feodorovitch!" he cried.

"To the sun in all its glory! To the Tzar! To Boris!" the people of Russia roared.

The blaze of the sun and the jewels on the robes of the boyars nearly blinded them, and the sound of ringing bells nearly split their eardrums; but when, with servile obedience, they looked up, they saw Boris. As he stood at the top of the steps with his arm around his two children, Xenia and Feodor, with his black eyes peering into the sunlight, the people of Russia felt that surely this was their savior. His great fur robes stood firm and strong in the gust of wind that swept the square, and his crown, the Cap of Monomakh, with its pounds of gold encrusted with rubies and emeralds, sat majestically on his head. All eyes focused on its cross of gold and pearls, then back to the Tzar as he spoke.

"I feel a great sense of sadness since I have yielded to your prayers," he said, looking both at the peasants and at the boyars. "My soul is filled with fear and foreboding. For Russia and for myself." The little Tzarevitch, Feodor, looked up at his father with great pride, and Boris smiled.

"I ask for the blessing of Heaven on me and on Russia," he continued. "I bid you kneel in prayer before the tombs of the great Tzars. Then you shall be my guests at a great feast!"

The bells peeled forth and the happy, hysterical mob broke loose, running toward the Tzar shouting, "Glory, glory to the Tzar!"

Boris watched as the police restored them to order. Their cries of praise rang in his ears as he walked into the palace. Already the gold and sable Cap of Monomakh felt heavy on his head.

ACT II

GREGORY'S boredom in the monastery, combined with Pimen's tales of royal grandeur, festered and boiled in the boy's brain until one day he ran away and headed for the Lithuanian border.

At an inn near the frontier the hostess sang to her guests about a duck as she filled their great tankards with wine. (Aria "Poymala ja siza seleznya.") She interrupted her song to greet Varlaam and Missail, two roguish monks, as they entered the inn.

"Blessings on you and your house," they said good-naturedly, and motioned for their companion to follow them into the great room with its roaring fire. The young man was Gregory, in secular clothes. They had met him on the road, and all they knew about him was that he was anxious to get to the Lithuanian border. He had told them his life depended on it.

Although neither Varlaam nor Missail really trusted their new-found friend, they bade him join them in a glass of wine and to stop worrying. "You should have my cheerful philosophy," Varlaam said as he drank tankard after tankard of the potent red Russian wine.

Gregory listened as the monks lustily reminisced about the glorious battles at Kazan when forty thousand Tartars were slain. (Aria "Kack vo gorode beelo vo Kazani.")

Caught up in memories of the past, the monks paid little attention to Gregory, which gave him a chance to talk with the hostess.

"How far am I from the frontier?" he asked.

"You can get there by nightfall, but you will have difficulty getting past the guards," the woman told him. "I have heard that someone has escaped from Moscow and orders have come from the capital to detain and search all travelers."

She ignored Gregory's frightened look and explained that there was another road into Lithuania besides the highway. They both turned and looked at the door. A captain, accompanied by several guards, walked in and headed directly for Varlaam's table. They searched Gregory and the two monks and decided that the young boy was not worth bothering with because his wallet was empty.

"The fugitive from Moscow is a heretic monk," the captain said to Varlaam. "You seem to fill the bill perfectly!" Since the captain could not read, he handed the warrant to Gregory, who leaned closer to the fire and began to read.

"An unworthy monk, Gregory Otriepiev, tempted by the devil, has fled toward the Lithuanian frontier, where, by order of the Tzar, he is to be arrested."

"And hanged," added the captain.

"There is nothing here about his being hanged," Gregory remarked.

"It is implied," the captain shouted, as he motioned to the young boy to continue reading. Gregory looked at the words on the warrant and then directly to Varlaam. "About fifty years old, of medium height, baldish, grizzled, and red-nosed."

The guards immediately fell on the old man, but the strength of his days at Kazan was still with him and he threw the men back and threatened them with his fist. Realizing that he was in grave danger, he grabbed the warrant from Gregory's hand and began to spell out every word of the description. He read, "about twenty years old, reddish hair, one arm shorter than the other." The monk saw the boy edging away from the table. "*You* are the man!" he roared, but Gregory was much too quick for them all. With a sudden thrust he overturned the table, spilling the red wine on everyone near it, ran to the window, and escaped.

(SCENE 2) While the hostess was laughing over Gregory's escape, Xenia, the Tzar's daughter, was weeping in the Kremlin. Her lover was dead and no one seemed to care. (Aria "Gdie ti gench moy!") The Tzarevitch, Feodor, sat at his desk near her, poring over a huge book. Their old nurse and then Feodor tried to amuse her, but to no avail. Feodor was glad when his father came into the room and dismissed his sister and the old nurse. Now he could get back to his studies with his atlas of Russia.

Boris listened attentively and proudly as the boy pointed out all the leading features of the country. He patted the boy's head with his great jeweled hand and gazed about the room.

"I have attained the highest power," he said, looking sadly at the tier upon tier of icons that covered the walls. "In the six years of my reign there has been nothing but disappointment. My daughter grieves for her lover; plague and famine have devastated the land."

Feodor did not speak. Though these matters rarely touched the royal family, even he, a child, had heard stories that for three years nothing edible had entered the capital.

Boris roamed the room, lost in thought. "In spite of all I have done for my people, they lay their troubles at my door. The Poles conspire against me, my nobles betray me." He sighed. "And worst of all, my crimes haunt me day and night. The bleeding body of the child I murdered is always before me, pleading for my mercy that was denied him." The Tzar leaned against a great chair and sobbed, "O God, in thy grace have mercy on me!" (Aria "Dostig ya visshey vlasti.")

A sound of confusion arose from the hallway and Boris sent Feodor out to see what was going on. As the Tzar stood looking at an icon, one of his boyars entered to tell him that Prince Shuisky was asking for an audience. "News has come from our secret agents that many of the boyars, Shuisky among them, are conspiring against you, great Boris. They have joined with Poland and our other enemies."

Boris' eyes blazed with anger, but he had to control his fury for Feodor had returned. Boris smiled. "I hope that one day I may see my son rule in my stead," he said, drawing the boy to him. Feodor's presence calmed his anger, but when Shuisky entered the room it was unleashed again.

"You traitor! You hypocrite," the Tzar raged as he strode across the room. "Do you think that I am not aware of what a schemer you are?"

Shuisky stood coldly near the door, ignoring his insults. "I have grave news for you, your Majesty. A Pretender to the throne has appeared and he is backed by Poland and the Pope. The people may just believe that he *is* the real Dimitri."

"Leave now, my son," Boris said to Feodor, "this is not for your ears." He waited until the door closed behind the child before he spoke.

"See that the Lithuanian border is closed at once!" he commanded Shuisky.

Boris could feel that his hands were shaking. "Tell me, Shuisky, have you ever heard of dead men rising from the grave to trouble Tzars who have been chosen by the people and annointed by the Patriarch?" Shuisky stood quietly watching Boris' fear mounting. "You recall," the Tzar continued, "it was you I sent to Uglich when I heard of the boy's death. Do you swear that it was Dimitri's body you saw?" Boris' jeweled hands encircled the Prince's sable collar.

"If you lie, Shuisky, your punishment will be greater than any that Ivan the Terrible could have dreamed of!"

Shuisky stepped back and looked Boris directly in the eye. "For some days, my Tzar, I watched the body of the child when it was laid out in the cathedral with the corpses of thirteen men slain by the mob. Corruption had already set in the bodies of these men, but the child was still whole. His face was as tranquil as if he were sleeping." He watched his poisonous words take their effect on Boris. Now the Tzar would believe that some miracle had occurred and that the child was really alive.

Boris began to choke violently, and he motioned to Shuisky to leave his sight. He fell into a great chair, gasping for air. "So this is why for thirteen years my dreams have been haunted by this murdered child," he thought as he tore at his collar. "Who is this new enemy of mine? A mere shadow, a name!"

He pulled himself toward the table, struggling to the window to get some air. "No one will take the throne from my son," he roared as he fell, knocking the candelabra to the floor. His guilty mind saw the body of the murdered boy. "Stay back!" the Tzar groaned. "I am guiltless of your death!"

The huge clock began to chime. Great spasms of fear shook the Tzar's body as he dragged himself along the floor trying to escape from the bloody vision. All the clocks in the Kremlin were ticking and chiming again. "Oh, Lord God, show me Thy grace! Have mercy on the wretched Boris," he sobbed as his body crumpled to the floor.

ACT III

GREGORY had escaped into Poland and established himself as the Pretender to the throne of Russia. There he was known now as Dimitri and welcomed by the enemies of Russia, particularly the daughter of the Voyevode of Sandomir, Marina.

Marina was a strong-willed aristocrat who had led a dull life among the Polish nobility until the arrival of Dimitri. He was going to be her route to historical fame. He would take her to Moscow as his wife, and there she would sit on the throne of Russia bedecked in jewels and admired by the boyars. Marina had been well coached by the Jesuit Rangoni, who saw in Marina and Dimitri his way to establish the Church of Rome in Moscow.

"Your beauty has bewitched this Pretender, Marina," Rangoni told her. "You must enslave him entirely and use him for the Church's end."

The young girl had only her personal gains in mind, but the fear that Rangoni inspired in her easily made her an instrument of his plans.

(SCENE 2) Rangoni also spoke to Dimitri one evening while he waited for Marina in the garden of the castle at Sandomir. "Marina is truly in love with you," the Jesuit said, "but you must realize that she suffers by being so . . . the people of the court are against it. I can help you win Marina and the throne of Russia despite these Polish nobles, if there is a reward for my services."

"Wherever my fortunes carry me, you shall be with me as my spiritual adviser," Dimitri promised.

At the sight of Marina entering the garden, Rangoni left Dimitri.

The clever girl listened to Dimitri's words of love. Then she said, "I will be with you, Dimitri, but only in Moscow. I also recognize you for what you are . . . an imposter!"

Tears of anger filled his eyes. "Whatever I was, I am the rightful Tzar. My cause is growing by the day. Tomorrow I will march on Moscow, and when I am crowned I will look down on you with contempt as you crawl toward my throne."

Marina quickly saw it was time to change her approach. "It was only because of my great love for you, Dimitri, that I had to insult you. Time is running out and you had to be incited into doing something at once. I am with you no matter what." (Duet "Sdyes moya golubka.")

Rangoni watched them from the top of the steps that led into the garden; the moon silhouetted the figures of Marina and Dimitri, embracing.

ACT IV

IF THE gardens of Sandomir were the perfect setting for the dreams of ambition and grandeur that plagued Dimitri and Marina, the gray and scraggy woods near Kromy were the perfect setting for the dreams of hatred and revenge that filled the minds of the poor people of Russia. There some vagabonds had captured and tied to a tree a representative of all their oppression, the boyar Kroutshov.

As they taunted him and insulted the name of the Tzar, the village idiot stumbled into the clearing. He was a pitiful figure clad in rags with an iron saucepan on his head. He ignored the boys who were teasing him and sat down on a rock. He looked blankly up at the gray sky and mumbled to himself: "The cats are crying in the moonlight. I will praise God and hope that the weather will keep fine." He smiled as he tossed his single kopeck up into the air.

Some of the boys continued to torment him, and one grasped the shiny piece of money and ran away. The poor simpleton howled, but his sad cries were drowned out by the rough voices of old Varlaam and Missail.

"The sun is dark and so is the moon. Even the stars have been eclipsed by the evils that have fallen on Russia. It is all because of the Tzar Boris!" they lamented loudly, inciting the crowd.

"Death to Boris! Death to the murderer!" the peasants cried.

Their cries of hatred changed to ones of joy as Dimitri and his troops rode into the clearing. The hungry people listened enrapt as he spoke to them.

"I am the lawful Tzarevitch of all the Russias, and I will protect you all from Boris. All of you who are for me, follow me to the final victory!"

This wild-eyed, young Dimitri, with his white uniform and his reddish hair, would save them, the people believed. So with a great surge of approval they followed him to their destiny.

Alone in the forest, the idiot sat on his rock. He was looking quietly for his kopeck. He looked through the black fingers of the trees toward the horizon, but now all he could see was the death glow of a great fire in the distance.

"What terrible doom is going to fall on the Russian people now?" he wailed. He tasted the drops of salt that ran down his dirty cheeks and straightened the battered pot on his head.

(Scene 2) The Douma was convened in the great Reception Hall of the Kremlin, and the boyars were arranging for a proclamation to be issued—a proclamation that condemned the Pretender as a traitor and threatened death to all who supported him.

Shuisky, whom no one trusted, rushed into the hall with disturbing news. "Recently," the Prince told them, "when I was with the Tzar, I chanced to look back at him as I left the room . . . he was in a terrible state." The boyars looked at each other.

"The Tzar was pale and wild-eyed. He was trembling," the Prince continued. "He kept seeing the image of the slain Dimitri. He kept shrinking back against the wall crying, 'Away! Away!'"

"Away! Away!" screamed Boris as he reeled into the hall. "Dimitri is alive! Shuisky must be punished for spreading the lie that I murdered him!"

The boyars moved uneasily in their chairs, but suddenly Boris regained his composure and seated himself on his throne. "I have summoned you all to give me counsel," he said.

Shuisky interrupted. "Outside, O Tzar, is a pious old man who has a great secret to impart to you."

"Admit the man," commanded Boris.

The old man was Pimen, and he walked boldly and directly up to the Tzar and began to speak. "One evening, a shepherd who had been blind from birth came to me and told me that he had heard a voice bidding him to go to the Cathedral of Uglich and pray at the tomb of the Tzarevitch." Boris gripped the arms of the throne at the mention of the name. "The Tzarevitch," Pimen continued, "is a saint in heaven and able to work miracles. As the shepherd prayed, his sight was restored." (Aria "Odnajdi v vetcherniy.")

Boris gave an agonizing cry and fell from the throne into the arms of several boyars near him.

"Bring me my son," Boris commanded, "and bring the vestments of death to me."

The boyars made way for the frightened Feodor as he ran up the great hall to his father. They helped the Tzar back onto his throne and filed slowly out of the room, leaving the two alone.

"I must bid farewell to you, my son, and to the world." The boy wept and put his head in his father's lap. Boris gazed about the huge hall. Its walls wavered before his eyes. He closed them for a moment and stroked Feodor's hair.

"Remember, my son, when you are the Tzar, be firm and trust but a few. Always respect the Holy Church and take care of Xenia. I ask heaven to protect my children . . . not me." (Aria "Protshay moy sin.") He kissed his son and fell back on his throne exhausted.

Feodor wept as the funeral bells began to toll.

"It is the mourners' wail," Boris said sadly. "Bring me the monk's robe. The Tzar goes to the cloister." The Tartar who had become the Tzar of all the Russias, without being born to the throne, knew that this was his end.

Pushing Feodor aside, he started up with a great cry, "I am still the Tzar here . . ." He fell against the throne and pointed to his son. "He is your new Tzar! Almighty God have mercy on me!"

Clutching at his heart, he fell backward down the steps that led up to the throne. He was dead.

Through his tears, Feodor watched the sun as it crept through the double tinted sheets of mica at the windows. Its colored rays caught the figure of the double eagle of Russia at the top of the throne and sent it down as a shadow to crown the head of Boris Godunov.

CARMEN

BY GEORGES BIZET

(1838-1875)

Libretto by Henri Meilhac and Ludovic Halévy

Based on the story "Carmen," by Prosper Mérimée

CHARACTERS

CARMEN	Mezzo-soprano
JOSE	Tenor
MORALES	Bass
ZUNIGA	Bass
MICAELA	Soprano
ESCAMILLO	Baritone
FRASQUITA	Mezzo-soprano
MERCEDES	Mezzo-soprano
REMENDADO	Tenor
DANCAIRO	Baritone

TIME: 1820's

Place: In and about Seville, Spain

FIRST PERFORMANCE: OPERA-COMIQUE, PARIS; MARCH 3, 1875

At the first production of *Carmen,* Paris audiences were shocked by its realism. The otherwise sophisticated Parisians were scandalized to see singers smoking on stage. However, contrary to legend, the critics hailed *Carmen,* and the opera had a very successful series of performances.

It is interesting that Bizet, who had never been to Spain or Cuba, was able to capture so completely the color and rhythms of the country. Cellestine Galli-Marie, the first Carmen, was responsible for the famous "Habanera." She asked Bizet to write a seductive aria for her, and Bizet's version of the Cuban habanera was the result. Unfortunately, Bizet, who died three months after the première of *Carmen,* never saw his work take its place among the most universally popular operas of the century.

ACT I

THE hot, sultry sun beat down on the white buildings of Seville. The walls of the factory and the neighboring shops reflected the white heat. In one public square, the Dragoons, in their flaming red uniforms, roamed about, awaiting the changing of the guard. Everything—the bridge that brought one into the square, the tobacco factory, even the children playing in the street—seemed to be affected by a strange pulse of excitement.

Catching sight of a young girl who was obviously looking for someone, Morales, an officer of the guard, courteously asked, "Are you searching for anyone I might know?"

"Yes, a corporal," she replied. "His name is José."

"He's not with my company, but he will be here soon. Stay and wait for him," Morales entreated, pointing to the shade of the barracks. Thanking him shyly, the girl moved across the square and was gone. "Obviously, this girl is not a Sevillian," Morales thought, watching her.

Suddenly, he was almost knocked down by a group of children in dirty clothes and ragged little paper hats, who were preceding the relief detachment into the square. Their bright, happy eyes denied the heat of the day, and their rough, raucous voices seemed content to do nothing more than imitate the sound of the soldiers' trumpets. As the guard marched dejectedly into the square, the light of the sun grew brighter and the shade grew more scarce.

Morales greeted the young corporal, José, and told him of the pretty girl who had been looking for him.

"That must be Micaela," José said, absentmindedly bidding farewell to the departing guard. "How can those children march and sing in this heat?" he thought. He looked across the bridge and began to mop his brow.

He was loosening his heavy, red jacket when he heard his captain, Zuniga, asking, "Isn't that big building across the square where the cigarette girls work?"

"Yes," José replied dully, "and they're a troublesome lot."

"Pretty, eh?" inquired Zuniga. José confessed that he had never paid much attention to them.

"I know where your thoughts are, my friend. With someone called Micaela, I wager!"

"You're right," José said proudly. "I love her."

A bell in the factory tolled, announcing that it was noon. Noon—the hour that offered a few moments' escape from the dirt and heat of the cigarette factory for the gypsies and Sevillians who toiled there. The sun sent down white shafts of heat, casting long shadows about the figures of the cigarette girls as they moved into the square. Some sat on the warm stone steps of the bridge. Others leaned against the white walls, unaware of the heat against their bodies. They wanted only to laugh for a few minutes and watch the smoke from their cigarettes as it curled into the sky. A voice cut through the heat and the chatter, and José heard someone ask, "Where is Carmen today?" And then, as if in answer, she was there.

As she descended the steps of the bridge, José noticed her dark hair and her even darker eyes—how they flashed in the sunlight! Her cool smile disclosed white teeth accentuated by the dark, gypsy hue of her skin. But his thoughts were elsewhere. He turned his back on her and began to clean his sword.

Carmen leaned against the railing of the bridge, bored with all the clamoring attentions of the men. She stared calmly and openly at the young corporal.

One of the men nearest her longingly touched her torn shawl and asked, "When are you going to love us, Carmen?"

Almost too bored to answer, Carmen moved away. "Perhaps never, perhaps tomorrow . . . certainly not today," she answered, darting a glance over her shoulder to make sure that José was aware of her. She laughed. Her lips were as red as her skirt. Its white polka dots moved in a sea of red as she moved toward him. He paid no attention to her, so she sat down on the steps to the factory and lit a cigarette.

"Love is just a rebellious bird," she said, flipping a match into the street. "No one can tame it. It's like a gypsy that has never obeyed the law." She ground her cigarette out under the heel of her shoe. "If I love you . . . you'd better take care." (Aria "Habanera.")

The men surrounding her laughed and begged her not to go into the factory today. But Carmen, ignoring them all, moved closer to José. He seemed still unaware of her presence and sat silently cleaning a golden chain.

With a gesture like the sudden spring of an arrow leaving its bow and heading directly for its mark, the gypsy tore an acacia blossom from her hair and threw it in José's face. As the petals fell past him, she ran into the factory.

The bell was tolling again, this time silencing the laughter and signaling everyone to return to work. "How good to be alone," mused José as he picked up the flower at his feet. Its strange fragrance suggested that the gypsy girl must surely be a sorceress.

"José! José!"

The sound of his name made him turn as Micaela came running across the square. It made him happy to have her here, to learn of his mother and his village. It was all so different from the heat of Seville and the strange gypsy ways of cigarette girls like Carmen!

Micaela bent over José shyly, and quickly kissed him on the forehead. "A gift from your dear mother," she said, smoothing her white apron. The atmosphere of evil that hung about him was quickly dispelled as Micaela told him the news of home and gave him the letter she had brought from his mother. (Duet "Ma mère, je la vois.")

"And now I must leave you so you can read your letter. Besides, I must be home before nightfall."

With love in his eyes, José watched her as she crossed the bridge. She waved and was gone. He would remember only Micaela and forget that gypsy witch—above all, he would throw her evil flower away!

Suddenly, the factory square was filled with excitement. There were women and girls everywhere, screaming for help. The bell began to toll with such vehemence that it brought Zuniga, who had been napping, out of the guardhouse. He and José could barely move. The hands of the cigarette girls were clutching at them from every direction. "It was Carmen!" one woman yelled. "No! It was Manuelita!" howled another.

"Quiet! Quiet!" ordered the captain. "Carmen struck Manuelita," cried one of the girls, shaking her gold bracelets in his face. "It was Carmen!"

"No, it was Manuelita!"

"José, take some men into the factory and bring that gypsy troublemaker to me," roared Zuniga. "We'll settle all this now!"

Obeying his commanding officer, the corporal went into the dingy building, returning minutes later with the twisting, screaming gypsy girl. The crowd was getting out of hand in their defense of her—or was it of Manuelita? One couldn't tell, for the noise was overpowering.

"Carmen will explain," said José, as the angry girl relaxed in his grip.

"Torture me if you will, but it will not make me explain. I defy heaven itself," she said, throwing her words at Zuniga. "But that is of no matter, for standing here beside me is someone I will die for!"

"You will find yourself in jail, too," said Zuniga.

As an answer to that remark, Carmen struck the woman closest to her. It was bedlam all over again! With that Zuniga informed the gypsy that her hands would be bound, and that José would have to take her to jail. When Zuniga left to fill out the orders, Carmen asked, "And where will the handsome young corporal take me?"

"I will obey my orders and take you to jail," replied José, trying to keep his eyes from hers.

Carmen smiled, mockingly. "The flower I gave you was under a magic spell, and now you will have to obey my every wish."

"I forbid you to talk anymore," José said in an unusual burst of temper. He wished that this day had never happened.

"Then, I shall have to sing," Carmen laughed.

The heels of Carmen's red shoes beat out a sinuous rhythm on the stones of the street. She tossed her head back and stared straight into the sun. Her long, black lashes shaded her eyes and she did not even blink. "Tonight I am going to my friend Lillas Pastia's. He has an inn outside of Seville. We could dance there." Slyly, she leaned toward José. "I will take you along, because you, only you, please me." (Aria "Près des remparts de Séville.")

"Be quiet," said the angry, confused José.

"Oh, I was only talking to myself," the gypsy girl retorted. "I meant you no harm."

José felt the sun beating down on his shoulders, and he also began to feel as if maybe he were under some magic spell. But he didn't believe in magic! Could it be Carmen? Moving to her as in a trance, he loosened the ropes that bound her hands. Free again, Carmen twirled about, and her red-and-white skirt swept small clouds of dust into José's eyes. But as she noticed Zuniga approaching from the guardhouse, she immediately placed her hands behind her back again, winking at José and whispering, "As we cross the bridge, I will trip you, and you will fall. I will meet you at Lillas Pastia's." Then, laughing insolently as the captain ordered José to take her away, Carmen moved along ahead of her escort.

The bridge ahead of them wavered in tiny spirals of heat. Carmen shouted with joy as she tripped José and disappeared into the crowd, leaving an echo of gold bracelets and red heels on the roadway.

ACT II

CARMEN did go to Lillas Pastia's, but José was forced to pay the price of his negligence—two months in the dark jail in Seville.

During those months, the dancing and singing with her smuggler friends at Pastia's tawdry inn rapidly became a bore for Carmen. Zuniga, who often visited her at the inn, trying to court her, was becoming a bore, too. The castanets and colored lanterns were losing their charm, and she wished that Zuniga would stop asking her companions, Frasquita and Mercédès, to make her come back to Seville with him. Chewing on an orange, she gazed sullenly at a dirty wine bottle and at the funny reflections the candle-light made in its contents.

Zuniga jealously remarked, "You're probably waiting for that corporal who was imprisoned when he let you escape. I can see it on your face."

"I suppose you've executed the poor man already," Carmen said caustically, tossing the orange rind into the fireplace.

"No, he's free," Zuniga sneered.

Delighted with the news, the gypsy decided to be charming and use her wiles to get Zuniga out of the inn. She needed time now to prepare for José's arrival.

She would have to be patient, she decided, for from the door she could see the torches of a procession and hear voices acclaiming the arrival of Escamillo, the bullfighter. Captain Zuniga brushed past her and called out to the toreador, "Join us for a drink. The evening is early."

Carmen glowered at Zuniga and the new frustration he had created. Dismayed as she was with this new delay, it was exciting to hear Escamillo tell of his triumphs in the bull ring. (Aria "Toreador Song.") She loved it all—the flaming red capes, the agile thrusts of the matador as he met his moment of truth, and, most of all, that moment when he paid homage to his favorite lady. That moment when the eyes of Seville were turned on Escamillo's lady!

Escamillo was quick to notice the intensity of Carmen's gaze, and he walked over to her, tossing his red cape over his shoulder. "What is your name?" he asked. "Tell me. I'd like to remember you when danger faces me in the bull ring."

"Carmen. Or Carmencita—it all amounts to the same thing," she said, calmly picking up a cigarette from the table.

"Since you won't leave with me, Carmencita," Zuniga growled angrily, "I'll have to come back later."

Carmen looked away from Escamillo to the captain. "I wouldn't advise that, my dear Zuniga," she replied. She walked away, casually pining some jasmine blossoms in her hair.

Escamillo was now aware that he, too, was going to be ignored by the only person in the inn who interested him, so he tossed his glittering cape over his shoulder and strutted out.

With both Zuniga and Escamillo gone, the room was momentarily quiet. But that lasted only a short while for Dancairo and Remendado, the smugglers, were soon discussing their plans for a new smuggling raid. After much haggling with Mercédès and Frasquita, they all decided that they would have to have the cooperation of the women if the raid was to be successful. Indeed, all forms of conspiracy need the assistance of women! Since Frasquita and Mercédès had already made up their minds to join them, that left only Carmen to be convinced. She, however, paced the room nervously, annoyed at their insistence. She was interested only in José's arrival. After all, wasn't she in love? (Quintet "Nous avons en tête une affaire.")

"A touching matter," remarked Remendado. "Being a soldier, he may well change his mind."

But José had not changed his mind, for his voice could be heard in the distance singing happily of the Dragoons of Alcal. Smiling in triumph, Carmen rushed to the door to greet him. All the months of waiting were forgotten. She danced for him, singing a strange, wordless song full of gypsy rhythms. Her skirt, tier upon tier of brilliant reds and maroons, cast shadows across the floor.

José's fascination was, however, short-lived. For above the sounds of Carmen's black castanets, he could hear the sound of retreat in the army barracks. His preparations for departure sent Carmen into a rage. She picked up his sabre and helmet, and hurled them at him, shouting, "Scamper away, little one. I was foolish to think I might please you!" Dancing about him, she imitated the call of the bugles and her rage subsided only when José showed her the flower he had saved since the first day they had met.

"Its perfume stayed on even when the petals had withered," he said, as he held it out to her. "I have thought of nothing but you since the first time I saw your face." (Aria "La fleur que tu m'avais jetée.")

Carmen was sullen and quiet, poking at the crumbs from a stale piece of bread on the table. "If you loved me, you would leave everything and follow me and my friends to the mountains. There we could be free. No retreats and no commands."

José's desperate protests were ignored as she relentlessly urged him to follow her. "I will never desert," he insisted. But her rage only mounted, and she heaped insult upon insult upon him. The angry words would never have stopped except for a knocking at the door.

It was Zuniga, returning as he had threatened. His jealousy at seeing the young corporal there resulted in a duel that was fortunately broken up by Carmen's friends. As they tied Zuniga to a chair, Carmen tapped him on the shoulder with her fan, remarking, "You see, my captain, you have arrived at precisely the wrong moment. You will be held prisoner here until we have departed for the mountains. Will you join us now, José?"

"What other choice have I now?" he asked.

"How ungallant," chided the gypsy, as she wrapped her shawl about her shoulders. She turned to José. "Come, little canary, we are on the road to freedom!"

ACT III

THEY went to the mountains, and the mountains meant freedom in many ways. Freedom from army commands, freedom from Zuniga, and freedom of time. Time for Carmen to think of Escamillo and the bull ring of Seville. Time for José to realize that this flirtatious gypsy child was a creature of fast-fleeting feelings who had grown tired of him.

Carmen was bored again. There was always the travel on little-known roads and sleeping among the rocks at night. She sat on the hard, cold ground, thinking—if only they could get this newest contraband delivered, then she might return to Seville.

Carmen watched José, who was gazing into space. "What are you staring at?" she asked curtly.

"I was thinking of my mother," he answered sadly. "She still thinks I am an honest man."

Carmen shrugged scornfully and said, "If you don't care for this life, why don't you go home?"

Furiously, José replied, "Don't say that!"

Carmen laughed. "You mean you might kill me?" She wandered over to watch Frasquita and Mercédès telling their fortunes with cards. Carmen casually turned up the cards to see what the future held for her. "Death," she said. "First for me and then for him. The cards don't lie." (Aria "En vain pour éviter.")

The smugglers decided to continue on and left José behind to guard the goods that remained. Suddenly, Micaela appeared. She shivered with fright and whispered to herself, "I must be brave. I must . . . for José's mother's sake. Oh God, watch over me, protect me." (Aria "Je dis que rien ne m'épouvante.")

Micaela looked up and saw José standing on a cliff. She called to him as he lifted his gun and fired at something or someone. Escamillo sauntered through the pass, inspecting his hat which had a bullet hole in it. José ran toward him shouting, "Who are you?"

The toreador answered proudly, "I am Escamillo, toreador of Granada. I have come for Carmen. I know she was in love with a soldier, but by now that has passed."

José drew his dagger and wildly lunged at Escamillo, but Carmen and the smugglers returned at this moment and stopped the fight. Escamillo casually brushed the dirt from his clothes and looked at Carmen, "I invite all of you to the bullfight in Seville. Especially those who love me." He gazed at Carmen once more and left.

Carmen was dreaming of the excitement of a new life as the love of a famous idol of the bull ring when Remendado brought in Micaela. "She was hiding behind some rocks," he said.

Micaela rushed toward José joyously, but he coldly asked, "Why are you here?"

Micaela stopped and said tearfully, "Your mother, José, is longing to see you. Come home."

Carmen shouted at him, "Go! You don't belong here."

José seized Carmen's arm and fiercely said, "You want me to leave so you can run off to Escamillo, but I never will. Only death will separate us."

Micaela stepped toward José and finally told him, "Your mother is dying. She wants to see you, José."

José cried with disbelief, "My mother is dying?" He turned to go with Micaela. Suddenly, he turned back to Carmen. "I will see you again."

Carmen was unperturbed by José's threats. The cold mountain wind swept through the pass and her memory traveled back to the heat of that day in Seville, when she stood on the bridge, seeing José for the first time. She had felt the same heavy pull of destiny she felt now. But gypsies live by fate she told herself, lighting another cigarette.

ACT IV

IT WAS Seville at the height of a festival day, and Carmen was a part of it all. It was Escamillo's day, and she was a part of Escamillo's life.

She was dressed in shimmering white, a mountain of white lace for her mantilla, and a crucifix of brilliants that shown in the sun and scattered bits of light on the red carnations at her waist.

Stepping away from the crowd outside the arena, Escamillo spoke to Carmen: "If you love me, you may well be proud of me today."

She answered, her dark eyes peering across her white fan, "I love you as I have never loved anyone." She glowed with admiration, for, after all, Escamillo was the favorite bullfighter of all Spain.

Frasquita and Mercédès were there also, and they had both seen José lurking in the crowd. Their warnings to Carmen were of little avail, for she only laughed. "I'm not afraid. Why, I'll even stay here and talk with him."

The people around them surged into the arena, and when the great wooden doors closed, Carmen was left alone. But not for long. She turned and saw José leaning against a large red poster. He came toward her.

"I've been warned to be afraid of you. My friends tell me that you are here to kill me," Carmen said.

"I am not here to harm you. Let's forget the past," José pleaded, "and begin over again."

Carmen bit her lower lip in an effort to keep from shouting in anger. "I will not lie," she replied, snapping her white fan open and shut in her hand. "Between us, everything is finished!"

"Carmen, I will do anything for you. I will even join the smugglers again if you will stay with me."

"Never!" the gypsy said, spitting the word through her white teeth. She could remember too well José's weaknesses and indecisions. Now, as he groveled before her, she hated them. "Carmen was born free, and she is going to die free!"

José's pale eyes and his unshaven face were beginning to anger her now, and the joyous sounds from the arena only enraged her more. Her pride demanded that she be where Escamillo was. The eyes of Seville would be searching for her, and this weakling was only wasting her time.

Attempting to get past José, who stood firmly before the gate, she shouted, "Kill me now or let me get by!" The cheers of the throng and the shouts of admiration for Escamillo incited José to curse Carmen, again and again. But she was oblivious to it all. She threw the ring he had given her into his face and moved to the gate. The maddened soldier seized her and plunged his dagger into her heart.

The sun was beating down again, and the white walls and the red posters blended with the white lace of the gypsy's gown. The sounds of *Olé! Olé!* blended with the blare of the brass and the rolling drums. The red carnations at the gypsy's waist were very still now.

CAVALLERIA

RUSTICANA

⚹ RUSTIC CHIVALRY ⚹

BY PIETRO MASCAGNI (1863–1945)

Libretto by

GIOVANNI TARGIONI-TOZZETTI AND GUIDO MENASCI

Based on a short story, "Cavalleria Rusticana,"

BY GIOVANNI VERGA

CHARACTERS

SANTUZZA	SOPRANO
MAMMA LUCIA	CONTRALTO
ALFIO	BARITONE
TURIDDU	TENOR
LOLA	MEZZO-SOPRANO

Time - 1800's   Place - A Sicilian village
First performance - Teatro Constanzi, Rome; May 17, 1890

Pietro Mascagni wrote *Cavalleria Rusticana,* when he was twenty-three, with hopes of entering it in an opera contest. It took him less than three months to write, but when it was finished modesty kept him from sending it in. His wife, who had no such qualms about her husband's music, entered the opera in the contest secretly. It won first prize.

The audience at the first performance of *Cavalleria Rusticana* went wild with enthusiasm. Mascagni later recalled that the crowd at the première was so tumultuous it was impossible for him to get into his own home. Finally, friends had to lift him through a window with the help of a rope.

MOUNT ETNA rises out of the island of Sicily like some unreal cloud—a thunderstorm always ready to unleash her fury on the people that live beneath her. The lava that has flowed from her anger has made black rivers and black earth over almost all of Sicily—black like the deep-rooted melancholy of its people, who were a blend of the Greek, Saracen, and Norman worlds.

They wake each morning to the blazing Sicilian sun and live their lives with proud, ferocious dignity. Only Sicilians with black eyes and black hair, as dark and brooding as the rivers of lava, could have lived this story in the white heat of this island.

In a small Sicilian village on Easter Sunday, as the sun came up over the church in the square and Mamma Lucia's tavern across from it, Turiddu, Lucia's son, could be heard by some of the early risers singing a passionate serenade. As he swaggered through the streets past Lola's house he smiled and thought of her flashing eyes. The tassel of his red fez danced in the breeze. Turiddu was as proud of his solder's uniform as he was of his ability to charm all the young girls of the town. (Aria "Siciliana.")

He had just come back from his term of service in the army and he had already charmed Lola and Santuzza. But this morning he was dreaming of Lola and her dark eyes and her cherry-colored lips. He cared little that she was now Alfio's wife and that rumor had it that blood had already been spilt before their door. Today he felt as if he could die for her.

As he sang in the morning air, so did the women of the village and the men who were in the fields. The square filled with people who talked of the holiday. Then they disappeared. Mamma Lucia came out of her tavern to hang up some brightly colored tablecloths in the sun, and saw Santuzza coming toward her from across the bridge.

"So it's you? What do you want?" Turiddu's mother asked.

Santuzza pulled her black shawl tight around her head. "Where is Turiddu?"

"Do you have to come here looking for my son?" the older woman asked, turning away.

"I only want to know where I can find him," the girl said sadly.

Lucia looked around. "He's gone to Francofonte to get some wine."

Santuzza's eyes flashed. "No! That is not true. They saw him here in the village late last night."

Lucia moved to the doorway. "If that is so, he did not come home last night." She looked at the young girl. "Come into the house, Santuzza."

"I cannot come in, Mamma. I've been excommunicated."

The old woman, who was devoutly religious, gasped and then blessed herself. "Just what is it that you know about my son, Santuzza?"

There was no time to answer her question, for Alfio was coming into the square with some of his companions. The men were anxious to compliment him on the magnificent Sorino mules that pulled his cart, and the happy man was anxious to tell them how good it was to be back from his travels and be with his wife, Lola, again. (Aria "Il cavallo scalpita.")

"How lucky you are, Alfio, to always be so merry!" Lucia said, waving to him.

"Ha, Mamma Lucia! Do you have any more of that old wine?" he asked, stepping into the cool shadows of the tavern.

"I don't know. But Turiddu has gone to get some."

"But he's still here," Alfio said, snapping his whip against his boot. "I saw him this morning near my house."

"What?" Lucia said.

Santuzza pulled at the old woman's dirty apron in an attempt to get her to keep quiet. Alfio changed the subject when he heard the voices of the choir coming from the church.

"Well, I'm going along. You others go to church." He kissed Mamma Lucia on the cheek, and with a crack of his whip he led his donkeys out of the square.

The villagers were coming over the bridge on their way to church. As she removed her apron, Lucia looked at Santuzza. "Why did you motion for me to be quiet?"

"You know, Mamma, that before Turiddu went into the army he was pledged to Lola." Santuzza sat down on the wooden bench and let her shawl fall back from her head. "When he returned and found her married, he turned to me. I loved him and he loved me. Now, Lola has forgotten even her husband and she has taken Turiddu from me. I am dishonored and they are together again!" (Aria "Voi lo sapete.")

"Why do you have to tell me this horrible story on this holy day?" Lucia said, not quite sure whether to be angered or frightened.

"You go to church, Mamma, and pray for me. Turiddu will be coming along soon and I will talk with him," Santuzza said.

The last of the villagers had gone into the church and Lucia hurriedly followed them. As the doors closed behind her, Turiddu sauntered over the bridge. "You here, Santuzza?" he asked.

"I was waiting for you."

"You're not going to church?" the young man asked.

"No. I must talk with you. Where have you been?"

"To Francofonte," Turiddu answered.

"Don't lie, Turiddu. I saw you come down the path. And people saw you at dawn near Lola's house."

"So! You've been spying on me," he said as he whipped around.

"No! It was Alfio who told me," Santuzza insisted.

"Go away—let me be!" said Turiddu.

"You love her. I can tell," Santuzza cried out.

Turiddu paced back and forth, afraid that someone in the church might hear them. "Be careful, Santuzza. I am no slave to you!" (Duet "Tu qui, Santuzza?")

The girl began to tell him that she had forgiven him, that he could do anything that he wished, but the sound of Lola's voice stopped the words in her mouth.

Lola's black heels clicked as they came down the steps of the bridge and she chewed at the stem of a rose as she spoke. "Oh, Turiddu, has Alfio been by?"

Turiddu looked at Santuzza in embarrassment. "I just came here. How should I know?"

Lola put the rose in her bodice and smiled. "Well, perhaps he stayed at the blacksmith's. I see that you two are hearing Mass in the square."

Santuzza watched Lola as she sauntered over to them. If a stream of lava had flowed into the village

it could not have been blacker than Santuzza's voice when she spoke. "I was telling Turiddu that today is Easter and that the Lord sees all things."

Lola answered, "Aren't you coming to Mass?"

"Not I. Only those may go who *know* they have not sinned," said Santuzza.

"I give thanks to the Lord that I can go," Lola sneered as she pulled her shawl over her head.

"Come on, let's go. We have nothing to do here!" Turiddu said, reaching for Lola's hand. But she was out of reach, almost into the church.

She turned and laughed. "Do stay there, Turiddu."

"Yes, do stay, Turiddu," Santuzza continued. "I have more to say to you."

Turiddu rushed at her in anger. "Must you pursue me even on the steps of the church?"

Santuzza fell on her knees before him and cried. "I implore you, Turiddu, do not abandon me . . ."

"Go away, I tell you. Stop pestering me!" He pushed her to the ground.

Santuzza's hand reached across the stones and touched the heel of his black boot as he ran into church. She lay quiet for a moment until the great door shut with a thud. She dragged herself to the steps and shouted after him, "The curse of an evil Easter be on you, Turiddu!"

She was sobbing on the ground when Alfio came into the square, but the sound of his footsteps alerted her and she pulled herself up and wiped her eyes with her shawl.

"How far are they in the Mass?" Alfio asked.

"It is almost over . . . but here is something else for you: Lola's in the church with Turiddu!"

He looked at her with great surprise. "What did you say?"

"I said that while you are working in the rain and the wind, Lola is betraying you! With Turiddu!"

Alfio grabbed her hand and held it tightly. "If you are lying, Santuzza, I will kill you."

"My lips are not used to lying. I have told you the truth," Santuzza cried.

"Then, I'm grateful to you, neighbor Santuzza," said Alfio. "Before the day is over I will have their blood."

From the look of hatred in his eyes and from the tone of his voice, Santuzza could tell that he was speaking the truth. She was suddenly filled with terror and loathing—terror for Turiddu and loathing for herself for having spoken these words to Alfio.

The Mass was over, and some of the villagers saw Alfio's red-shirted figure with Santuzza slowly following behind, but they thought little of it. They were anxious to return to their homes and proceed with the festivities of the day.

Turiddu stopped Lola on the steps. "You're not leaving without even saying good-by, are you?"

"I'm going home. I haven't seen Alfio yet," Lola answered.

"Don't worry about that," he said, putting his arm about her. "He'll be along." He turned to the townspeople: "Come along, let's drink a glass of wine together."

Mamma Lucia agreed and urged all their friends to come into the cool tavern. There, under the great beams covered with green vines that protected them from the blazing sun, they all joined to toast the red Sicilian wine.

Turiddu raised his glass to Lola: "To your loves, Lola."

"To your good fortune," she laughed. (Drinking Song "Viva il vino spumeggiante.")

"To you all, good health!" Alfio shouted with a voice like the crack of a whip.

"Welcome," Turiddu said. "Join us in a toast." The young man handed Alfio a full glass of wine.

"Thank you," Alfio said, waving the glass aside. "It would poison me!"

"As you wish," Turiddu snapped back as he threw the wine against the wall.

"What is the meaning of this?" Lola asked, looking first at Alfio, then to Turiddu, and then to the spilled wine that was running across the stones. Sensing that something was about to happen, the villagers dragged Lola out of the tavern and left Alfio with Turiddu.

"Do you have something else to say to me?" Turiddu asked.

"I? Nothing!" whispered Alfio.

"Then I am ready," Turiddu replied.

They embraced in the manner prescribed by their country's custom which meant preparation for a duel to the death, and Turiddu bit Alfio's ear.

"Neighbor, you have bitten well," Alfio sneered. "We understand each other perfectly."

Turiddu drew back. "I know, Alfio, that I am in the wrong. I should let you kill me like a dog. But if I do, Santuzza will be alone. So, you see, I shall have to kill *you!*"

"As you see fit," Alfio said coldly. "I will wait for you beyond the garden."

He was gone when Mamma Lucia came out of the back room.

"I have drunk too many glasses of wine today, Mamma," Turiddu told her. "I think I'll go for some fresh air." He put his arms around her. "But before I go, I want you to bless me the way you did when I went off to be a soldier."

She kissed him warmly on the cheek.

"Kiss me. Kiss me again, Mamma. If I do not return, you must promise to care for Santuzza." (Aria "Ma prima voglio.") The young man embraced her quickly and ran over the bridge.

Lucia ran screaming after him. "What are you telling me, Turiddu?"

Santuzza caught her as she was about to fall, and they stood huddled together while a deathly silence hung about them.

Then, suddenly, as though an earthquake had split the day in two, a scream tore through the town. Like the thrust of a knife it ripped through the sunlight and plunged into the square. "Turiddu has been killed! Turiddu has been killed!"

Santuzza thrust her hand to her mouth to stifle a scream that never came, then fell to the ground.

CAVALLERIA RUSTICANA

DON

GIOVANNI

BY

WOLFGANG AMADEUS MOZART

(1756-1791)

Libretto by LORENZO DA PONTE

CHARACTERS

Don Giovanni, BARITONE.
Don Pedro, Commandant of Seville, BASS.
Donna Anna, SOPRANO.
Don Ottavio, TENOR.
Donna Elvira, SOPRANO.
Leporello, BASS.
Zerlina, SOPRANO.
Masetto, BASS.

TIME: THE EIGHTEENTH CENTURY

Place: In and around SEVILLE, SPAIN

First performance: NATIONAL THEATER, PRAGUE;
October 29, 1787

The story of Don Juan, upon which Mozart's *Don Giovanni* is based, is an old one which appeared first in sixteenth-century Spain and later in plays by Molière and Goldoni. Lorenzo da Ponte, author of the libretto for *The Marriage of Figaro,* collaborated again with Mozart on this opera. Though both Da Ponte and Mozart regarded the work as a *dramma giocoso,* or a merry drama, audiences and critics have tended to think of it as a serious opera.

Don Giovanni has legions of devoted admirers who claim that it is the greatest operatic achievement of all time. When Mendelssohn heard the work, he told the poet Goethe that it was "the most beautiful music in the world." *Don Giovanni* also inspired Robert Schumann to write his first treatise on music, in which he named Mozart a genius.

ACT I

IT HAS been said that cities are like mirrors—the older the glass, the deeper the reflection. Seville was an old city, and her shadowy reflections at midnight were far different than those at the height of day. At noon, Don Pedro's palace was white and imposing. At midnight it was black and ominous. The moon did soften the outline of the black walls, but not for long. The palace had the Spanish quality of an alternating feeling of sadness and happiness.

Leporello, too, alternated between sadness and impatience as he waited for his master, Don Giovanni, to end his visit with Donna Anna, the daughter of the Commandant Don Pedro. Leporello was Don Giovanni's servant, and he was used to waiting endless hours for his master. During these periods of boredom he often dreamed of better days. Days when he would be a fine gentleman. When he would no longer be a peasant. When he would not have to follow his selfish master from country to country in a never-ending search for beautiful women.

"I'm just a watchdog," Leporello thought, looking up at the moon as it disappeared behind a cloud. (Aria "Notte e giorno faticar.")

The courtyard was black as Giovanni rushed from the palace. Leporello hid himself behind a column. As was usual, his master was not alone. This time, Donna Anna was clinging to him desperately and trying to pull the Don's black cape away from his face. Giovanni pushed her away and the young woman stood looking at him and trembling with rage. She began to scream, and the sound of their struggle awakened the entire palace. Its heavy mahogany doors opened, flooding the street with light. Donna Anna's father appeared with his sword drawn.

"I won't fight with you," Giovanni said quietly to the old man. Leporello could see his master's hand reaching for his jeweled rapier. He trembled, watching the old, white-haired Commandant as he moved toward Giovanni. He knew that his younger master could put an end to the Commandant in no time at all. Anna rushed into the palace.

"Not fight me?" the Commandant shouted, lunging at Giovanni.

"You are a fool!" Giovanni smiled. "You must want to die."

The Commandant was indeed no match for the brilliant swordsmanship of Giovanni. It took only one carefully and stealthily driven thrust and the old man fell to the ground, mortally wounded.

"That was well done," Leporello commented with unsuspected daring. "First, you betray the daughter, and then you kill the father."

The dark streets of Seville swallowed them up as Donna Anna ran from the palace, followed by her fiancé, Don Ottavio.

"Father!" she cried, taking her father's cold hand.

"Take the body out of her sight," Ottavio ordered. Tears of anger and despair filled Anna's dark eyes as she watched the servants carrying her father's body into the palace.

"You might as well go with them, Ottavio," she said. "Let me die, too."

"Listen to me, Anna. Look at me. You know I live for you. You must forget the memory of tonight. I will be a husband and a father to you."

Donna Anna took the young man's hand. "Do you promise to avenge my father's death?"

"I swear that I will," Ottavio said, kissing her gently on the cheek.

They walked quietly into the palace. Anna faltered for a moment on the last step and turned to Ottavio. "We will avenge him together!" (Duet "Fuggi crudele, fuggi.")

(SCENE 2) Morning found Giovanni and Leporello leisurely walking down a country road. Giovanni was dreaming of his rendezvous with a new love, and Leporello was trying to summon up the courage to make known some of his real thoughts concerning his master.

"May I speak freely with you?" he finally asked.

"Of course. But hurry it up."

"You're leading an evil and very dangerous life."

"And it's very bold and dangerous of you to speak to me like that," Giovanni said angrily, putting his hand on the dagger in his belt.

He squinted in the early morning sun and motioned for his servant to be quiet. "There's a lady coming up the road. Let's step into the trees and observe her for a while. She might be pretty."

Completely amazed by his master's uncanny sense of perception as far as lovely women were concerned, Leporello followed the Don without arguing. Sure enough, a lady did appear. Even the black folds of her mantilla could not hide the fact that behind the intricate lace there was the face of a beautiful woman. Leporello sighed.

It was Donna Elvira, a noble woman of Burgos, on her way to her summer house. From their hiding place in the shrubs along the road, the two men could easily see that she was upset. They could hear it, too. She was talking angrily to herself.

"If I ever find him," she said, "I'll tear his heart out. He's my husband and he promised he'd never leave me." (Aria "Ah! chi mi dice mai.")

"Hear that?" Giovanni asked, slapping Leporello on the back. "A lady in distress. Let's try and console her."

"You have already offered consolation to hundreds of ladies," the servant said under his breath. Giovanni, however, was already approaching Donna Elvira.

"Don Giovanni! You monster!" Elvira screamed, pushing her mantilla back from her face.

Giovanni quickly regained his composure and took Elvira's hand. "Please, my dear, don't be angry. Let me explain . . ."

"Explain?" she cried, her brittle voice growing higher and higher with every accusation. "You abandoned me after swearing you would marry me."

"I had good reasons for doing that," the Don lied, motioning for Leporello to join them. "Didn't I?"

"He had good reasons," Leporello agreed as he pushed his big, broad-brimmed hat down over his eyes, trying to avoid the anger of Elvira's glance.

"Reasons?" she screamed. "I'll have my revenge!"

"If you don't believe me, then ask this gentleman." Giovanni laughed, pushing Leporello in front of him. "He'll tell you all!" Flashing a smile of perfect white teeth, he ran up the road.

Elvira was speechless—for a moment. Leporello laughed at the arrogance of his master and at the look of frustration on Elvira's face.

"You wretch," she screamed, stamping her black shoes in the dust. "How can you laugh at my bad luck?"

"Oh, let him go," Leporello said, wiping his forehead with his dirty handkerchief. "He really isn't worth the time."

"He betrayed me."

"My dear woman," the peasant replied, taking a black book from his torn pocket, "this is a record of all the women my master has loved and deserted. Why, he's notorious in Germany, in France, in Italy. Women mean nothing to him. Rich, poor, beautiful, or ugly . . . they're just a passing thing." (Aria "Madamina! il catalogo.")

"Well," said Elvira, staring up the road, "I will have my revenge." Leporello shrugged his shoulders as though he doubted that she would ever see Don Giovanni again. Elvira paid little attention. The sun was rising high now and the heat of the day would soon be upon her. She vigorously and angrily began to fan herself.

"Too bad," thought Leporello, watching Elvira's taut, straight back as she disappeared over the horizon, "nothing can come of all this . . ." He put his catalogue back into his pocket and lazily sauntered up the road.

(SCENE 3) In the village, there was to be a wedding celebration for Zerlina and Masetto.

At least it would be a change for Leporello. He would be among his own kind. Zerlina was an adorable village girl and Masetto was a charmingly stupid country bumpkin. What the appeal of the event was for his master, Leporello did not care to consider, except of course there was always an abundance of pretty girls at such weddings.

Don Giovanni and Leporello watched the happy dancing of the peasants. In their naive way, they liked the Don. It took only a broad smile and a few words from him to have them all in the palm of his hand.

"Good day, my friends. Don't let me interrupt your good time." He winked at Zerlina. "Are we having a wedding?"

"Yes, my lord." She smiled, smoothing the folds in her flowered skirt. "I'm the bride."

"And I'm the groom," Masetto said, taking off his hat and pushing back an unruly lock of hair.

"Dear Masetto! My dear Zerlina!" Giovanni said cheerfully. "We will all be friends. I offer you both my protection. Leporello, take all these good people to my villa. See that they have chocolate and coffee . . . wines and ham. Everything for a festival day!"

Masetto's big calf-eyes looked to Zerlina. "And," continued the Don to Leporello, "see that my friend, Masetto, is amused. I will bring Zerlina along later."

"My lord," Masetto stammered, pulling at the pink ribbon on his hat, "Zerlina must not stay here."

"Come now," Giovanni said with fatherly devotion, "Zerlina is in the hands of a gentleman. We'll be along shortly."

"But, what about me?" Masetto continued.

"We will," the Don said impatiently, "put an end to all this dispute if you don't go immediately." He put his hand on his sword. A little smile played about Zerlina's mouth, for although she was pleased by this nobleman's attentions, she was in love with Masetto. She reached out and touched his hand.

"I understand very well, my lord," Masetto said, turning to go with Leporello. "I am sure of your kindness and I am sure that you are a gentleman. Your noble manners will make a lady out of her, too."

By this time all the villagers were halfway up the hill, and Leporello could feel the growing anger of his master, so he pushed Masetto along.

Don Giovanni took Zerlina's hand as she waved good-by to Masetto.

"Well, at last we got rid of that fool!"

Zerlina took the garland of flowers from around her neck and tossed them aside, smiling. "But I'm engaged to marry him."

"What?" Don Giovanni roared. "Do you think that an honest man like myself would allow a lovely girl like you to marry a clod like him?"

"But I've given my word," Zerlina replied, running under his outstretched arms.

"You were not meant to remain a country girl," the Don went on.

"Well," Zerlina said coquettishly, "I do know that gentlemen of high quality are not always honest with women."

"That's a rumor. Why, I want to marry you."

Zerlina laughed, thinking of the times she had looked in her mother's old and cracked mirror and dreamed of being a great lady.

"You?" she exclaimed.

"Of course," said the Don. "Once we are in my little house over there, you'll give me your hand and say 'Yes.'"

"I'd like to go, but . . ."

"Come along," the Don urged. "I'll change your whole way of living."

"He might be telling the truth," Zerlina thought. "I'd like to . . . but I can't," she said in complete confusion. Giovanni's long-lashed, flashing black eyes and the gleaming jewels on his fingers did appeal to her though, and she was just about to go with him. (Duet "Là ci darem la mano.")

"Stop! You scoundrel!" Elvira yelled, coming up behind them.

Giovanni stopped. He knew that voice well.

"Can't you see, my love," he said, "this is only a little game."

"And I know the game you're up to," Elvira continued, taking Zerlina's hand from the Don's and patting her on the cheek. "Get away from this monster. Every word he tells you is a lie. Even his face is a lie!"

Zerlina, now wide-eyed with amazement, was glad to be free of the whole situation and she happily went off with Elvira, leaving Giovanni sputtering and annoyed over his lack of good luck.

"Everything is going wrong today," he said, kicking at the garland of flowers that Zerlina had thrown on the grass. Looking up, he saw Ottavio and Donna Anna coming into the village green. "This is the last straw," he thought, trying to plan an escape.

"We have found you just in time, sir," Anna called out, not recognizing Giovanni as her assailant of the night before. "Do you have a brave heart?"

"Why do you ask that?"

"Because we need your assistance."

"Just command me," the Don said, relaxed in the knowledge that he had not been recognized. "My sword, my possessions, my blood are at your disposal."

Donna Anna wiped her eyes with her long black handkerchief, and looking up saw Elvira glowering in rage at Don Giovanni.

"Don't put any trust in this man," Donna Elvira remarked, looking at Anna's grief-stricken face. "He has already betrayed me. You will be next."

"She has quite a noble air and a sweet face," Ottavio said quietly to Anna. "She fills me with a strange pity."

"Pity?" Don Giovanni laughed. "Why, she's demented. Just let me stay with her and perhaps I can calm her."

"Don't believe him!" Elvira pleaded, pulling away from him. "His soul is as ugly as his thoughts."

Ottavio looked at Don Giovanni. "This lady seems . . ."

"This lady is mad," Giovanni assured him. "Be quiet, Elvira, or we will have a crowd with us. You must not be talked about. Let us discuss this elsewhere." (Quartet "Non ti fidar, o misera.")

Elvira smiled sadly and walked away with Don Giovanni close behind her.

It was broad daylight, but to Donna Anna there seemed to be dark, cold shadows everywhere.

"Ottavio," she whispered, clutching the black crucifix at her throat, "he is my father's assassin."

"What are you saying?" Ottavio asked, as he took her in his arms.

"There is no doubt," Anna continued. "His voice

DON GIOVANNI

. . . it's the same voice of the man who was in my room that night."

"It cannot be. Giovanni is a great nobleman. He is our friend."

"It was this same man. I *know* it!" Donna Anna continued, gripping Ottavio's hand. "He killed my father."

All Anna's blazing Spanish temper flared up as she gazed into Ottavio's bland blue eyes. Their innocence and bewilderment annoyed her.

"I ask you for vengeance, dear Ottavio. If you should ever forget that, remember the bleeding wound in my father's chest. It will revive your hatred, as it does mine." (Aria "Or sai, chi l'onore.")

Troubled, but glad to be alone for a moment, Ottavio watched Anna as she walked up the path to the villa.

"How can a man of such high birth be guilty of such a crime?" he asked himself. He could still feel the strength of Anna's hand on his, and her strong conviction about Giovanni somehow gave him a strength he had never known.

"Her happiness is my happiness and her anger is mine, too," the young man thought to himself. "So, there is nothing for me to do but to find out the truth." (Aria "Dalla sua pace.")

(SCENE 4) When the late afternoon sun was about to sink, Don Giovanni was in his garden, making plans for an evening of wine and romance. Leporello arrived and Giovanni asked, "Is everything going well, dear Leporello?"

"Everything is going badly," his servant replied, sitting down wearily on the edge of the fountain. "I have tried to entertain them. I have lied to them and coaxed them. Masetto, too. He is so jealous!"

Don Giovanni smiled.

"Can you imagine who arrived here with Zerlina?" Leporello asked.

"Donna Elvira?"

"Yes. She shouted and screamed and said terrible things about you in front of everyone. Finally, when she got out of breath, I pushed her out of the garden and locked the gate."

"Excellent!" Giovanni roared. "Tonight, we shall have an even better party. These country people intrigue me. Ask everyone to come. There will be dancing and singing and drinking! And tomorrow we will add some new names to my book. Come, we must make some preparations." (Aria "Finch' han dal vino.")

Leporello wiped his face and followed his master into the villa, and Masetto and Zerlina came into the garden.

"I won't put up with you any longer," Masetto said to Zerlina as he flopped down beside the fountain. "I certainly don't deserve this treatment."

Zerlina picked a rose from one of the bushes and tenderly brushed its petals against Masetto's face. "But I'm innocent, Masetto. He didn't touch me at all. Beat me if you want to. You can put my eyes out and I will still kiss your hands. Let's be friends again." (Aria "Batti, batti.")

"I must be weak in the head," Masetto thought, listening to her cajoling words. "But she does get around me."

They both began to tremble as the sound of Giovanni's voice in the villa echoed in the stillness of the garden.

"Why are you afraid?" Masetto asked. "Do you think that I will find out what really happened between you two?" Looking about, he added, "I'm the one who should be afraid. That's why I'm going to hide in these rosebushes. You stay here, and speak very loudly."

Thinking that she had better conceal herself, too, Zerlina ran behind the fountain. But it was too late. She heard the Don calling out to her and then she felt his hand pulling at her belt of ribbons.

"I see you, little Zerlina," he laughed, "so, don't try to run away."

"Please let me go!"

"Can't you see that I love you? Come with me."

Over the coronet of flowers on Zerlina's black curls, the Don could clearly see Masetto's face peering through the trees.

"Is that you, Masetto?" he asked. "Why are you hiding there? Can't you see that Zerlina cannot bear being without you?"

"That's very true, sir," Masetto said with a touch of irony.

"Come along, the two of you. Don't you hear the music?" Giovanni put his arms around both of them, urging them to come into the villa and join in the dancing.

The day that was ending had been long for the two country youngsters. They were tired and confused, and they no longer had the energy to play games with the noble Don. They smiled weakly at each other, and followed him into the ballroom.

When the sun had set, three people dressed in black-and-white domino costumes walked into the garden. Leporello, watching from the window, could not hear their conversation for their voices were drowned in the relentless splashes of the fountain.

"Let's have courage, my friend," Elvira said quietly, "and we will be able to uncover all of his crimes."

"She is right," Ottavio agreed, looking at Donna Anna.

"I am afraid for all of us," Anna replied, looking at her reflection in the fountain. She adjusted her black mask.

Leporello called over his shoulder to Don Gio-

vanni. "Look, my lord, at the richly dressed masqueraders in the garden!"

"Tell them we would be honored to have them join us," Giovanni shouted back.

"His voice reveals him," the masked trio said, almost as one.

"My lord invites you all to come in and join the dancing!" Leporello called out cheerfully.

With forced "Thank you's," and smiles that denied their true intent the unmasked figures joined hands and walked toward the villa, asking heaven for protection and vengeance. When they reached the palace they put the masks on again. (Trio "Protegga, il guisto cielo.")

(SCENE 5) As Elvira, Ottavio, and Anna were making their way down the great candlelit hall that led to the ballroom, an angry Masetto was having a difficult time with Zerlina. Chocolate and sherbert had revived her sagging spirits, and she was rather obviously flirting with Don Giovanni. The masked trio drew a deep breath, and looked quickly at each other as the doors to the ballroom opened and they were greeted by Leporello.

"Everybody is welcome here!" Giovanni said, saluting them with a goblet of champagne. "Three cheers for freedom!"

"We are grateful for your kindness," Elvira and Anna responded. They were joined by Ottavio, who was busy admiring the magnificence of the ballroom.

"Start the music again!" Giovanni roared. "Everyone take a partner!"

The room was a swirling mass of dancers, and the air was filled with the sounds of first a minuet, then a country dance, and then a waltz. Everyone was dancing, even Leporello. He was clumsily whirling around with Masetto, and trying to distract him from the Don's obvious attentions to Zerlina.

From behind their masks, Donna Anna, Donna Elvira, and Ottavio watched the Don as he took Zerlina from the room. Leporello had seen this latest move, too, and quickly followed.

At Zerlina's first cries for help, all the villagers were stunned into silence. En masse, Don Ottavio and the men rushed for the door, but the wily Giovanni was thinking fast. He pushed Leporello ahead of himself into the ballroom.

"Here's the real villain!"

"What are you doing?" Leporello asked, struggling in the Don's strong grip.

"You are going to die for this," Giovanni went on.

Ottavio stepped away from Anna and Elvira, brandishing a pistol. "You won't escape this time."

"This pretense won't work tonight," Anna and Elvira said, ripping off their masks.

Don Giovanni recognized the three of them and momentarily drew back. Then his eyes took in the entire scene and every possible escape route. He could see the angry villagers, led by Masetto, coming at him, but their fury only added to his courage.

"*I* am afraid of nothing!" he laughed, holding them back with his sword. "Even though the world should end, I'm not afraid."

A roll of thunder from an approaching storm shook the crystal chandeliers, and a gust of wind blew in from the garden, sending the filmy silk curtains at the windows up into the air in ghostly billows.

With the energy of a cornered animal, Don Giovanni pushed Leporello through the doorway. Then, with a dangerously close lunge, he stabbed at Don Ottavio and jumped from the window.

"A bolt of lightning will strike you down," the villagers shouted after him. But he was gone. Nothing was heard but raindrops on the pebbles of the pathway and the singing of the fountain.

ACT II

EVEN for one of Don Giovanni's unlimited daring, it seemed wiser to allow a few days to pass before returning to Seville, and further exploits. So he and Leporello were not seen for several nights, and when he did return to Seville it was to see Donna Elvira.

Standing before her house, Leporello decided to leave his master, once and for all.

"What have I done," Giovanni said innocently, "to make you want to leave?"

"Oh, nothing! You only tried to kill me!"

"It was all a joke, you fool. Come, let us make peace," he laughed, throwing Leporello a bag of gold pieces.

"Well, I accept, this time."

"Good!" Giovanni slapped his companion on the back. "Now, do you have the courage to do as I ask?"

"If we are going to leave women alone."

"Never!" laughed Don Giovanni. "I have just seen Elvira's beautiful maid. We're going to try an experiment. I would like to talk with her, but I think it will be more interesting if I change clothes with you."

"Why not your own?"

"With such ordinary people, my dress would excite suspicion."

"Master, for many reasons . . ."

"No more arguments, Leporello!"

So there were no more arguments, and they completed their change just as Donna Elvira came out onto her balcony.

"Elvira, my love?" Giovanni called out, winking at Leporello. "I have come to ask your forgiveness."

Elvira fell against the iron railing, not believing her own ears.

"She still loves him," Leporello thought. "What a fool!"

"Come down and talk with me," Giovanni begged. Against her better judgment, Elvira did.

"Now," said Giovanni, "when she comes out the door, you walk up to her. Disguise your voice . . . make love to her . . . get her away from here!" (Trio "Ah, taci, ingiusto core.")

When Elvira appeared, Giovanni carried the plot even further by acting the part of a street hoodlum, terrifying them both until they ran away. He then serenaded Elvira's maid who remained inside.

He had no sooner finished his serenade when Masetto and his friends, in search of the Don, came into the square. Giovanni pulled Leporello's big hat down over his face and called to them.

"Masetto? Is that you?"

"It is. Who are you?"

"Don't you recognize me? I'm Leporello."

"Well," said Masetto, stupidly putting down his lantern, "where can we find your master? We intend to kill him!"

"I'll tell you what to do. If you come across a man and a woman near the square, it will surely be him, making love again." The Don smiled at the serious look on Masetto's face. "You can't miss him. He's wearing a black hat with white plumes. Now, half of you men go *that* way and the rest, *that* way. Masetto, you come with me."

It took but a little of the Don's versatile play-acting to relieve Masetto of his musket and pistol, for the unwise boy would do anything he was told. And then, when the last of the villagers had disappeared down the empty streets, Giovanni struck out at the unsuspecting Masetto and beat him violently until he fell to the ground, screaming for help.

Zerlina was the first to find her unhappy sweetheart. "Didn't I tell you, Masetto, that your jealousy would get you into trouble? Who did this to you?"

"Leporello, or somebody dressed in his clothes," Masetto sobbed, rubbing his head.

Zerlina smiled tenderly. "You *seem* to be in one piece." And, taking her sad-looking country bumpkin in her arms, she told him that she had a remedy for his aches and pains. "My love will make you well again." (Aria "Vedrai carino.")

(SCENE 2) While Zerlina was consoling Masetto, Leporello was busy with Elvira. He was busy maintaining his disguise as Giovanni, and busy trying to escape from the searching villagers. Their hurried flight brought them directly to Donna Anna's palace. Leporello saw Anna and Ottavio coming from the gate to the courtyard, but all his desperate gyrations could not move Elvira fast enough to get them both out of sight. Also, Zerlina and Masetto were approaching from the opposite side of the square.

Thinking that he was Giovanni, they all confronted him, crying out, "Kill him!"

"Spare him," the deceived Elvira sobbed. "He's my husband!"

Seeing Ottavio's and Masetto's drawn swords, Leporello decided that it was time to give up acting the role of his master. Squirming in fear, he begged them to let him live. "I am not the man she thinks I am."

"Good Lord, Leporello!" Donna Anna cried.

"So it was you who beat Masetto!" Zerlina wailed.

"Take pity on me," Leporello cried, running from Elvira to Ottavio to Masetto. "I didn't want to do anything. My master made me do it."

In their confusion as to who was who, Leporello easily escaped and ran into the darkness.

"Well, there is no doubt now," Ottavio said, "Giovanni is the murderer of Donna Anna's father. All of you stay in the house with her until I return. I am going to get help."

Anna smiled with pride at her lover. Elvira was sobbing in embarrassment and shock, and Masetto was rubbing his head. Ottavio stood watching the strange group as they walked into Donna Anna's palace.

"Stay with my loved one. Try and comfort her grief. I am going to avenge her. When I return, I will be able to tell her that he is dead!" (Aria "Il mio tesoro.")

The great iron gate closed and Ottavio ran down the street alone.

(SCENE 3) In his fright, Leporello stumbled quite accidentally into a cemetery and hid behind the magnificent statue of the Commandant—a huge equestrian figure that guarded the tomb.

Giovanni, too, went to the same cemetery, to hide from Elvira's angry maid. Spying Leporello in the moonlight, he called out.

"Hi! Leporello! Don't you recognize your master?"

"Is that you?"

"Tell me what's happened."

"I was nearly killed again, because of you!"

Giovanni roared with laughter. "I just met a friend of yours on the road. She thought that I was you!"

The mouth of the gray marble statue seemed to move in the moonlight. "You will stop laughing before dawn!"

"*Who* said that?" Giovanni asked, drawing his sword.

65

"Leave the dead in peace, you villain!" the statue continued.

"It must be someone outside trying to tease us," the Don said flippantly. "Look! Isn't that the statue of the old Commandant? Read the inscription to me."

"I've never learned to read by moonlight," Leporello answered, trembling so he could barely stand on his feet.

"Read it!" Giovanni commanded.

"I AM WAITING HERE TO TAKE VENGEANCE ON THE VILLAIN WHO KILLED ME."

"The silly fool," Giovanni said, swaggering around the tomb. "Tell him that I will expect him to dine with me tonight."

"I can't do it, Master. My heart is pounding so."

"Do it, or I'll put this sword through your fat body!"

"My . . . my master wants you to come to supper with us," Leporello said.

The statue nodded.

"Will you come to supper with us?" Giovanni shouted, amused by the sight of Leporello shaking in his boots, and by the thought that any piece of cold marble could move.

"Yes," the statue replied.

"Well, this whole thing is indeed strange," Giovanni mused. "But, if we are having a guest for supper, I suppose we should go and prepare for him."

Leporello had already scaled the wall. He was all too willing to leave. Giovanni followed, slyly taking a bemused look at the ominous figure on horseback. Don Giovanni laughed.

(SCENE 4) During the hour of Giovanni's and Leporello's mysterious encounter with the statue, Ottavio visited Donna Anna. He hoped that with the assurance of the proper authorities, who were going to find her father's murderer and make him pay for his crimes, he would be able to convince her that she should marry him. Anna, however, was too grief-stricken to think of a wedding. She did not mean to be unkind but she could not rest until the entire matter involving Don Giovanni had been resolved. (Aria "Non mi dir, bel idol mio.")

(SCENE 5) In his villa, the Don had dressed himself in his most lavish doublet and cape, and he proceeded to consume many glasses of vintage wine.

"I spend my money to enjoy myself," he laughed, throwing an empty glass in the direction of the orchestra that was seated in the gallery. "Play! And you, Leporello, bring in the food!"

The Don was not, as he had hoped, destined for a quiet evening, for Elvira frantically interrupted his supper to declare her love and to beg him to give up his evil way of living.

"You do amuse me, Elvira," Giovanni laughed. "At least let me eat in peace. Join me, if you like."

"You are the most terrible example of sin and evil that I know," Elvira screamed, and ran from the room.

Don Giovanni, hardly able to contain himself, threw back his head in great peals of laughter.

Elvira shrieked in the hallway, and Leporello ran into the dining room, crying out to his master, "Don't go out there! I could see his face."

"What are you babbling about?" Giovanni demanded, getting up from the table. "Someone is knocking at the door. Answer it!"

"I cannot," Leporello sobbed, crawling under the table.

"Then I will!"

As the Don swung the door wide open, a gust of wind tore through the dining hall and almost knocked him down. It was the statue!

"You asked me to supper, Don Giovanni. I have come," said the statue.

"I do not believe it," Giovanni said quickly, regaining his composure, "but I'll do the best I can."

"We are all dead," Leporello moaned as he obeyed his master and started to leave to prepare another place.

"Stay for just a minute," the statue said in deep, rumbling tones. "I have no need for the food you mortals consume."

"Then what do you want?" Giovanni asked.

"Will you come to supper with *me?*"

"I'm not afraid," Giovanni answered. "I'll come."

"Give me your hand as proof," the statue said, extending his marble, gloved hand. At his touch, Giovanni screamed in pain.

"This is your last chance, Don Giovanni," the statue went on. "Repent and change your ways."

"No! Never!"

The statue of the Commandant, refusing to release his grip, continued to drag the Don to the door. "Say 'Yes,' Giovanni," he asked again.

"No! No!"

A flash of lightning struck the golden knobs of the door, and a sheet of flames burned into the dining hall. The black-and-white marble squares of the floor seemed to give way under some unseen pressure, and Giovanni and the Commandant were dragged down into hell. Just as suddenly, the marble floor moved back into place and calm settled over the villa.

Leporello opened his eyes to see Elvira, Donna Anna, Ottavio, and Zerlina with Masetto. "You will never see him again," Leporello cried. "The statue took him away. The Devil helped to avenge us all."

"It is a just end for an evil man," Elvira said.

"It is the rightful doom for the wicked," Donna Anna said to Ottavio as he took her in his arms.

"The end for the evil is always like the life they lead," Masetto and Zerlina joined in, looking at the trembling Leporello.

The fat little peasant looked around the great dining hall. Everything was as it had always been—except for Don Giovanni's favorite mirror against the wall. It was shattered into a thousand, dagger-like splinters.

ELEKTRA

by Richard Strauss

(1864–1949)

Libretto by HUGO von HOFMANNSTHAL

CHARACTERS.

ELEKTRA ....Soprano
CHRYSOTHEMIS ....Soprano
KLYTEMNESTRA ....Mezzo-soprano
ORESTES ....Baritone
AEGISTHES ....Tenor

Time: Antiquity   Place: Mycenae
First performance: Hofoper, Dresden; January 25, 1909

Elektra was the start of Richard Strauss's association with the brilliant Austrian writer Hugo von Hofmannsthal. The work was presented as a "dramatized symphonic poem," and created a furor at its opening in Dresden. Strauss's music made extraordinary demands on both the orchestra and singers, who had to fight against the overwhelming volume of more than 100 instruments. Mme. Schumann-Heink, who played Klytemnestra, related that, at the first rehearsals of *Elektra*, Strauss cried to the orchestra conductor, "Louder, louder! I can still hear the singers!" Mme. Schumann-Heink left after one performance.

FROM the cool shadows of the roadway that led to the palace, one could see nothing but the heavy boughs of eucalyptus and oleander. Then, almost suddenly, the great city of Mycenae loomed up, impressive and forbidding. Its entrance, called the Gate of Lions, and every stone of the fortress bespoke the first rule of military art for which the Greeks were famous: "See without being seen."

All Greece and all the kings of Greece had once paid tribute to Mycenae's ruler, Agamemnon. But now that he was dead, the palace and its legends of murder and horror were left to his heirs and survivors. Agamemnon's two daughters, Elektra and Chrysothemis, their mother Klytemnestra, and her new husband, Aegisthes, lived and hated there.

If it were true, as the Greeks believed, that the gods lived in the trunks of the olive trees and circled the sky in the form of eagles, then the gnarled trees and the great birds could have observed much on one particular night. In the courtyard shadows, several serving maids talked among themselves as they drew up cool water from the well and poured it into their jugs.

"Where is Elektra?" one asked, as she wiped her hands on the edge of her skirt.

"This is the time of night when she laments the death of her father," her companion said quietly. "You will hear her soon. The echo of her wail will resound through the whole palace."

The youngest of the servants spilled some water on the ground as she turned suddenly and saw Elektra standing in the shadows. Elektra's dress of rags was covered with the red earth so typical of that part of Greece, and her unkempt hair hung about her face, almost hiding her burning eyes.

"I cannot understand why the Queen allows her to walk about the palace looking like that!" exclaimed one of the maids. "If she were my daughter, I would lock her up."

Another servant spoke more compassionately. "We should not talk that way against her. You know that she is forced to eat with the dogs, and that Aegisthes beats her."

The youngest girl smiled. "I would like to kneel before Elektra, wash her feet, and dry them with my hair." The overseer pushed the girl aside and ordered her to go into the palace, but the child continued defiantly, "Elektra is the daughter of a great king. She should not be made to suffer."

The overseer dragged the weeping girl to the great doors of the palace and pushed her inside. Elektra watched them in silence as they wrangled among themselves. Then, taking up their jugs, the women slowly walked into the palace, leaving Elektra alone in the courtyard. The night was quiet except for the screams of the young servingmaid who was being beaten for having spoken out in Elektra's defense.

"Agamemnon! Agamemnon!" Elektra cried. "I am alone! Father!"

The nightmare of her father's horrible murder was with Elektra day and night, and in the shadowy rocks she could clearly see all the bloody events that had occurred on that night years ago. She could see Klytemnestra and Aegisthes as they threw the fatal net over Agamemnon while he was bathing. His arms were tangled in its tough fibers, and he was unable to defend himself as the axe fell. Eyes wide open, he had died at the hand of his own wife!

"Oh, Father," Elektra wailed, "come to me and give me strength for the day that is coming, your day of vengeance, when all your mighty horses will go with all your faithful dogs to be sacrificed on your grave." She danced to the memory of her dead father. She danced as she and Orestes, her brother, would dance with Chrysothemis on the day when their father's murder was avenged.

"Like this, Father, we will dance over your grave on that triumphant day! Agamemnon! Agamemnon!" she called, beseeching her father's spirit to come to her. (Aria "Allein! Weh, ganz allein.")

Chrysothemis came out of the palace and, for a moment, stood in the doorway, watching her sister groveling and weeping on the ground. "Elektra," she called.

Elektra stood up and looked disdainfully at her pretty, blonde sister.

"What do you want? Tell me, and go!" Elektra said, moving stealthily toward her. As if to defend herself, Chrysothemis raised her hands to her face.

"Why do you raise your hands like that?" Elektra screamed. "That is the way our father lifted *his* hands the day the axe fell on him! What do you want, daughter of Klytemnestra?" Her words were like the snarl of a dog.

Chrysothemis rushed to her sister's side, and hysterically told her of their mother's newest plans. "They intend to lock you in the tower, Elektra. The tower where you will never see the light of the sun or the moon." Elektra laughed.

"It is true, Sister! I heard them talking as I stood near the door."

"Do not listen at doors, Chrysothemis. Do not open doors. Sit by the gate with me and wait. Wait and pray with me for the day of judgment that will fall on them!" Elektra sat on the steps and beckoned her sister to join her.

"I cannot sit in the dark, Elektra. All I can do is roam the hallways and rooms of the castle . . . but I never find rest. I hear voices in all the rooms and vaults . . . but when I reach them, there is no one there. I am so afraid, Elektra. I cannot even weep. Have some pity, Elektra."

"On whom?"

"If it were not for you, we could have long ago been free of this place. They are afraid of your hate and they keep us here. Elektra, I don't want to die here. I want to live and know the joy of marriage and children." Elektra turned away.

"Listen to me, Sister." Chrysothemis was insistent. "Our father is dead and our brother will never come. Must we go on waiting and waiting? Orestes will *never* come." She began to weep.

"Why are you howling?" Elektra asked, kicking at the red dust. "What is that noise in the palace?"

Chrysothemis knew the sound. It was Klytemnestra walking through the hallway. "You had better hide, Elektra. Do not let her find you here. She is angry and upset because she dreamed that Orestes found her. You must not cross her path tonight!"

Elektra pushed her hair from her eyes and smiled. "I want to speak with my mother tonight, as I have never wanted to before!"

"I will not listen," Chrysothemis said as she ran away from the palace and into the night.

Elektra watched her sister's white figure disappear. "A weak, frightened bird," she thought. "One must have the strength of eagles to cope with Klytemnestra!"

Suddenly the windows of the palace were blazing with light, and the sound of a frantic procession grew nearer. Elektra turned and watched. The sound of whips and staggering bodies did not frighten her. She was not afraid. She stood straight and tall. Her heart was filled with loathing as she turned to face the Queen, her mother, Klytemnestra!

Klytemnestra leaned on the arm of her serving maid, and peered into the night. Her scarlet robe fell about her. The flames of the torches danced in her heavy eyes, and on her blood-red jewels, and on her sallow skin. She raised her ivory staff and pointed it at Elektra. "Look at that! Look, she still defies me. She would strike me dead with a glance if she could!"

Paying no attention to her servants' warnings, the Queen slowly walked toward Elektra. "Since you are not in a hostile mood, Elektra, I will come closer to you." At a wave of her jeweled arm, all the attendants left the Queen and Elektra alone. The dim light from one remaining torch cast strange shapes and shadows in the gray courtyard.

Wearily, Klytemnestra told Elektra of the nightmares that were racking her mind and body. She had been unable to sleep for months, and she hoped that the demons who were haunting her could be appeased by some blood offering. "These jewels that adorn me bring me no rest. I cannot sleep, Elektra. But I believe that you can help me."

"I, Mother?"

"Yes. You are strong. You think clearly. You can see that I am ill. And yet, I am not ill. I am dead! And yet I feel that I am living. . . . I know, Elektra, that if blood is made to flow, if the *right* blood is made to flow, I can be free of this curse." (Aria "Ich habe keine guten Nächte.")

Elektra looked at the red earth behind the well where she had hidden the bloody weapon of her father's murder. She smiled, knowing that there was one secret that Klytemnestra would never know. "Blood will flow from under the axe, Mother, and when it does, you will dream no more," she said, turning to face the old woman's ravaged and beseeching eyes.

"Who will be the sacrifice? Tell me quickly! Tell me the victim's name!"

"A woman."

"One of my servingmaids? A child? A wife?" Klytemnestra frantically clutched one of the gold bracelets on her arm. "A mother?"

"Yes. A mother!" Elektra answered.

"Must I be the one who strikes with the knife?" asked the Queen.

"No! This time you do not go to the chase with your net and the axe. A man will deal the blow. A stranger will help you . . . one who is our kin."

With a furious gesture Klytemnestra pounded on the stones with her staff. "Enough of these riddles, Elektra. Take care!"

Elektra was ecstatic at being able to frighten her

mother, and had she not controlled herself she would have joined the flickering shadows that seemed to call to her to come and dance with them.

"Have you called Orestes back from exile, Mother?" Elektra asked.

Klytemnestra whipped around in anger. "I have forbidden that his name be spoken here!"

"Why do you tremble, Mother? Are you afraid of him?"

"Why should I be afraid of one whose mind is gone? He stutters and stammers and plays with the dogs."

"But once he was strong and beautiful!" said Elektra.

Klytemnestra leaned against her staff, trying to hold her drooping eyelids open. "He is well cared for. I have sent gold for his care. He is treated as a king's son."

"You lie!" screamed Elektra. "Your gold was used to kill him. Your eyes tell me that you are lying."

Klytemnestra pointed a bony finger at Elektra. "I am in command here," the Queen shouted, "and I fear no one who roams in foreign lands. I will find the way to make you disclose the words I must know to relieve me of these nightmares. If you will not tell me now, as you roam this palace in freedom, then I shall have you put in chains!"

Elektra sprang threateningly at her mother. "Do you want to know from whom the blood must flow? From your own neck. From *you!*"

Klytemnestra recoiled in horror. "I see it all, Mother," Elektra went on. "The huntsmen chasing you down the stairway, through the vaulted hallway, chasing you with great, black nets, until you are struck down. And I who sent them will chase you, too. You cannot escape. When you are dead, you will dream no more!"

Klytemnestra could not breathe. In fear, she dropped her staff. Then, as she gasped for air, the lights in the palace grew brighter, and the Queen's two servingmaids came excitedly out of the door. One whispered to the Queen. Klytemnestra looked up into Elektra's eyes. "More light! More light!" she screamed as her servants helped her up the steps. At the top of the stairs she turned and raised her arms in a threatening gesture, then threw back her head and laughed triumphantly.

Elektra stood confused and angered. What had the train bearer whispered to her mother? What could she have said? Now she could see the procession of servants and their torches moving into the palace. She could hear the sound of Klytemnestra's gold sandals slithering along the stones. What had she been told?

Chrysothemis came running into the courtyard and fell at Elektra's feet. "Orestes is dead!"

"Be still!" screamed Elektra, pushing her sister aside.

"Orestes is dead. I went outside the palace, and out there everyone knows. Two strangers, an old man and a young boy, brought the news. Orestes was dragged to his death in a chariot race!"

Elektra was stunned by the news, but she also realized that now, more than ever, everything depended upon her and Chrysothemis. "It is not true! I know it is not true. But we cannot wait. We will do the deed ourselves." Elektra pulled Chrysothemis to her. "I have hidden the axe."

"You cannot mean that we will kill our mother!"

"Both of them! Mother and Aegisthes. You are strong, Chrysothemis. We can do it while they sleep."

"We cannot. We must escape."

Elektra wiped the tears from her sister's eyes, and took her hand. "I will be your slave, Chrysothemis, if you will help me do it. We cannot escape until we have done it!"

"I cannot, Sister. I cannot do it, Elektra." Chrysothemis pulled her hand from her sister's and ran into the palace.

"Then be accursed!" roared Elektra as she hurled a handful of red earth at the white figure closing the huge doors. "I will do it alone!"

She began to dig near the well. Her hair fell into her eyes, and tears of anger and hatred almost blinded her. She stopped digging and listened. Everything was quiet. Then she saw a shadow move across the courtyard. A man's figure stopped near the steps.

"What do you want here, stranger? Leave me to do my work in peace," Elektra said.

"Are you a servingmaid from the palace?" he asked.

"Yes," she smiled sarcastically, "I serve the royal palace."

"Then I must wait until I am called," the stranger said, looking at the great doors. "I have come with tidings for the Queen." He looked at Elektra. "We can give witness that her son Orestes is dead."

Elektra got up from where she had been crouching. "Take your tidings elsewhere. You are alive, and he who was a thousand times more noble than you is dead!"

"Peace to Orestes. He loved life and brought much to it," the stranger continued as he moved closer to Elektra.

"But I am alone and he is dead," Elektra moaned. "I cannot bear to think of him as dead."

"Who are you? Are you any kin of Agamemnon and Orestes?"

Elektra rubbed a dirty hand across her throat. "Kin? I am the blood of Agamemnon and Orestes. I am Elektra."

The young boy started back. "No! *You* are Elektra?"

"Yes," she answered sadly, "but leave me now."

"Elektra, listen to me. I have little time to spare. Orestes is alive!"

"Alive? Is he safe?" She stood transfixed, staring at the young man's golden, curling hair. Strange thoughts whirled through the mist of her mind. That robe he was wearing, embroidered with wild beasts, was it familiar to her? And above his shining eyes, was it a scar she had seen as a child?

"I am frightened. Who are you?" she asked.

He reached out to her. "The dogs in the courtyard know me well . . . my own sister does not?"

"Orestes!" Elektra cried out, hiding her face in her hands.

The moon passed over the courtyard, catching her young brother in its light. "Let me look at you, Orestes. If you are just a vision, please do not vanish." Orestes knelt before her and tried to embrace her, but Elektra drew back. "Do not touch me, Orestes. I'm ashamed to stand before you like this. I was once beautiful and now I am a corpse. This matted hair of mine was once beautiful, too. I am ugly and hateful now. I am ashamed to stand before you in the moonlight like this. But I must speak to you, Orestes. You must not be afraid." (Aria "Orest! Orest!")

Orestes nodded. "I have come at the bidding of the gods. They will protect me."

"You are blessed, Brother, because you will do the deed. And blessed is he who finds the axe to help you!" Elektra saw her brother tremble. She also saw another man in the courtyard. It was Orestes' tutor.

He spoke quietly and firmly. "Now is the time, Orestes. No man is in the palace now."

Conquering his fear, the young boy drew himself up and strode to the doors. He paused for a moment, then went in. His tutor followed him and as they closed the doors behind them, Elektra ran up the steps and began to pace back and forth like a caged animal. Suddenly she stopped, horror-stricken. "I have forgotten to give him the axe! I forgot! It is still hidden."

She ran to the well, but before she could reach it a piercing scream came from the palace. It was Klytemnestra. Elektra threw back her head. Her eyes blazed in the moonlight.

"Strike again!" she cried out like a wild woman. Another scream tore across the sky. Elektra stood still. She did not even see Chrysothemis and the servants rushing out of the palace. Elektra saw only Aegisthes coming into the courtyard, and the sight of him stumbling in the dark brought her back to reality.

"Is there anyone here? Bring me some light," he grumbled. Elektra rushed up the steps and removed a torch that stood beside the door.

"May *I* bring you some light?" she asked, bowing before him.

"Where are the strangers who have brought us the tidings of Orestes?" he asked.

Elektra pointed. "In the palace," she said.

"Is it true that he is dead?" Aegisthes asked.

"They tell the truth, and not only with words, my lord, they bring proof. There can be no doubt." Elektra's black eyes stared at Aegisthes and she circled about him in a strange dance.

She threw the torch into the shadows, watched Aegisthes disappear into the palace, and waited.

A little later Aegisthes' cries of "Murder! Help! Murder!" rang through the air.

Elektra thrust her hands toward the sky. "Only Agamemnon hears you!" she answered.

In minutes the courtyard was filled with the fire of torches and the sound of voices. She heard Chrysothemis calling, "Sister, come with me. Orestes is here! Our brother is here, and he has killed them." The sounds of swords filled the night as Orestes' soldiers battled the guards in the palace. Elektra fell against the great doors, shaking with joy.

"Can't you hear the sounds?" Chrysothemis asked. "The sounds of freedom?"

Elektra crouched on the threshold and looked up into the sky. "How could I not hear the music?" she said. "It comes from me. I shall lead the dance of triumph."

Chrysothemis ran to the window. "Look, Elektra, look. They are carrying Orestes on their shoulders."

Elektra paid little attention to her. "We are with the gods now. I was once a blackened corpse, and now I am a living flame." She rubbed her eyes with her hands and pushed the matted hair from her face. The moonlight fell on her, and the years of hatred that had aged her beyond her time dropped away. She was young again.

"See the light that comes from my face," she called to her sister, "Love does destroy, but no man can be with the gods if he has not known love!" (Duet "Wir sind bei den Göttern.")

She flung her arms about and lifted her legs in a wild and nameless dance, her head thrown back, joyous, free, happy at last.

Chrysothemis called her name.

"Do not speak, Chrysothemis. Dance! I will lead the sacred dance to Agamemnon!"

She performed a few more steps of uncontrolled triumph and then fell lifeless down the steps.

Chrysothemis beat her fists against the huge doors calling, "Orestes! Orestes!" and the black eagles soared over the Lion Gate, over the valley of the orange trees, over the fields of poppies, and out to the gray and swelling sea.

FAUST

BY

CHARLES GOUNOD
1818–1893

LIBRETTO BY JULES BARBIER AND MICHEL CARRE

BASED ON THE POEM "FAUST" BY GOETHE

FAUST	TENOR
MEPHISTOPHELES	BASS
WAGNER	BARITONE
VALENTIN	BARITONE
SIEBEL	MEZZO-SOPRANO
MARGUERITE	SOPRANO
MARTHA SCHWERLEIN	SOPRANO-MEZZO

Time: In the sixteenth century
Place: A German village

FIRST PERFORMANCE: THEATRE LYRIQUE, PARIS; MARCH 19, 1859

The legend of Doctor Faustus had attracted many writers and composers before Charles Gounod wrote his opera *Faust* in 1859. Both Marlowe and Goethe wrote plays about the legend, Wagner composed a Faust Overture, and no less than four composers, including the Frenchman Hector Berlioz, based operas around it. None of these operas, however, has proved so enduring a work as Gounod's. Slow to win favor with Paris audiences, *Faust* later became renowned on two continents, a special favorite of Queen Victoria, and so successful that it has been performed as many as seventy times a year at the Paris Opera, where it opened!

ACT I

THE folds of the heavy, reddish-brown curtains that hung at the huge windows of Faust's study, barring the entrance of the early morning sun, were streaked and thick with gray dust. An odor of fatigue and age hung over everything. Even the once-brilliant leather-bound books and the parchments illuminated with gold letters lay wearily against each other on the shelves, their red leather now dull, and their gold now tarnished. A single candle cast tired shadows on the lined face of the bearded old man turning the pages of a once-magnificent book. He pushed it aside in fatigue and desperation, and stared dejectedly into space.

"There is *nothing*," he cried out, as if in answer to some dark question from the shadows. "Everything is in vain . . . my searching . . . my learning. I will never find the answer to the mystery of life. I call out to Death and even *he* will not come to me." Dr. Faust moved the candlestick to one side and gazed at the blood-red flacon that had been hidden by it.

"If Death will not come to me . . . then, I will go to him!"

The old man poured the contents of the little bottle into a crystal goblet, its once-shining prisms now dimmed with dust, and raised the glass to his lips. His wrinkled hands trembled and faltered, as the sound of the villagers singing in the fields rose and fell in the morning air, eventually reaching his almost deaf ears. The old philosopher shook his head sadly at their songs of joy, and putting the poisoned goblet down on the table cried out, "There is nothing for me! I curse them all! Happiness . . . love . . . everything!" With great effort he rose from the chair and pushed a stack of gold-edged books onto the floor. "I call upon the Devil to help me now!"

The clouds of dust from the falling books settled on the floor, and a great burst of flame took their place.

"Well, I'm here," answered the Devil, or Méphistophélès as he was called. "Speak up, wise man, and tell me what it is that you want."

Faust reeled backward, staggering in the blazing light of the sudden flames and the red of his visitor's costume.

Méphistophélès smiled as he watched the old man. "Are you afraid?" he asked. "My clothes should not annoy you, I'm dressed as noblemen are. Tell me, are you afraid?"

"No."

"Do you doubt my powers to help you?"

"Perhaps," said the old man, squinting just a little to get a better look at the Devil. "You had better go."

"Come, is that a fitting greeting?" Méphistophélès asked, sitting on the edge of the table. "You called for me and now you tell me to go! Is it gold you wish?"

"What is gold," asked the philosopher, "to one who yearns for something else?"

"Glory, perhaps?" asked Méphistophélès.

"No!" shouted the old man. "My youth is what I want."

"That is easily done," said the Devil, throwing his cloak over his shoulder.

"And what price do you ask in exchange?" Faust said, looking straight into the man's black eyes.

"Nothing really," replied Méphistophélès. "On earth, I'll wait upon you. Below you will wait upon me!"

Then, unfolding a scroll, Méphistophélès said, "Sign this."

Dr. Faust turned away. He was not sure that even in his despair he was prepared to give up his soul.

Méphistophélès laughed, and with a great flourish he pulled the shabby curtains back from the window. There, in a cloud of morning sunshine, was a vision of Marguerite, a young village girl, at her spinning wheel.

"How marvelous! I will sign. Give me the parchment," the old man said excitely.

Méphistophélès rolled the document up and put it in the belt of his sword. "Drink the contents of this goblet. It's not poison. It is the foaming gift of life!"

Faust took the crystal glass and turned toward the vision of Marguerite. "I drink to you!" he cried, draining the goblet dry.

The sun flowed into the dingy library, and instantaneously the old doctor became a young man. "Will I meet her again? And when?" he asked.

The Devil laughed as he placed his red, plumed hat on his head. "You will meet again, without a doubt . . . today! Let us be on our way to our life of pleasure." Méphistophélès roared with delight, bowing before the young Faust. (Duet "A moi les plaisirs.")

The young man smiled and walked out into the sunlight, never once looking back into his study.

ACT II

IN THE square of a simple German village where soldiers and townspeople had gathered, village students were gaily singing and dancing.

Everything was right for the day of the fair. The flowers were in bloom and the sun was shining. A breeze was gently swinging the golden sign of Bacchus that hung over the doorway to the inn.

Valentin, Marguerite's brother, strode into the square, pausing just long enough to admire the medallion that his sister had given him. The feel of the metal in his hand gave him confidence. He knew that he would be protected by it when he went away to war.

"What's the matter? Aren't you ready to go?" Wagner, a student, chided the soldier.

Valentin put his tankard down. "I'm worried about Marguerite. While I'm gone, she'll have no one to care for her."

"I will always be near her," said Siebel, who as everyone knew was in love with Valentin's beautiful sister.

"Thank you," Valentin replied, taking the young boy's hand." "Oh God," Valentin prayed, "guard my sister and give me strength in battle." (Aria "Avant de quitter ces lieux.")

"No more of this melancholy." Wagner laughed. "Let's have more wine, and I'll sing you a song about a rat and a cat who sat in the Abbot's cellar."

"Pardon me," Méphistophélès said, breaking into the group. "May I join you? When you have sung your song, I'll sing a more amusing one." (Aria "Le veau d'or.")

The villagers were both amazed and amused by this dashing newcomer. Not quite knowing why, except that it was a festive day and the man's rather diabolical eyes urged them on, they joined him in a rousing chorus about the way all men worship the power of gold.

"He's a strange and sinister man," Valentin commented, watching the Devil as he brandished his red cape, finishing his song with a cascade of evil laughter.

Wagner offered Méphistophélès a drink. The Devil held the student's hand for a moment, looking at the lines in his palm.

"I see that you are going to die in battle," Méphistophélès said.

Siebel was intrigued and asked Méphistophélès to tell his fortune. The Devil closed the youth's hand and smiled. "I can see that every flower that you touch will wither and die, especially those you give to Marguerite."

"Marguerite? How dare you speak her name?" Valentin shouted angrily.

"Take care, brave soldier," the Devil answered, pushing the young man aside. "I know a weapon that is waiting for you, too!" He snatched a glass from Wagner's hand to drink a toast, but spit the bitter wine out. "What terrible wine! I'd better see if I can find a better vintage."

The Devil struck the golden sign over the door of the inn and watched as, miraculously, red wine began to flow from it. "Drink a toast to Marguerite!" he shouted to the amazed villagers. "Drink!"

"That's enough," Valentin said angrily, drawing his sword. "I'll silence your tongue now, if it takes my life."

Méphistophélès laughed and the stream of wine burst into flame. Seeing Valentin's sword, the Devil stepped back, drawing a circle around him with his own rapier. Valentin lunged at the mysterious stranger, but drew back. His sword was shattered in his hand.

Suddenly, realizing that they were all in the presence of some evil force, Wagner and Siebel joined with the others, raising the hilts of their swords in the sign of the cross. (Chorale "De l'enfer qui vient.") All they could hear as they slowly backed away from Méphistophélès and out of the square was the sound of his laughter and the beating of their hearts.

"We're sure to meet again, my friends," the Devil called after them as he tossed his cape around his shoulders and sat down on the empty table.

"What's the matter now?" Faust asked, coming into the courtyard.

"Nothing, dear doctor. What can I do for you?"

"I want to see the girl . . . the one in the vision. Or was she *just* a vision?"

"She was real," Méphistophélès answered, "but you may have trouble winning her. She's protected by heaven."

Faust sat on a bench, absent-mindedly watching a group of young girls as they danced into the square. They called out to Siebel, who was searching for Marguerite.

Impatiently, Faust scanned every face. Then suddenly he saw her. She was more beautiful than all the rest—more beautiful than anything he had ever seen. Marguerite smiled to her friends, and walked calmly across the square.

"She *must* be protected by heaven," Faust thought to himself. There was an aura of tranquillity about her, and the white prayer book she held seemed to have been written to be carried in her fragile hands.

"There she is!" he cried out.

"Well, have you no tongue? Speak to her!" the Devil said, rocking back and forth on the table.

"Marguerite," Faust called, running up to her.

Siebel had the same idea at the same moment, but Méphistophélès stepped in front of him. "Not gone yet?" the boy asked angrily.

"Since I'm here, I've not gone," the Devil replied, keeping an eye on Faust and Marguerite.

Marguerite stopped at the sound of her name.

"Forgive me," Faust blurted out, "but may I walk with you to your home?"

The girl smiled naively and lowered her eyes. "No. I have no need of anyone to walk me home." She quietly continued on her way, leaving Faust staring in wonder after her.

"So," said Méphistophélès, as he walked up to him, "what happened?"

"She would not listen to me."

"I can see," said the Devil, slapping him on the shoulder, "I shall have to teach you how to win her."

Siebel stormed off, leaving Méphistophélès and his protégé surrounded by the laughing village girls who had witnessed the entire scene.

ACT III

SIEBEL ran up the road to Marguerite's house. Seeing the thatched roof of her cottage and the wooden gate that led into her garden, he paused for a few moments to catch his breath and to pick a bouquet of flowers. The boy had intended that they would speak for him, and tell Marguerite of his love for her, but he noticed that as he plucked them, they wilted. "The dark stranger told my fortune well," he thought to himself. "Every flower I touch dies. I'll dip my hands in holy water and rid myself of this curse."

Once in the garden, he went to Marguerite's shrine for the Virgin and then he picked a few more blossoms. Their little red heads remained straight and strong on their stems. "His power is gone already," Siebel laughed. He set the bouquet down tenderly and ran out. (Song "Faites-lui mes aveux.")

Méphistophélès said to Faust as they entered the garden, "Wait here while I leave a more worthy gift." Méphistophélès left the garden and returned with a magnificent casket of jewels. He held it out for Faust to see. Faust seemed unimpressed, and barely noticed that the Devil placed the jewels on the wooden bench near Marguerite's spinning wheel before he walked away.

The young man turned toward the cottage, admiring its utter simplicity and the calm happiness that surrounded it. "I have *never* felt this way," he thought. "This is surely the home of some angel. Everything here surpasses any mortal beauty. This feeling of innocence is the real wealth that I have dreamed of." (Aria "Salut! demeure chaste et pure.")

"Take care," the Devil hissed, "she's coming into the garden."

"Let's leave," Faust said sadly, closing the garden gate. "I will never see her again."

Marguerite, too, seemed more than usually affected by the calm of the early evening. She was grateful for the cool breeze against her face. It was still flushed with pale pink from her encounter with the young stranger. She sat down at her spinning wheel and carelessly began to wind the golden flax.

For some reason an old song about the King of Thule kept going through her brain. What on earth did this old legend of the king's golden goblet have to do with the sound of the stranger's voice that was still ringing in her mind? (Aria "Il était un Roi de Thulé.")

She turned her thoughts to Valentin, hoping above all else that he would return safely from the war. "I'm so very lonely," she thought, letting her hand fall from the spindle. It touched Siebel's bouquet.

"Poor, faithful boy," she laughed.

A ray of twilight sun, setting over the thatched roof, fell on the casket of jewels. "What is this?" Nervously turning the little key in its lock, she opened it. The sparkling jewels beamed against their red velvet lining.

"I have never seen anything so beautiful!" Marguerite exclaimed, kneeling on the ground so that she might admire the gems more closely.

"I can't resist trying them on," she said, noticing a tiny hand mirror in their midst.

"Is it really you?" the girl asked her reflection. "With these earrings and bracelets, why, I am a king's daughter." (Aria "Je ris de me voir.")

Coming from the cottage, her nurse, Martha, found the girl bathed in a shower of dazzling, dancing reflections from the jewels and the mirror.

"Saints above!" she said, rocking back and forth on her big feet. "Who gave you all this?" She slapped her pudgy hands together in amazement.

"I'm sure that they were left by mistake," Marguerite said sadly.

"Nonsense," said the older woman. "They are yours. They were obviously left by a nobleman."

"Could you be dear Madame Schwerlein?" the Devil called out to Martha, swaggering into the garden with Faust behind him.

"I am."

"Forgive us for intruding," Méphistophélès said gallantly. He turned to Martha and said, "I bring you news of your dear husband. He is dead, but he sent you his blessing." Martha gasped in surprise.

Marguerite began to hurriedly take off the jewels. "Why take them off?" Faust asked. "You wear them beautifully."

The Devil flattered and cajoled the old woman into taking a stroll with him, and Marguerite was alone with Faust.

"You need not be lonely any longer," he told her, taking her in his arms.

Marguerite said, breaking away, "I'm frightened by words like yours. You must go."

"I only speak what is in my heart. I love you," Faust answered.

"I beg you to go," Marguerite whispered. "It is *late*. You *must* say good-by. I will see you again tomorrow. Then we will be together forever."

"Forever!" Dr. Faust sang out happily as he ran into the garden, almost falling over Méphistophélès, who stopped him at the gate. (Duet "Laisse-moi contempler ton visage.")

"I see that you are still in need of lessons, dear Doctor."

"Let me alone," Faust shouted angrily.

"Stay for just a moment," the Devil replied, barring his way with his flaming cape. "Listen to what the girl has to say to the stars."

"He loves me," she said, smiling and loosening her yellow braids.

Faust ran back to her, calling her name again and again. But the Devil remained behind, doubled up in a fit of diabolical laughter. He kicked the gate open with his foot and walked into the darkness. Looking up, he saw a falling star blazing a path of crimson in the sky as it plunged into nothingness.

ACT IV

THE days passed slowly for Marguerite. The boredom and lack of faith that had tormented Faust as an old philosopher remained with him in his new-found youth. He soon tired of the innocent girl and left her alone, waiting for the war to end. At least then, she thought, Valentin would return to her.

Marguerite hesitated even to go to church for fear of hearing Méphistophélès' raging voice, tormenting her. One day he had spoken to her and told her that all the devils in hell were calling for her. Since then she had refused to visit the great cathedral, even if it meant depriving herself of the solace that she needed now that she was about to bear a child.

(SCENE 2) The spring changed into the summer and the summer into fall. Eventually it was the day of Valentin's homecoming. The soldiers returned in a flurry of colorful, tattered banners, and their rousing song of triumphant joy was wildly acclaimed by all the villagers in the square. (Chorus "Gloire immortelle de nos aïeux.")

Valentin, looking in vain for his sister in the crowd, reluctantly accepted Siebel's excuse that she might be in church. He bade his friends farewell and walked toward his home. He was tired, but he hummed happily to himself as he walked up the road. In a spurt of happiness at being alive and free, he swung into the garden with both of his muddy boots firmly planted on the creaking gate.

"Come on," he cried out to Siebel. "Join us."

"No. Wait a while."

"Your eyes have avoided mine all day," the soldier said. "Come, now, tell me what is the matter."

"I cannot!"

"I cannot wait for you to tell me, either!" Valentin said, pushing the boy aside and running into the house.

"You have to forgive her," Siebel said, trying to hold back his youthful tears. But his words went unheard and he ran back to the square. As he ran down the cobblestones he saw Méphistophélès and Faust walking in front of Marguerite's house.

Dr. Faust seemed preoccupied as he lingered in the background, barely listening to the Devil's taunting serenade advising a lovely girl not to admit her sweetheart into her home before he had placed a ring on her finger. (Serenade "Vous qui faites l'endormie.")

Every accompanying chord from Méphistophélès' guitar annoyed the doctor, and he was almost glad when he saw Valentin running out of the house. "What do you people want?" the soldier shouted.

The Devil laughed. "My serenade was not meant for your ears."

"I know. But my sister heard all the words," Valentin continued, knocking Méphistophélès' guitar out of his hands with his sword. "Whom do I fight to avenge her honor?" Valentin asked.

Without thinking, Faust drew his sword and, as if hypnotized, plunged it into Valentin's chest.

Méphistophélès sneered. "So, the hero is finally stretched out before us."

Martha ran into the square, followed by Marguerite. Valentin raised himself up on his elbow upon seeing Marguerite, and then pushed her aside brusquely. "Listen to me, Marguerite," he said, breathing heavily, "everyone must give way to the Will sublime. You will meet your fate."

Marguerite drew back at her brother's ominous words. Valentin gasped, reaching for the cherished medallion that his sister had given him months ago. "You are cursed, Marguerite!" he shouted. The poor girl reached out to grasp his hand. "You will die alone! But I die like a soldier!" he whispered, drawing back from her.

"Forgive her," some of the villagers summoned up the courage to say. But Valentin refused to listen. He fell backward, clutching at his wound. Martha and Siebel ran to Marguerite's side, ignoring the warnings of the Devil, and enveloped her as she fell over her dead brother's body.

ACT V

To MARGUERITE, everything was over. In her insanity she killed her child and was sentenced to death by the court. Much against the advice of the Devil, Faust had decided to try and save Marguerite and help her escape from the dark dungeon into which she had been thrown.

Together, unseen by anyone, they entered the prison on the day of Marguerite's execution. It was gray and quiet everywhere. So quiet that one could almost hear the dripping of the water down the gray walls and hear the scurrying gray feet of the rats as they escaped from the first signs of dawn.

They were nearing the girl's cell when Dr. Faust stopped. "You must leave me alone now," he ordered his companion.

"You haven't much time," Méphistophélès said, dangling the jailer's keys in front of the young man. "You must convince her to join us. Your mortal hand will be her salvation."

"Leave me alone!" Faust said angrily, as he took the keys.

"I'll be waiting at the door," the Devil replied. "Don't lose any time."

Faust could see Marguerite through the great iron bars of her prison cell. The dirty, mad-looking creature huddled on the straw in the corner was a far cry from the beautiful child he had fallen in love with, but he was determined to save her.

"Marguerite," he called to her.

She looked up, dragging herself toward his voice.

"He is here, somewhere. He is here to save me." She reached out for Faust, but the chains that held her to the wall gripped at her wrists and cut into her flesh. She fell back on the straw, crying.

"You have come to save me . . . you have!"

"I love you, Marguerite." Faust whispered, pushing the creaking iron gate open. "And I have come to save you."

In her madness, Marguerite pulled at the chains and finally staggered to her feet. In the dank shadows of her prison she saw all the events of her life. Like the gray, murky dreams of her childhood, she saw Faust as he was on the day they met. Young and gallant in the sunlight. The myrtle and roses of her garden were blooming in the dirty straw at her feet. The walls of the prison were no longer gray. They were blue, like the sky, and filled with stars.

"You must come away, Marguerite. Now!" Faust called to her.

"No, no . . . stay with me a moment."

Faust realized that she was not speaking to him but to a dream.

Méphistophélès strode up behind him. "If you stay here any longer, I'll not pay the price," he warned, pulling at the young man's arm. (Aria "Alerte! Alerte!")

Marguerite screamed, trying to hide her eyes from the sight of him. "What does he want here? Make the demon leave this church!"

"My horses are waiting for us in the courtyard. There is little time to save her," the Devil protested.

Marguerite fell on her knees, imploring God to save her.

"Come with me, Marguerite," Faust cried out, wrenching his arm away from Méphistophélès' grip. But the girl did not hear him. "Marguerite!" Faust called again, reaching out to touch her.

"Get away from me," she screamed. "Your hands are dripping with blood!" With a pitiful little gasp of horror she staggered back and fell dead. (Trio "Anges purs, anges radieux.")

Dr. Faust hid his face in his hands. Unable to exert his own will, he felt Méphistophélès' hands pulling him into a roaring eternity of flames. "You are condemned!" the Devil shouted, dragging him away.

The philosopher looked back, and thought he saw the entire wall of the prison opening next to where the dead Marguerite lay. The girl, now young and beautiful as she had been on the day they had met, took the hand of a golden archangel and slowly walked up the stairway to heaven. There was a flurry of angels' wings and the sound of voices singing in the wind.

"She is redeemed. Christ has risen again!" (Chorus "Sauvée! Christ est ressuscité!")

Dr. Faust strained to see and to listen, but it became impossible. The blood-red flames licked at his eyes and seared his ears, obliterating everything but the sound of Méphistophélès' ugly laughter as they both fell into oblivion.

LA GIOCONDA

The Ballad Singer

BY

AMILCARE PONCHIELLI

(1834—1886)

••·•——◆——•·••

LIBRETTO BY TOBIA GORRIA (ARRIGO BOÏTO)

BASED ON THE PLAY

Angelo, le Tyran de Padoue

BY

Victor Hugo

CHARACTERS

Barnaba	Baritone	Alvise Badoero	Bass
La Gioconda	Soprano	La Cieca	Contralto
Enzo Grimaldo	Tenor	A Monk	Baritone
Laura	Mezzo-soprano	Zuàne	Bass

••·•——◆——•·••

TIME—1600's IN ITALY   PLACE—VENICE

First Performance: La Scala, Milan; April 8, 1876

Amilcare Ponchielli, who numbered Puccini and Mascagni among his pupils, emerged from relative obscurity at the age of forty-two when his opera *La Gioconda* was produced at La Scala in Milan. Based on a play by Victor Hugo, the opera was a huge success at its première in 1876, not only because of its beautiful melodies, but also because of the sumptuous extravagance of its costumes and settings. *La Gioconda* is a spectacularly "grand" opera, set in festively decorated ducal courtyards and splendid halls; the pageantry of the costuming, which calls for silks, furs, jewels, and brocades, has rarely been equaled in the history of opera.

ACT I

THE warmth of the spring afternoon and the festive decorations in the courtyard of the Palace of the Doges belied the undercurrent of terror and hatred that was common in Venice, now that it was under the reign of the Inquisition. The brightly colored flowers and the blue sky contrasted with the forbidding inscription over a carved opening, in the shape of a lion's mouth, in the wall: "For Secret Denunciations to the Inquisition against any Person, with Impunity, Secrecy, and Benefit to the State."

Barnaba, one of the most feared spies of the Inquisition, cynically looked at the lion's mouth and then back to the crowd of merrymakers in the square. As a fanfare of trumpets announced the start of the festival regatta, Barnaba watched the Venetians disperse. He strummed his guitar and laughed. "They sing and dance on their own graves," he said to himself, "while the minstrel Barnaba spins his web. I can hear everything and so does the State! If only I could find a way of trapping Gioconda—for myself!" He moved behind a column as he saw an old blind woman being led into the square by a beautiful young girl. It was Gioconda and her mother.

Cieca gripped her daughter's hand and walked in faltering little steps. "Come," Gioconda said, "it is quiet and peaceful here. You can rest on the steps of the church. Your prayers will guide me as I sing my songs."

Barnaba stood quietly, admiring her dark beauty. Her green dress was cool and soft like the waters of the canal, and the sun shot her dark braided hair with shafts of gold.

"It is still and safe here, Mother. Now I must go and find Enzo."

"God bless you, my child," Cieca said.

As Gioconda turned to go, Barnaba stepped out in front of her. "I bar your way, Gioconda, only because I love you."

The young girl drew back and put her arm around her mother. "I told you once that I cannot bear your face," she said angrily.

"Stay for just a moment. Enzo will wait."

"You disgust me," Gioconda said, stepping away from him. Barnaba reached out to touch her, but, with a fleeting glance at her mother, she quickly ran away.

"My child, my child," cried Cieca, feeling about for Gioconda, "You are my eyes. Where are you?" Barnaba watched her as she fumbled along the steps.

"If the mother were in my power," he thought, "I could capture Gioconda." The old woman fell to the ground and Barnaba laughed. Turning his attention to the crowd that was returning, he observed the winner of the regatta being carried on the shoulders of his friends. He also watched Zuàne, who had been defeated. He approached him.

"You have a sickly look, Zuàne. Obviously, you did not carry off the pennant in the regatta."

"To the devil with you," the young man snapped.

"Suppose I told you the reason for your misfortune?" Barnaba said.

"I know it. My prow was overweighted."

"Nonsense," Barnaba said, looking at Cieca, "your boat was bewitched. See that blind woman? I saw her cast a spell on your boat this morning."

"Good Lord!" exclaimed Zuàne. The poor woman looked so absolutely harmless, sitting quietly on the steps saying her rosary.

Barnaba whispered in his ear. "Although her sockets are empty, she sees us all! Her curse will make your boat your coffin."

Some sailors who had overheard their conversation drew closer. "She *sees* us?"

In moments, Barnaba's evil plan had taken over. Zuàne told his companions of Cieca's curse, and the crowd dragged the poor woman to the center of the square. They demanded that she be burned at the stake as a witch, and in the fever of the excitement she would have been, but Barnaba stepped between them. "No, we will take her to prison." His patrol of henchmen was pulling her away just as Gioconda returned with Enzo.

"Mother!" screamed Gioconda, rushing to her.

"You murderers!" shouted Enzo. "Let her go or I shall draw my sword. Has a race of cowards been born to the winged Lion of St. Mark?"

"She must die!" the wild mob shouted.

Calling out for his shipmates, Enzo ran for help.

The angry crowd was thirsty for blood, and they were goaded on by Barnaba. As Gioconda looked up to the sky to pray for deliverance, she saw Alvise and Laura coming down the steps to the square.

For a moment the populace was quiet. They knew that they were in the presence of Alvise Badoero, the chief of the State Inquisition. And behind her black velvet mask, they recognized his wife Laura.

Alvise spoke. "What is the meaning of this rebellion within the ducal walls? How dare you all assume the right of judge and executioner?"

"She is a witch," the people cried.

Laura looked at Alvise. "She is blind, my lord. Let her live!"

"Is she guilty, Barnaba?" Alvise asked.

"Yes," whispered Barnaba.

"You lie!" cried the young ballad singer, throwing herself at Alvise's feet. "Have mercy . . . let *me* speak. She is an angel. All she does is pray to God, while I sing my songs to keep us alive."

Laura saw Enzo coming through the crowd, the same Enzo to whom she had once been betrothed. What had brought him here?

Gioconda also saw Enzo. He had drawn his knife. "No, Enzo . . . not now. This great lord will save her."

Barnaba watched the three of them, and wondered how Laura dared to stare at Enzo in such a way, her blue eyes flickering behind her mask. "Cieca is a witch," the spy said to Alvise. "Her silence proves it."

Laura smiled. "But she has a rosary! Witches have no such piousness. Save her, Alvise."

"Saved she shall be!" her husband said.

Cieca moved toward the sound of Laura's voice. "The voice of a woman or an angel has saved me. I pray that you accept this rosary. It will bring you luck. My benediction is upon it." Laura took the delicate beads gratefully and kissed the old woman. (Aria "Voce di donna.")

"Come, it is time for church," Alvise said, taking his wife's arm.

As Gioconda and Cieca joined the crowd going into the cathedral, Barnaba deliberately lagged behind and managed to stop Enzo as he reached the steps.

"What are you thinking, Enzo Grimaldo, Prince of Santafior? Perhaps you are dreaming of Laura Badoero?"

"Who are you?"

"*I* know everything. Genoa is your birthplace . . ."

Enzo tried to walk past him, but Barnaba's arm barred his way. "I am only a sailor. I steer a ship."

"To everyone else. But not to me. Venice has outlawed you, but some desire pulls you back. Once you were in love with Laura, but fate arranged a family marriage to Alvise."

Enzo removed Barnaba's arm from the archway. "I have sworn fidelity to Gioconda!"

The spy laughed. "You love that singer like a sister. Laura is still your real love. Since I wish to help you, I shall arrange for her to be on board your ship tonight."

"But who are you? Why should you be my benefactor?" Enzo asked. (Aria "O grido de quest' anima.")

"I am one who detests you," Barnaba answered as he opened his jacket. Enzo could see the silver letters C. X. glistening in the sun. "I am a member of the powerful Council of Ten!" Enzo drew back in anger and disgust as Barnaba continued. "I could have put you to torture, but it will be better this way. Gioconda hates me and I have sworn to ruin her. You will do it by betraying her. Go to your ship and wait." He watched the sailor walk across the square; then he called out for Isepo, a public scribe, who by way of blackmail was in his service.

"For as long as you live, Isepo, I control your destiny. I am the hand and you are the pen—write!"

While Barnaba was dictating his treacherous letter, Cieca and Gioconda appeared at the door of the church. "Hide yourself, Mother. Barnaba is still there," Gioconda said. She stood behind a pillar and listened.

"To the Secret Head of the Inquisition . . . your

wife will escape with Enzo, the sailor, tonight aboard a Dalmatian ship . . . signed The Lion's Mouth." (Aria "O monumento.")

With a cry of despair Gioconda ran into the church.

As a mob of masqueraders came into the square, Barnaba laughed over his revenge and, with a flourish, dropped the letter into the lion's mouth. The ballad singer leaned wearily on Cieca and looked out into the crowd. The dancing had stopped and everyone was kneeling on the marble squares answering the call to vespers.

"I have been betrayed, Mother," Gioconda wept.

"Put your hand on my heart, my child. I know your sorrow."

ACT II

ENZO'S ship, the *Hecate*, lay quietly at anchor at the shore of a deserted island near Venice. The sailors did not know that the two men coming on board dressed as fishermen were really Barnaba and Isepo.

"Who goes there?" asked the pilot.

"I wish you a fine evening and a good catch, fishermen," Barnaba greeted him. "I am just a fisherman awaiting the tide. My boat is down there in the shallow water."

Barnaba turned to Isepo. "We're safe. They do not suspect us." Isepo glanced about the deck, and listened as Barnaba noted the size of the crew and the armament of the ship.

"Go and warn the sentries, Isepo. I will stay here and finish the job." Isepo lowered himself over the side of the *Hecate* and left his master with the crew.

"A fine evening and a fine catch, fishermen," Barnaba repeated, looking up at the stars. "Tonight a siren will fall into your net."

A cool northeast wind swept over the lagoon as Enzo came on board. "Be ready to cast off at my first sign," he ordered. "Now, all of you go below and get some rest. I will take the watch alone." The crew respectfully bade their captain good night and Enzo was alone.

In the sea and the sky he saw Laura's face. The moon's reflection shimmered on the water and the waves seemed to kiss the horizon. Would Laura come from out the water or from the sky? He leaned against the rail and waited. (Aria "Cielo e mar.")

"Captain! Ahoy!" It was Barnaba's voice.

Enzo saw Laura's face, like marble in the moonlight. Barnaba had brought her as he had promised.

On board and in Enzo's arms she felt safe again, but Barnaba's farewell words as he rowed away sent a shudder of terror through her.

"That sinister voice . . ." Laura looked out into the night. "That infernal smile of his frightens me. We must be careful."

"We have nothing to fear. When the moon sinks we will weigh anchor and sail into the wind." (Duet "Deh! non turbare.")

Enzo went below to prepare for their departure, and Laura knelt to pray to the Madonna for protection. The wind in the sails and the sound of the water against the side of the ship covered Gioconda's footsteps as she emerged from the shadows and walked up to Laura.

"Who are you?" the noblewoman asked, looking up at the masked face.

"I am a shadow that waits for you. I love the man that you love!"

Laura pulled her cloak about her and got to her feet. Gioconda pointed to the bow of the ship. "I waited there, like an animal in its lair. You want to escape? Does love consume you? Everything is ready. Go and escape!"

Laura trembled. "You're afraid," Gioconda said. "And you *dare* to love a hero like Enzo?"

"I love him as you never can," Laura replied quietly, "like the air of creation that comes from heaven."

Gioconda moved closer to her rival, and Laura could see the hatred in her eyes. "I love him like a lion . . . I could kill you for him!" (Duet "Là attesi e il tempo colsi.")

Gioconda pulled Laura to her and showed her a gleaming dagger. "No . . . that is not your fate." She forcibly turned Laura's face to the sea. "Look, there . . . in that boat approaching!"

Laura screamed. "I am lost! It's Alvise!"

"Yes," answered the singer, putting her dagger away, "Death rows on the lagoon and no one can save you now."

Tears came to Laura's eyes as she held up her rosary to Gioconda. "Help me. Help me."

The sight of Cieca's rosary softened Gioconda's anger, and she quickly pulled Laura to the railing. "Here, take my mask. It will help to disguise you. Get into my skiff. These sailors will save you. Go!"

"Will you tell me who you are?" Laura asked as the little boat pulled away.

"I am Gioconda."

As the skiff pulled out into the black lagoon, Enzo came on deck. "Gioconda! What are you doing here? Where is Laura?"

The young girl looked past him. "She has gone. She does not love you. But I am here!"

Enzo pushed her aside. "You have only hate in your heart, Gioconda, and you lie!"

A gunshot echoed over the lagoon as Gioconda pointed to the gondola on the horizon. "You've been betrayed. Someone revealed your name to the

LA GIOCONDA

Grand Council. If you sail now, you can save yourself."

Instead, Enzo helped Gioconda into a small boat and sent her to the shore. "I will not surrender and I will not run away from them," he told her, and seizing a blazing torch, he set the *Hecate* afire.

When the last of the crew had escaped, Enzo jumped into the sea.

From the shore, Gioconda heard him call Laura's name, and she hid her face in the folds of her green cloak. "It is always 'Laura,'" she cried as, with a crash of timbers, the *Hecate* sank into the cold water.

ACT III

ALVISE'S magnificent home was called the Ca D'oro, the House of Gold. It was one of the proudest ornaments of the Grand Canal. Many Venetians had never set foot inside its walls, but those who had would never cease to marvel at its painted and gilded furniture and its golden brocades.

Alvise looked out of the window, over the canal. His hands gripped the iron bars in anger as he thought of Laura. He had hoped to surprise her at her rendezvous aboard the *Hecate,* but she had escaped. "She will have to die," he said aloud. "No one can live who has betrayed the name of Badoero!"

He drew back the golden draperies that cut off the entrance to another room, and looked at his guests who were singing and dancing together. "Look at them whirling about the floor . . . Little do they know what is in store for my wife!" (Aria "Sì, morir ella de'!") He watched her blue eyes and the gold of her dress as it trailed softly across the marble floor. The pearls woven into her golden braids made her even more beautiful, he thought.

"You called for me?" she asked.

"It is time for you to drop the pretense, Laura. I almost caught you yesterday. You saved yourself then, but you cannot now. You must die!"

In his anger, Alvise threw her violently to the floor. Laura clung to his knees, weeping.

"But death is too great a punishment for even the greatest guilt."

Alvise raised the curtains to an adjoining room and pointed to the golden bed. A cry of horror escaped from Laura's throat, only to be drowned in the melody of a serenade coming up from the lagoon. Neither Laura nor Alvise saw Gioconda enter and hide herself.

"Do you hear the song?" Alvise asked. "You will take this vial of poison, and before the last note has sounded, you will drink it. There is no escape." He put the golden vial into Laura's hands and stalked out of the room. Laura stood motionless with fear, and barely recognized Gioconda as she quickly stepped from the shadows and replaced the golden bottle with a silver one.

"Drink this instead! It will only give the appearance of death. Hurry and drink it. My singers have almost reached the end of their song."

Laura drank Gioconda's potion and walked into the room with the golden bed. With great haste the singer then poured the poison into the silver vial and ran from the room. The last note of the serenade drifted away as Alvise returned. Taking note of the empty golden flacon and Laura's presumably dead body on the bed, he went to join his guests. Had he been seconds earlier he would have passed Gioconda in the hallway that led to the great salon, and heard her call out to her mother: "It was because of you that I saved her . . . for him."

(SCENE 2) The ballroom was a mass of gold. The polished marble floors reflected the golden threads of the masqueraders' costumes. Behind golden masks were noblemen, their wives, the most beautiful women of Venice, and, of course, Barnaba.

Alvise greeted his friends regally, and suddenly through the bronze doors there appeared a full company of dancers. The host had brought them to the Ca D'oro to entertain his guests with a Dance of the Hours. Their filmy costumes of pink and blue and yellow seemed to float on the air. A hush settled on everyone.

As the last dancer soared out of the ballroom, Barnaba returned, dragging old Cieca with him. Gioconda cried out to her, but Alvise motioned the singer to stay where she was.

"Why are you here?" he asked the old woman.

Barnaba spoke up. "She was in the forbidden room, casting an evil spell."

"I was only praying for the dead," Cieca said.

A heavy bell began to toll in the distance.

"A death toll!" Enzo exclaimed, coming from out the crowd. "For whom?"

"For Laura," Barnaba answered sinisterly.

"Come now," Alvise said. "If *I* am happy, why should you all be so sad. Who has the right to grieve?"

"I, more than the others," Enzo said.

"You? And who are you?"

"I am Enzo Grimaldo. You have robbed me of my country and my love. Why not complete the crime?"

Enraged, Alvise turned to Barnaba. "You will answer with your head for this insulting coward, Barnaba!" Gioconda looked at Enzo. She knew now that he really loved Laura. He had come to die for her.

Cieca stared at Barnaba with unseeing eyes. "*You* are the informer! If anyone was killed, you are the murderer."

Barnaba reached out to strike her but restrained

himself. "Laura saved you once, Cieca. But you will never escape again."

Through her tears Gioconda spoke to the spy. "If you will save Enzo and take him to the Church of the Redeemer, I will fight you no longer and go away with you."

"It is a desperate gift, Gioconda, but I accept it."

Alvise pushed his way through his shocked guests, and raised the draperies to the death chamber. "Look at her! She dishonored my name. I was the one who killed her!" At a signal from him the guards seized Enzo and dragged him away. Cieca reached out for her daughter's hand, but Gioconda was gone. Instead the old woman felt Barnaba's fingers tightening around hers as he pulled her from the golden room into a dank secret passageway. The blackness settled over her as she silently called out for Gioconda.

ACT IV

GIOCONDA stood silently in the shadows of the ruined palace on the island of Guidecca. The night air was damp, and the distant lights from St. Mark's square that flickered through the ruins cast a green and deathly light on the ballad singer's white face. She looked at the dirty old table and the strange lights the lantern cast on the dagger and the vial of poison near it.

Soon two hired street singers arrived bearing Laura's body.

"You are sure no one has seen you?" she asked.

They nodded. "Put her on the bed. Here is the gold I promised you."

The singers refused her bag of money, assuring her that they were her friends and they had only wanted to help her. Gioconda smiled gratefully. "You are very generous and I thank you. But I have one more favor to ask. Will you search the streets for my mother? If you find her, I will meet you tomorrow at Cana reggio."

"Trust us, Gioconda," they said and bid her good night.

Gioconda picked up the golden vial. "Suicide! That is all that is left for me," she thought. "My mother is gone. Enzo is lost to me." She tilted the little bottle and watched its contents flow back and forth. "I'll take Laura's poison, and I will not have to look at them again." She threw the bottle to the ground. "But who would help them escape?"

Gioconda looked at Laura's body on the bed. "I could always kill her and throw the body in the canal!" The evil thought amazed her, and she felt tiny beads of perspiration forming on her forehead. The distant voices in the gondolas frightened her, and the festival lights in Venice seemed to be grow-

ing brighter. She turned away from Laura, and saw Enzo standing in the ragged shell that had once been a doorway.

"Enzo!"

"You have gotten me out of prison. What do you want of me?"

"Want of you? I want to give you back the sun and your life."

"Oh, Gioconda," Enzo said, as he put his hand on his knife, "don't mock a man who is going to die."

"Stay and listen to me, Enzo," Gioconda begged.

"I am going to Laura's tomb . . . to see her for the last time."

"Well, good speed, faithful hero!" the singer said jealously. "Her crypt is empty. I have removed her body!"

"You lie," shouted Enzo. "You are jealous even in death. Now you are prowling the cemetery." He grabbed the young girl and drew his knife. "Tell me where she is . . . tell me!"

"No," Gioconda replied, hoping that he would kill her, but Laura's voice called out faintly from the bed. "Enzo."

By the time he had dropped his knife, Laura was standing beside him. The couple fell on their knees before the young singer. Gioconda listened to the melody that was coming in from the canal. "Do you recall that song, Laura? It is the song of your fate. Those same singers will carry you both away tonight. Your escape has been arranged."

From the doorway she could see the black prow of a gondola. "Here is the boat. It is time to say good-by." She looked at Laura's blue eyes, and then at her rosary. "So be it. Love each other and give a thought once in a while to Gioconda. Farewell." (Trio "Sulle tue mani l'anima.")

Gioconda wiped her eyes, and turned to the cross on the wall. "Help me, Holy Virgin. Help me to find my mother." Drawing her mantle about her, she walked to the door and put her hand on the greenish-bronze handle. As it turned in her grasp she was confronted by Barnaba.

"This is how you keep your pact? By trying to escape?"

"I will keep the pact," Gioconda answered. "I have not lied. I have not run away. I only want to make myself more beautiful for you." She took the dagger from the table and plunged it into her heart.

With a howl of rage he bent over her. "I strangled your mother yesterday!" he shouted. Then he raged, "She does not hear," and stormed out the door.

The green waters licked at the shore and splashed gold reflections against an empty gondola and its moorings. Far, far out the first vague sign of dawn was breaking through, pink and warm.

HANSEL

AND

GRETEL

By Engelbert Humperdinck

(1854–1921)

LIBRETTO BY ADELHEID WETTE

Based on the fairy tale "Hansel and Gretel," by Grimm

CHARACTERS

Hansel	MEZZO-SOPRANO
Gretel	SOPRANO
Peter	BARITONE
Gertrude	MEZZO-SOPRANO
The Witch	MEZZO-SOPRANO
Sandman	SOPRANO
Dewman	SOPRANO

Time: Long, long ago   **Place: The Black Forest**

First performance: Weimar, Germany

DECEMBER 23, 1893

When Frau Adelheid Wette, Humperdinck's sister, wrote a children's play based on the famous fairy tale "Hansel and Gretel," the composer added some incidental music so that it could be performed as an opera for the family. The work that resulted was so charming that it was produced by the Royal Theater in Weimar, and since then it has become traditional in many countries to present it for children every year at Christmas time. *Hansel and Gretel* was the first opera to be broadcast complete from the Metropolitan Opera House stage. This took place on December 25, 1931.

ACT I

THE tall trees of the Black Forest cast weird, grotesque shadows all around the cottage of Peter, the broommaker. The evening sun crept cautiously through the green leaves and tinged the thatched roof and the heart-shaped shutters with designs of lavender and pink. Hansel sat near the door. He was making a broom and listening to his sister, Gretel. She was singing that stupid little song again about the geese who had no shoes!

"You're singing, and there isn't a penny in the cookie jar to buy some milk and bread," Hansel said, tossing his far-from-finished broom against the wall. "I wish Mother would come home."

"So do I," said Gretel. "I'm getting so hungry."

Hansel kicked at the bits of straw that cluttered the floor, and tucked his white shirt into his pink lederhosen. Gretel looked out the door, into the dark woods, and quoted her favorite proverb, "We mustn't forget Father's good advice, 'When need is direst, God lends His hand.' Now, stop grumbling and get back to work."

"Work, work, work! I'd rather dance and sing," said Hansel, skipping across the floor.

"All right, Brother, let us dance as Auntie once taught us to do. Like this . . . Tap, tap, tap, clap, clap, clap." They whirled about the room and finally fell to the floor in happy laughter. (Song "Brüderchen, komm tanz' mit mir.")

As they lay there, completely out of breath, they could hear their mother's voice, calling them from down the road. Before they could get back on their feet, she was in the door. Gertrude, their mother, was tired and angry, and certainly not interested in hearing why the work for the day was not done. "A thrashing is what these children need," she thought. Losing her temper, she reached for a stick and knocked over a gleaming, white pitcher of milk! The cool liquid made little puddles on the floor.

"Look, what you have made me do," their mother wailed. "Now there is nothing for supper. Off to the woods with both of you! And don't come home until you have gathered enough strawberries for supper!"

Gretel wiped the tears from her eyes with the hem of her lavender dress, and picked up two straw baskets from the table. Hansel took her hand as they left the cottage, carefully closing the door behind them.

After arguing which path to take, they set off into the deepening shadows. Soon they were so far away that they could not hear the jolly voice of their father, who was singing as he returned from the village tavern.

All the way up the dusty road, Peter, their father, had thought of the wonderful meal they would have tonight. Opening the door, and seeing no one there and hearing no sound from the big kettle over the fireplace, he roared, "How can I prove what a great cook I am, when the big, black kettle has nothing in it?"

Gertrude, who had been napping, woke up. Immediately, she started scolding her husband. "Can't you do anything but waste time? You're always at the tavern . . ."

"Forget your troubles, dear wife. Look at what a glorious dinner I have brought you and the children. There was a great celebration in the town today and I sold all my brooms."

Gertrude was delighted and she took her husband's arm and began to dance with him.

"Where are Hansel and Gretel?" asked Peter.

Sitting down in an old rocking chair, their mother told him what had happened during the day—how the children had made her spill the milk and how she had sent them off into the forest.

"Into the forest?" Peter stormed. "Haven't you heard of that horrible place in the woods where the old witch lives? At midnight she rides out on a great broomstick with all her pink goblins. And when the sun is shining she coaxes little children into her house and turns them into cookies!" (Aria "Die Knusperhexe.")

Gertrude shivered, and with a sad, little cry of "Help," ran out of the cottage.

Peter followed her, shouting, "Wait for me! We will find them together!"

(SCENE 2) Things were quieter in the dark-green forest where Hansel and Gretel were taking time out to catch their breath. Gretel sat on a soft bank of cool moss. She looked like a Dresden doll, engrossed in making herself a necklace from some tiny, white blossoms. She laughed as the evening breeze swept the petals up into her face. She was not afraid, for Hansel was close by searching for strawberries. And anyway, her song about a tiny man in a rich purple cape and a black hat always kept her from being frightened. She especially liked the part about how he was able to stand on one leg for such great lengths of time. (Song "Ein Männlein steht im Walde.")

So, she sang until she heard Hansel's voice shouting, "We can go home now. I have a basket full of strawberries." But, instead, they decided to eat the strawberries. They could always find more.

In the distance a cuckoo called. Looking up to the sky, they discovered that it was very dark. The shadows were no longer pink and lavender. They were deep-purple and black! Hansel took Gretel's hand and confessed that he did not know the way home. "Oh, Hansel, there are ghosts coming out of the trees," Gretel sobbed. "We will never see home again."

An eerie mist settled over the forest, and from the center of this mist the terrified children saw a little gray man emerging, carrying a sack on his back. He was the Sandman. He smiled, and his eyes sparkled like two little black currants in a cookie. "I love children," he said, "so you needn't be afraid. And all I have in this little bag is some magic sand that will make you sleep." (Song "Der kleine Sandmann bin ich.")

Hansel and Gretel felt safer as he danced around them, strewing his silver grains of sand. Soon they began to feel drowsy. They knelt in the grass and said their prayers, asking their guardian angels to protect them while they slept. (Children's Prayer) Then, as the little man disappeared into the mist, they fell asleep in each others' arms. And as they slept, and as the shadows thickened and enveloped them, their golden angels descended and began to dance.

At the first sign of the new day, the angels left, stepping ever so lightly, careful not to disturb the drops of dew on the wild strawberries.

ACT II

A TINY man, the Dewman, stepped out from a pile of pink leaves, and glanced at the sleeping children. "Ho, ho!" he laughed, in a tinkling, little voice. "Two more pairs of eyes to waken with my golden shafts of light." Then, sprinkling some glis-tening drops from a flower in his hand over Hansel and Gretel, he laughed again and bounced away.

Gretel awakened, rubbing her eyes, rather astonished to find herself still in the forest. She was very unhappy with the crinkles in her lavender dress, and she wished she were at home, sitting at the big table with a steaming bowl of porridge before her.

"Wake up, Hansel! The birds are already awake," she said, poking at her brother.

"I had a wonderful dream last night," he said sleepily, "about fourteen golden angels."

"You see, I told you they would always protect us." Gretel smiled. "I had the same dream!"

"Look!" Hansel cried out, as the morning mist dissolved. "Look!"

There, just a few feet away, in the rosy light of the sun, was a magnificent gingerbread house! The children marveled at the house and how good it would be to eat. (Duet "Von Kuchen und Torten ein Häuslein gemacht.")

Hansel, paying little attention to his sister's cautioning words, walked right up to the side of the house and broke off a piece from its corner.

"Who is nibbling away at my house?" asked a croaking voice from inside.

A very surprised Hansel dropped his piece of cake. "Did you hear that, Gretel?"

"It was only the morning breeze, Brother," Gretel said, looking at the golden crumbs and the lavender icing at Hansel's feet. "I think I shall taste a bit of cake myself." It was delicious they decided, particularly the icing.

They were so hungry and they enjoyed the gingerbread so much, they failed to see the ugly witch coming out the door. Cackling in fiendish glee, she tossed a rope around Hansel's neck and drew it tight. "Come inside, little ones. Come inside, pretty ones, and I will give you all the sweets you can eat."

"No," said Hansel, squirming in the rope. "Help me get loose, Gretel, and we'll run away."

They tugged and pulled and were quite surprised suddenly to find themselves running back into the forest.

"Hokus, pokus, pokus, hokus! This is the witch's spell!"

Neither of the children could take another step.

The end of the witch's black stick began to glow. Then she dragged Hansel to a great iron cage and tossed him inside. Gretel stood motionless under the magic spell, as the hag disappeared into the house.

"Gretel, listen to me. Watch everything the witch does and pretend to obey her. We will save ourselves, somehow," Hansel said as he curled up, pretending to be asleep.

Hurrying out of the house to the big oven in the

yard, her black cape spread out behind her, the witch threw a handful of wood on the roaring fire. She cackled and danced about, rubbing her hands together as she planned how she would coax Gretel into the oven. "I will ask her to bend down and look inside," she thought, "and with one push she will be inside. Hokus, pokus, the witch's spell! And I will have a beautiful gingerbread!" Delighted with her evil plan, the witch jumped on her broomstick and raced deliriously around the house.

When she stopped, she called to Gretel. "Come, my pretty one, and take these raisins and almonds to your brother. We will fatten him up a bit. He's so bony." Gretel refused to move, so the witch had to carry the sweets to the cage herself.

But as the witch put down her stick, clever little Gretel picked it up and sang the magic words. "Hokus, pokus, pokus, hokus, the witch's spell."

Turning to look at the oven, the old witch did not see Hansel escape from the cage.

"Pretty one," she said, coaxingly, to Gretel, "look into the oven and see if the lovely gingerbread is done."

"But I do not know how to, dear witch," said Gretel, pretending to be very dumb. "Will you show me how?"

"Stupid child!" the witch screamed. "This is how it is done." And as she bent before the door, Hansel dashed out from behind a tree and he and Gretel shoved the witch into the fiery oven.

They slammed the great door and shouted and danced with joy. (Song "Knusperwalzer.")

"The awful witch is dead at last," said Hansel as he ran into the house. In a moment he appeared at an upper window, laughing and throwing down oranges and apples, lovely pink candies, and golden pears! All the things they had dreamed of those nights when they had gone to bed without any food. Gretel tried to catch them all in her apron.

Trying to taste them all, she was munching on a particularly lovely pale blue bon-bon when the oven exploded with a thunderous sound. Gretel dropped everything, and stood silently staring at the smoke and debris.

As in a dream, the gingerbread children that made up the body of the house came to life. They walked as in a dream, too, for their eyes were closed, and in quiet little voices they begged Hansel and Gretel to touch them so that they might waken. Gretel was afraid, but she took the hand of the littlest child. The pretty girl smiled and opened her eyes.

"Come, Hansel, we will waken them all," Gretel said eagerly.

Soon they were surrounded by happy, beaming faces. Hansel waved the witch's wand, repeating the magic words, and the spell was broken. (Chorus "Die Hexerei ist nun vorbei.") The sound of their joyous laughter rang through the forest, joining with the song of the birds.

The singing birds swooped and circled around Peter and Gertrude, who were searching for their lost children in the forest. The friendly birds directed them to the spot where their children were. Hansel and Gretel pushed open the white gate and ran to their mother and father. Looking back, they saw two of the children dragging the body of the old witch from the shattered oven. She was a tremendous gingerbread!

"You see, my children," said Peter, "how the witch was destroyed by her own evil magic? It is thus that Heaven punishes all evil!"

"When need is direst, God lends His hand," said Hansel and Gretel as the happy throng joined hands and started for home.

The tall trees of the Black Forest whispered in the wind and smiled, for they had hated the evil witch, too.

HANSEL AND GRETEL

Madame Butterfly

by GIACOMO PUCCINI (1858-1924)

Libretto by LUIGI ILLICA and GIUSEPPE GIACOSA
Based on JOHN LUTHER LONG's story
and DAVID BELASCO's play, **Madame Butterfly**

CHARACTERS

CIO-CIO-SAN	Soprano
B. F. PINKERTON	Tenor
GORO	Tenor
SHARPLESS	Baritone
SUZUKI	Mezzo-soprano
THE BONZE	Bass
PRINCE YAMADORI	Baritone
KATE PINKERTON	Mezzo-soprano

Time: 1800's
Place: Nagasaki, Japan

**First performance: La Scala, Milan;
February 17, 1904**

To the tremendous surprise of Puccini, the first performance of *Madame Butterfly* was a complete failure. The cast was good; Puccini was a popular composer; and he had worked for three years on the opera, but it still was a failure. Sometime after the performance Puccini said, "It was a terrible evening. The failure of *Butterfly* hurt me all the more because it was a complete suprise. . . . The morning after I felt I would never be able to write another note of music. For two weeks afterward I couldn't force myself to leave the house. . . . I was so ashamed!"

Puccini, however, revised the opera, and that same year it was performed again and was a great triumph.

ACT I

CIO-CIO-SAN stood at the top of Kazagashira hill, looking out at the blue sea and the mountains. Below her, the buildings of the city of Nagasaki were soft in color, and the gardens with their graceful painted bridges blended into the fields of seedling rice that stretched on into the mountains. Cio-Cio-San was happy, as she always was when she looked at the mountains, for here was the resting place of departed souls who were now her ancestral gods. But today she was rapturously happy, for she was about to marry the American naval lieutenant B. F. Pinkerton.

On another hill also overlooking the harbor of Nagasaki, Lieutenant Pinkerton and Goro, the marriage broker, were inspecting the lovely house and gardens that the young American had leased for himself and Cio-Cio-San.

"These sliding panels are as frail as parasol paper," Pinkerton remarked.

"No, they are as strong as a fortress," the little man replied, bowing and smiling. He clapped his hands three times, and Pinkerton turned to see two men and a woman coming from the house. Humbly they went down on their knees before him.

"And who are they?"

Pointing to the woman, Goro said, "This is your bride's companion, Suzuki, or, as we call her, Miss Floating Cloud in Heaven."

Suzuki looked up and spoke. "Your excellence is smiling? A smile has the power to destroy all hurt."

Pinkerton, who did not understand or appreciate this wisdom, turned away, and the servants went back into the house. Goro scurried over to the young man's side and assured him that he had nothing to worry about. Everything had been taken care of; the marriage ceremony would be simple and the relations would not be bothersome. Smiling mysteriously, he added, "Her uncle, the Bonze, will not grace us with his presence."

The lieutenant and Goro were interrupted by the arrival of the American consul, Sharpless. Hat in hand and mopping his brow, he walked into the garden, talking all the while about the steep ascent to the house.

"Nothing else to say about my house?" asked Pinkerton, pointing to its fragile paper walls. "I have just bought it for nine hundred and ninety-nine years! Japan is fantastic! I can cancel my lease any month I wish." He smiled and sipped his drink. "My marriage is to be on the same terms!"

Sharpless looked at Pinkerton thoughtfully as he seated himself in a wicker chair. "Young man," he said, "your free and easy philosophy may hurt you someday." He continued seriously, "Your bride-to-be came to the consulate last week. She is very lovely, I was told, and it would be shameful for you to bring any unhappiness to her."

"Do not worry, Sharpless," the young man said, brushing a cherry blossom from his white uniform.

Goro rushed into the garden, pointing toward the path up the hill. "Listen, listen! They're coming. You can hear them like a swarm of bees."

Coming up the path with her mother and her friends, Cio-Cio-San smiled contentedly to herself. "I know I am the happiest girl in all Japan. In fact, in all the world!" she thought. "I have answered love's call, and I am happy to be standing at this door to a new life."

She paused for a moment on the curved bridge before coming into the garden. The quiet water mirrored her almond-shaped eyes and her black hair, entwined with many silver pins and flowers that tinkled in the breeze. Lieutenant Pinkerton watched her tiny feet in their delicate rounded getas as they moved down the steps, and he was dazzled by the many colors of her kimono and obi. The sleeves of her wedding dress dragged along the ground and caught the tiny blossoms along the path in their train.

Motioning to her friends, Cio-Cio-San closed her parasol and went down on her knees. "Bow before B. F. Pinkerton," she said softly. And they did. Rising, she introduced her relatives to the lieutenant and the consul.

Sharpless approached Cio-Cio-San. "Your name, Miss Butterfly, fits you perfectly. Are you from Nagasaki?"

"Yes. And once my people were very wealthy." She turned to her companions and they nodded in affirmation. "But," and she smiled shyly, "we are no longer rich and I have had to earn my living as a geisha. I do not hide it. I am not ashamed."

"And how old are you?" the consul asked.

"I am well on in years. I am fifteen." Sharpless admired her honesty and pitied her frailty. But he was afraid that her devotion to the young officer was more sincere than Pinkerton's was to her. The consul looked away at a flowering plum tree, as Butterfly spoke to Pinkerton.

"Do not be offended, but I have brought a few treasured keepsakes with me." She emptied her sleeves, placing their contents, one by one, on a tiny stool.

Pinkerton looked at them all as she explained each one—the little ivory fan, the mirror, and a tiny jar of rouge.

"And this one?" Pinkerton asked, pointing to a long sheath.

Her happy smile left her face as she replied, "It is something sacred. Please forgive me, but there are too many people around for me to explain it to you now."

Goro crept up behind the officer, whispering and smiling wryly. "It is the dagger the Mikado sent her father with the request that he use it."

Butterfly was looking at some small ivory Buddhas. She calmly put them aside and led her husband-to-be away from the crowd. "Early this morning I visited the temple of my gods to renounce them. I am starting a new life with you and I must begin it with my new religion. My uncle, the Bonze, does not know. Neither do my people. But I know my husband's God will protect me. To make you quite happy, I must forget the faith of my home and my people."

The chattering guests, enjoying their tea and Kasutera cake, were asked to make a circle around the happy couple and prepare for the wedding ceremony. Some tinkling of bells, some words, and the ritual of drinking saki nine times, and it was quickly over. When the signatures were set to the papers, Sharpless decided to return to town. His departing admonition to his American friend, to be faithful to Butterfly, fell on deaf ears. The happy bridegroom was calling for saki, this time for everyone, and the consul descended the hill with the sound of joyous toasts ringing in his ears.

A sudden breeze swept through the garden, bringing with it the angry voice of the Bonze. As he appeared on the bridge, all Cio-Cio-San's friends and relatives stood as though they were thunder-struck. Pointing his bony finger at the girl, he roared, "You have disgraced us all! You have renounced your people! No one must stay here. Come away from this place, all of you! The curse of the temple is on you, Cio-Cio-San." Butterfly fell weeping to the ground as her husband rushed to her side.

"I order you all to leave," the Bonze shouted again. Butterfly's mother tried to go to her, but the terrified crowd pulled her away, and the old woman followed them into the city. Butterfly held her ears, so as not to hear the shouts and curses of the priest and her friends.

Pinkerton consoled her by telling her that there was not a Bonze in all Japan who deserved as much as a single tear from her. Feeling safe with him, she smiled and wiped her eyes with the corner of her long sleeve.

The night began to fall, and from the house Cio-Cio-San could hear Suzuki offering her evening prayers. As Mrs. B. F. Pinkerton, there would be no more Shinto prayers. Now that she had renounced her people, she was really alone. But that did not matter, for she was happy.

She called to Suzuki, who appeared quickly on the terrace holding a beautiful white gown. Butterfly bowed to Pinkerton and followed Suzuki into the house.

Pinkerton roamed about the garden, watching the fireflies as they swooped and blinked in the night. With only the shrill of the locust in the distance, it was quiet enough to hear the falling petals from the plum and cherry trees. He turned and saw his new wife in the doorway. The moonlight sifting through the trees fell on her in her shimmering white yukata. He had never seen anything, or anyone, quite so beautiful.

"We have a thousand million stars to protect us tonight," Cio-Cio-San said softly.

"They named you well, Butterfly," Pinkerton said, walking toward her. "You are very beautiful."

At the name, "Butterfly," Cio-Cio-San's face clouded over and she sadly remarked, "In the lands across the ocean, when butterflies are caught,"—she cringed in fear. "I've often heard it is the custom to pin them to a cardboard." She shuddered.

The lieutenant took her hands gently. "That's true, I can't deny it. But shall I tell you why?" The girl nodded.

"So they can't fly away! To hold them forever, as I want to hold you."

Butterfly, happy again, looked up at the stars. It was difficult to distinguish them from the fluttering blossoms on the trees and the sparkle of the fireflies. Lieutenant Pinkerton put his arm around his lovely wife as they went into their new home. (Duet "Viene la sera.")

ACT II

THE lieutenant was recalled to the United States, but Butterfly thought little of this change of events. After all, it would only be a matter of months before he would return.

As the seasons flew by, she began to wonder if her husband would return. Three times she saw the heavy rains of autumn make way for winter with its silver snow, and then it was cherry blossom time again.

Standing beside a screen brightly decorated with the Seven Grasses of Autumn, Cio-Cio-San watched Suzuki at her morning prayers.

"Your Japanese gods are dull and unhearing, Suzuki. The God of my new country would grant me all that I ask, if only that God knew where to find me." She looked out into the garden and asked, "How much money do we have left, Suzuki?"

"Only a few coins," Suzuki answered. "Unless your husband comes soon, we'll have nothing to live on."

"He *will* come. Otherwise, why did he order the consul to pay the rent every month? And didn't he tell me when he left that he would return when the roses bloomed again and robins came to nest?"

"Yes. He will return," Suzuki said, weeping.

"You have no faith, Suzuki," Butterfly said, brushing the tears from her maid's eyes. "Look out into the garden and past the bridge to the harbor. One day we'll see a tiny smoke cloud there, and it will be his ship. It's a mighty warship coming into the harbor. Can't you hear the cannon roaring their welcome? He has come back, but I shall not go down the path to meet him. No, I will wait here. I will wait among the flowers until I see him in his white uniform coming over the bridge." She laughed and ran to the terrace. "I will hear him calling 'Butterfly, Butterfly,' but I will hide and tease him for a while." She extended her arms to Suzuki and smiled. "But when he calls me his lovely silver goddess, I will rush into his arms. It will come true, Suzuki. You must believe me." (Aria "Un bel di.")

Butterfly watched Suzuki leave the room. Her sad, bent body said she did not believe it at all.

There was a knock at the door and a voice asked for Madame Butterfly. Without even looking at the door, Cio-Cio-San answered, "I'm Madame Pinkerton, if you please."

Turning around, she saw the consul and clasped her hands with joy. "It is an honor, Mr. Consul, that you come to visit me."

"So, you remember me," he said, taking off his hat and bowing low.

"You are welcome. This is an American house," Butterfly said, motioning Sharpless to be seated.

Over tea they discussed many things: the weather, his health, and when the robins nested in America. The consul was ill at ease, for he had come to tell her Pinkerton had written him a letter saying that he was no longer married to Butterfly, as he had taken an American girl as his wife. The consul could not quite bring himself to tell her the news, and soon it was too late. They heard Goro's laughing, cackling voice, and turned to see him and Prince Yamadori just reaching the top of the hill.

Butterfly smiled. "Ever since my husband went back to America, Goro has been trying to marry me to the wealthy Prince. He does not seem to understand that the lieutenant is coming back!"

But she welcomed Yamadori to her house with great dignity, and graciously accepted the flowers he had brought. Sharpless watched, shaking his head sadly, as she told Goro that it was not possible for her to marry again. She did not recognize the laws of Japan that said she was free again. She recognized only the laws of America. Heartbroken, Yamadori left, and Butterfly laughed behind her ivory fan as she watched his grotesque figure disappear down the hill. Goro was trailing behind.

The consul looked at her with grave concern. "We're alone now. Come, sit here next to me and I'll let you read the letter from America."

"I'll be very quiet, I promise," Butterfly said, sitting down on a red pillow. But she chattered away, happily commenting on every word of endearment, until Sharpless realized he would have to tell her the truth.

"What would you do if he should never come back to you?" he asked.

Butterfly sat motionless, then bowed her head and almost stammered. "I would have two choices. I could return to entertaining the people with my songs . . . or else, even better . . . I could die."

"Perhaps you should marry Yamadori," Sharpless suggested.

"You, even you, are against me," Butterfly said. "Your words upset me and I beg you to leave." She walked toward the door and would have fallen had not Sharpless rushed to her side.

"He forgot me!" she cried, and ran from the room.

The look of pity on the consul's face changed to one of surprise and disbelief when Butterfly came back carrying her child on her shoulder. Her eyes were shining with pride. Putting the child down on the floor and holding him close, she spoke. "Could he forget this beautiful child?"

"Does Pinkerton know about him?" Sharpless asked.

"No. He was in America when 'Sorrow' was born.

But now you can write and tell him. He will return soon, I am sure. Then we will call our son 'Joy.'"

She kissed the baby tenderly. "I would rather die than have my child see me dancing and singing to support him. I will not live without honor!" (Aria "Chi vide mai.")

"I promise to tell your father about everything that has happened," the consul said, patting the little boy on the head. "I promise."

Sharpless had not been gone more than a few seconds when Suzuki appeared, dragging Goro into the house. She had overheard him spreading vicious gossip about Butterfly and her baby. Butterfly was enraged, and threatened to kill the screaming, pleading Goro. Suzuki took the baby from the room as his mother, in disgust, pushed Goro out of the house. Watching his dumpy little figure scurrying out of sight, Butterfly dreamed of the day when she could take Sorrow away from Japan to America where he belonged. A shot from a cannon brought her back to reality, and she heard Suzuki saying, "It's the cannon from the harbor. It is a warship of gleaming white! And it's flying the American flag!"

Picking up a telescope, Butterfly looked for the name of the ship. "There it is! *Abraham Lincoln!* He has come back."

Rejoicing, she ran out to the terrace and to the cherry tree that stood in front of it. Climbing up into its branches, she gazed out toward the harbor. Shaking the blossoms down, she called to Suzuki, "Go into the garden and bring all the flowers, as many as there are stars when night has fallen. Bring all the lilies and all the iris, all of them!"

"The garden will be as barren as winter," Suzuki replied, running down the steps.

"I want the house to be filled with springtime when he arrives," Butterfly said, as she climbed down from the tree.

Soon, Suzuki returned from the garden, her arms filled with flowers of every description. She and Butterfly sang together as they covered everything—the floors, the pillows, the chests—with lilies and violets and slender green branches.

"I want the jasmine and cherry blossoms to be everywhere," Butterfly said happily.

"There are no more flowers, Cio-Cio-San. The garden is empty. All April is here in the room." (Duet "Scuoti quella fronda di ciliegio.")

The sun was beginning to set as Suzuki brought the baby to his mother. They would all wait together. He sat on a tiny pillow while Butterfly gazed into her lacquered mirror.

"How time has changed me, Suzuki. Give my face a touch of color. And a spot of rouge for the baby, too. The hours of waiting may rob his face of its glow."

"Do not move so much while I am arranging your hair," Suzuki scolded, but Butterfly did not hear her. She was thinking how surprised all her relations would be to know that her husband had come back. She would have her triumph at last!

"Bring me my wedding gown, Suzuki. He must see me just as I was that night." She looked at herself again in the mirror and was pleased, particularly with the crimson poppy in her hair. With child-like grace she motioned to Suzuki to close the shosi. She made three little holes in the paper panels—one for each of them. The baby's was nearest the floor, for after all he would become tired. She would stand, looking out of the highest panel.

As the voices from the town drifted up the hill, the moon appeared. Sorrow fell asleep, and so did Suzuki. But Butterfly stood rigid and motionless, staring into the night. She knew that he would arrive soon.

ACT III

WHEN the first streaks of the pink dawn appeared, Butterfly was still waiting. She watched the sun rise and fill the house. She touched Suzuki on the shoulder, and she awoke with a start.

"Is it morning, Cio-Cio-San?"

"Yes. And I know he'll come soon." She picked up her sleeping son and carried him up the stairs, repeating to herself, "Tomorrow our grief will turn to joy. Tomorrow . . ."

While she was gone, Pinkerton and Sharpless arrived, bringing the lieutenant's American wife. Suzuki listened as they explained their reasons for wanting to take Sorrow back to America. They must all think of the child's future. She fell wailing to the floor when she thought of what this would do to Butterfly.

Although he was touched and aware of what great misery he had brought to Butterfly, Pinkerton could not stay and tell her himself. He walked out of the house, crushing the now dead flowers beneath his feet. Kate, his American wife, watched his figure disappear. She sighed and turned to Sharpless. Together, they went out on the terrace, leaving Suzuki to confront Butterfly with the sad news.

Cio-Cio-San came excitedly into the room just in time to see them walking into the garden. Suddenly, it was all clear to her. Pinkerton was not coming back, and that lady was his new wife. She raised her hand to Suzuki, who came close to her. Gathering her last bit of courage, she spoke to the consul and Kate and assured them that it would be best for Sorrow to go to America. Bowing low, she bid them good-bye and instructed Suzuki to darken the house.

"Go and stay with the baby. I wish to be alone."

Reluctantly, Suzuki left the room, and Butterfly stood looking at the shrine of Buddha and the sheathed dagger on the wall next to it. She knew the inscription on the dagger from memory: "He shall die with honor who can no longer live his life with honor." She felt that she would faint, but caught herself against the great lacquered chest. One of the drawers came open and exposed the tip of a long white veil. Butterfly, as in a trance, pulled it out. Its full length trailed behind her as she roamed about the room, looking at every object for the last time. Taking the dagger from the wall, she placed it on the floor beside her. The door flew open, breaking the deadly silence, and Sorrow came rushing in. Butterfly smothered him with kisses and then blindfolded his eyes. "You will be happy in America, little one," she sobbed, and placed a small American flag in his hand. "Play for a while. You will be happy soon." (Aria "Tu, tu piccolo Iddio.")

Butterfly went behind the screen, and picking up the dagger, she plunged it into her body.

The knife clattered to the floor and the dying Butterfly crawled to Sorrow. Pinkerton and Sharpless rushed into the room as Butterfly died. The crimson poppy that had been in her hair blazed vermilion-red among the dead flowers on the floor.

MADAME BUTTERFLY

THE MAGIC
FLUTE

Die Zauberflöte

by

WOLFGANG AMADEUS MOZART
(1756-1791)

Libretto by EMANUEL SCHIKANEDER and K. L. GIESECKE
Based on Liebeskind's story,
"LULA, ODER DIE ZAUBERFLÖTE"

Tamino	Tenor	Pamina	Soprano
Three Ladies	Two sopranos, Mezzo-soprano	Three Genii	Soprano, Mezzo, Contralto
Papageno	Baritone	Speaker of the Temple	Baritone
The Queen of the Night	Soprano	Sarastro	Bass
Monostatos	Tenor	Old woman (later Papagena)	Soprano

Time: Around the time of RAMESES THE FIRST
Place: EGYPT, near the TEMPLE OF ISIS
First performance: Theater-auf-der-Wieden,
VIENNA; September 30, 1791

Many people consider *The Magic Flute* Mozart's greatest opera. E. Schikaneder, the librettist, and Mozart wrote the opera in German, for the public preferred opera in their own language rather than Italian, which was popular with the aristocracy. Both Schikaneder and Mozart were Freemasons, and it is fairly certain that they used *The Magic Flute* to glorify Freemasonry.

At that time, the ideas of brotherhood that the Freemasons supported were opposed by both the State and the Church. The struggle for and against Freemasonry is thought to be symbolized by the various characters in *The Magic Flute.* Pamina represents the Austrian people; the Queen of the Night is the Empress Maria Theresa, who opposed Freemasonry; Tamino symbolized Emperor Joseph II, who was generous in his attitude toward the Freemasons; Sarastro is a Freemason who was well known to Mozart; and Monostatos personifies the Church.

ACT I

TAMINO ran breathlessly down the rocky pass that led into the valley. He could hear the giant serpent slithering along the rocks behind him, and he could feel the heat of its breath as its fangs shot perilously close to him. Even as he stumbled against a sharp rock, the young Prince wished desperately that he had just one arrow left. Then he could kill the terrible beast. Tamino gripped his silver bow tightly in his hand and ran on. The giant snake followed hungrily behind.

The young man had barely enough breath to call out, "Help me, help me! Merciful gods, help me," as he ran into the clearing. Those cries took his last bit of strength and he fell exhausted in front of what appeared to be a dark cave. He toppled against a rock and slipped into unconsciousness.

The serpent loomed above him, breathing fire and ready to strike. The opening of the cave suddenly grew bright with light. Three ladies in flowing silver robes stepped out, pointing their silver darts at the monster. It fell dead.

"He is certainly handsome," the First Lady said, looking at Tamino.

"I have never seen anyone so handsome," said the Second Lady, wondering quietly at the strange Oriental design of his clothes.

"Yes," commented the Third Lady, "someone should paint his portrait." She made a quiet note of the odd slant of the young man's eyes.

"We should really tell the Queen of his arrival," one said.

"You are right," agreed another. "Who will stay with him?"

"And who will go?" asked the Third.

After much jealous arguing as to who would go and who would stay, they mutually decided that the beautiful stranger would be safe until they all returned. They disappeared, as mysteriously as they had just appeared, into the cave.

Tamino regained consciousness and looked about wildly. He was rather amazed to see the serpent dead at his feet.

"How odd and mysterious," he thought to himself. "This could happen only in Egypt, certainly not in my homeland."

The musical sound of a pipe of Pan was dancing down from the direction of the pass. Tamino jumped up quickly and hid himself behind the leaves of a nearby tree. He cautiously peered out at the strange figure coming into the clearing. This odd person was happily singing to himself. From time to time, Tamino could catch the words of his song. From them, he gathered that this strange character was a birdcatcher. The man kept talking about the bird calls he knew, and how much he wished that he might capture a lovely girl and make her his wife. (Aria "Der Vogelfänger bin ich ja.")

Tamino pushed the leaves aside to get a better look. Why, the little man looked like a bird! His suit was made of thousands of tiny feathers—silver and gold, yellow and white, pink and blue—every color of the rainbow bird world. Gradually, Tamino realized that some of the dazzling colors were living birds, tiny birds in silver and gold cages strapped to the man's back.

Tamino stepped out from the protection of the green leaves and spoke to the stranger. "Who are you, happy man?"

"I am a man, like you," the man answered, seeming not at all surprised to see a new face. "May I ask who you are?"

"My father is a King, I am called a Prince."

"I don't like the way he stares at me," the birdman thought to himself. "I'll frighten him away." He raised his hand. "Don't come near me. I have gigantic strength."

"So you were the one who saved me from this serpent?"

Noticing the monster near the opening of the cave, the little man began to tremble. "Is it dead or alive?"

"But you have no weapon," Tamino continued, "how could you have killed him?"

"With my bare hands," the birdman said, boasting, "I strangled him."

From the cave came the loud cries of "Papageno!" The Three Ladies were back again.

"Who are they?" Tamino asked.

"I don't really know who they are. But they're calling me," Papageno replied.

As the Three Ladies angrily approached the birdman, the Prince noticed that one was carrying a vase of water, the second a stone, and the third was holding a golden padlock and a medallion in her hands. Their faces were veiled in white silk that fluttered in the wind, and then clung quietly to their silver robes.

"They must be very beautiful," Tamino said to Papageno.

Papageno shook his head and cooed at the birds in their cages. The poor things were trembling nervously. "I do not think so," he whispered. "If they are, why do they hide their faces?" Papageno motioned for Tamino to be quiet. "I have brought you the birds, fair ladies, just as you wished."

The First Lady handed Papageno the vase of water. "And in return, our ruler sends you clear water instead of wine."

"And this stone instead of cake," said the Second.

"And," said the Third, "instead of sweet figs you shall have this golden padlock for your mouth!" She turned to Tamino. "It was *we* who saved you. Our ruler has sent this gift to you. It is a portrait of her daughter."

Two of the Ladies lifted the shimmering bird cages from Papageno's back and moved toward the cave, laughing to themselves as Papageno tried in vain to remove the padlock from his lips.

Tamino looked in wonder at the portrait. "I have never seen anyone so beautiful," he said to himself. "I do believe that I have fallen in love with this picture. I wish that she were here before me. I would never let her get away." (Aria "Dies Bildnis ist bezaubernd schön.") The young Prince kissed the medallion.

Suddenly, a great clap of thunder, short but frightening, echoed through the valley. "What is that?" he asked.

"You must have courage now," the Three Ladies replied. "Our Queen is about to appear."

The sound of thunder grew closer and then, with a sudden burst, the entire mountain opened wide. Bluish-silver moonlight settled over everything. Tamino opened his eyes and saw the Queen of the Night standing majestically next to her star-

studded throne. She smiled, extending her hand to Tamino. Bits of diamonds, like tiny drops of water, seemed to fall from her silver fingernails.

"Don't tremble, my boy. You are innocent and you are wise. You are just the one to put my heart at rest. A monster has stolen my daughter! You shall save her and return her to me." (Aria "Zum leiden bin ich auserkoren.")

Tamino did not know what to answer.

"If you save her, she shall be yours forever!" The Queen tossed a glittering star into the air, and with a sudden roar of thunder she was gone.

Papageno pointed to his padlocked mouth and began to hum. The Three Ladies appeared again from the shadows. The First removed the padlock from Papageno's mouth, saying, "Fortunately, the Queen is merciful today."

"You may speak, but you must never lie again," the Second said.

"Oh, I shall never, never lie again," Papageno sang, happily dancing around. "Never again."

"If every tongue that spoke a falsehood could have its lips sealed," the Three Ladies chanted together, "we would have a feeling of love and understanding." (Quintet "Dies Schloss soll deine Warnung sein.")

The First Lady stepped forward and presented the Prince with a silver flute. "This rare gift is for you. Our Queen has sent it to you. It possesses the magic power to keep you free from danger and will move the coldest heart to love."

To Papageno they said, "The Queen has commanded that you escort the Prince to Sarastro's palace."

"No. I cannot."

"You will be safe with the Prince," the First Lady said, smiling at Papageno. "This treasure is yours." She presented him with a golden casket containing a set of silver chimes. "With these chimes, and with Tamino's magic flute, you will both be protected always."

"But how do we find our way to this great castle?" Tamino and Papageno asked simultaneously.

"Three youthful genii will meet you and show you the way," the Ladies replied, dissolving into the mist.

They were gone, leaving the Prince and the birdman alone. The huge green leaves were beginning to move in the cool air, and the silver, night-blooming flowers were coming to life as the two young men walked into the unknown.

(SCENE 2) At the very moment when the three genii were leaving Tamino and Papageno at the gold-and-white gates of Sarastro's castle, Monostatos, a Moorish slave in the employ of Sarastro, was dragging the Queen of the Night's beautiful daughter, Pamina, into a sumptuously appointed room. She was to be kept a prisoner there until Sarastro had returned from his daily hunt. The giant shoved the girl roughly across the floor, and she fell weeping into a mass of silver cushions. When Monostatos tried to pat her hand, the Princess pushed him away.

"Your life is over, little dove," the Moor said.

Pamina answered him by kicking him. "I'm not afraid of dying," she said calmly. "But my poor mother will die of grief."

"Tie the girl to the couch!" Monostatos roared to several slaves who were watching the proceedings from behind a gold-laquered screen. As they attempted to secure Pamina with some silver ropes, she promptly fainted. Now everyone, including the Moor, was in a state of consternation.

Papageno had strayed away from Tamino and now he was standing in the doorway that led to Pamina's golden prison.

Seeing Papageno in his wild and colorful costume of feathers, Monostatos was certain that this stranger was the Devil himself. Papageno's reaction to the dark, bearded face of the Moor was exactly the same. In their fright, they both raced for the door that led into the garden.

When she awakened, Pamina saw Papageno returning through the same door from which he had so recently exited. "You must be the daughter of the Queen of the Night," he said.

"I am she," Pamina said sadly.

"Well, I'll know for sure right away," the birdman said, looking at the portrait that Tamino had received from the Queen. He scrutinized the girl closely. "Yes . . . everything tallies."

"May I see?" Pamina asked. "Yes, it is certainly I. How did you come by it?"

Papageno looked about the room and sat down on a huge white cushion.

"I came to your mother's palace to deliver my birds, as I do every day, and I met a Prince there. He so entranced your mother that she gave him this portrait of you. She commanded him to come here and free you. I'm afraid that his decision to do so was as hasty as his love for you. The thing now is to get you back to your mother."

"We might attempt it, if I were sure that you were not another villain hired by Sarastro," said Pamina.

"A villain?" Papageno said, jumping up from his cushion. "I'm the best man on earth."

"Please forgive me," Pamina added, seeing the genuine look of hurt on the poor man's face. "I can tell you have a loving heart."

"Yes? What good is it," Papageno said, "since I have no loving wife."

"Man can always give an abundance of love," Pamina said, taking Papageno's hand. "And he will never lack a goodly heart to spend it on."

"It is love that makes life worth while," said Papageno. Pamina agreed with him about that. (Duet "Bei Männern, welche Liebe fühlen.")

(SCENE 3) Meanwhile, the three genii led Tamino into the sacred grove. "This is the path you wish to take," the youths said, pointing to three magnificent temples at the end of the road.

Over the portal of one, Tamino could read THE TEMPLE OF WISDOM. Over the portal of the second was THE TEMPLE OF REASON, and over the third THE TEMPLE OF NATURE.

"Do you really think that I can save Pamina?" he asked.

"We have no power to help you now," they answered, waving good-by. "But, be brave and be a man. All will go well."

Tamino approached the temple on the right. "Stand back!" a voice said from within.

The same words greeted him at the door to the temple on the left.

"I'll try the middle door," Tamino thought. "Surely someone will let me in."

He had not even reached the top of the marble steps when the door slowly opened. He was confronted by a tall, stately old man.

"What are you searching for here, young man?" the priest asked, barring Tamino's way.

"I am looking for the home of virtue and love."

"Those are high-sounding words, my boy," the priest said, folding his arms. "How do you expect to find that home, when vengeance has brought you here?"

"Vengeance against a villain has brought me here," Tamino said bravely.

"You will not find him here."

"Doesn't Sarastro rule this country?"

"Yes," replied the old man, "in this Temple of Wisdom."

Tamino turned to go.

"If you value your life, you had better stay," the priest said. "Stay and talk to me. Do you hate Sarastro?"

"Yes. He is a tyrant. He has made the Queen of the Night miserable and unhappy. He has stolen her daughter."

"Don't listen to such foolish chatter from such a foolish woman."

"Where is Pamina? Have they already sacrificed her?"

"I cannot answer that," the priest replied. "My tongue is bound by an oath. You will learn the truth, young Prince. The hand of friendship will lead you, and make you one of our eternal brotherhood."

All these riddles were swimming in Tamino's head, and the sound of voices chanting within the temple only confused him more. The old priest walked away. "Tell me," Tamino cried out, "tell me! Is Pamina still alive?"

"She lives," mysterious voices answered.

"Thank you, thank you!" Tamino shouted with joy. "I wish I had the power to thank each and every one of you. I'll play you a song on my silver flute, perhaps its music will show you a little of what is in my heart."

The Prince sat down on the marble steps and began to play. A serene stillness settled over everything. The silver notes seemed to float on the air.

Tamino said, "Can Pamina hear it? Where is Pamina?"

Then he heard the sound of Papageno's pipes. "Perhaps," thought the Prince, "Papageno has found her. I'll follow the sound of his pipes. Maybe I'll find them both." He listened for a moment and walked into the shadows of the silver-green forest.

Quite naturally, Pamina and Papageno had had a similar idea, to follow the sound of Tamino's flute, for they soon appeared in search of the Prince. Before they could cross the clearing in front of the temples, they were stopped by the angry Monostatos and a horde of slaves.

"Stop them! Tie them up!" he shouted.

Miraculously, Papageno thought of his magic chimes. He began to play. The Three Ladies had not failed him. The tinkling little sounds shimmered all about the evil Moor and his followers, and in seconds they were completely under the spell of the music. They danced and laughed as the notes twisted and curled into the air; and finally they dashed off into the forest in search of the music.

"I think we should all own such magic chimes," Pamina said, laughingly. "Then all our enemies would run away, and we would always be happy."

The tinkling sounds of the chimes had no sooner disappeared than a loud blast of trumpets was heard from within the temple.

Pamina began to weep when she heard the voices shouting, "Long live Sarastro!"

"We're lost now," she cried, running to Papageno. He was trembling as much as she was. "No matter *what* happens," Pamina said bravely, "we will speak the truth."

The voices cried praises to Sarastro. Then Pamina and Papageno were surrounded by Sarastro's soldiers and priests. Everyone, even the ferocious lions drawing Sarastro's golden chariot, was silent as he walked past them toward Pamina.

She threw herself at his feet. "I did try to escape, my lord. I am guilty of trying to run away from you. But it was because I was frightened of that evil, wicked Moor."

Sarastro helped Pamina up. "Rise, Pamina, and be happy. I know that I can never force you to love me. Yet I cannot give you your freedom."

"I must get back to my mother," the young girl said, wiping the tears from her eyes.

Sarastro shook his head. "Your mother is a proud and haughty woman. It is time for a man to guide your heart."

At that moment, Monostatos came out of the forest, dragging Tamino after him. In the second that it took for a ray of sunlight to leap from Sarastro's gleaming chariot to the golden necklace at Pamina's throat, Tamino knew that he was gazing at a portrait come to life.

"It is she!" he cried.

"It is he," Pamina whispered. "This is no dream."

They ran into each other's arms. The Moor tore them apart, shouting, "This is too much! He tried to rob you of Pamina, my lord. It was I who tracked him down."

"You shall have your just reward," Sarastro said solemnly. "Take the Moor away and give him seventy-seven bastinado stripes!"

The wicked Monostatos was carried off by the slaves, roaring and wailing as he went.

"Lead these two to our temple," Sarastro commanded, looking at the Prince and Pamina.

Pamina gripped Tamino's hand. She was frightened by the feel of the cool, silk veil that was placed over her head. There was a veil for Tamino, too. Its folds almost hid his almond-shaped eyes. Pamina could feel their soft, brown warmth, steadfast and strong. She knew she would be safe.

Over a soaring song of praise for Sarastro, she could hear a choir of a hundred voices singing, "The earth will be heaven, when virtue and justice are joined together. Then mortals will be equals of the gods."

With Tamino's hand in hers, these words made very good sense, so she walked calmly toward the temple with her head held high.

ACT II

SARASTRO stood solemnly in the center of the vast subterranean temple of Isis and Osiris. The low, blue flames in the slender silver braziers on either side of him cast tall shadows of the priests against the wall as they marched into the chamber. The priests formed a circle around their leader, and two Speakers moved to his side, lowering their heads to signify that all was ready.

The wise, old man began to speak. "You have all been called together to take part in the initiation of the royal youth, Tamino. He is virtuous, silent, and well-meaning. If you hold him worthy, as I do, I ask you to show your approval."

There were no words and there was no indecision. As one, they drew their ornate silver horns from the folds of their white robes. They put the horns to their lips. Three chords echoed through the blue shadows.

All was quiet again.

"I thank you," Sarastro said. "The gods have ordained that the lovely Pamina is to belong to Tamino. For this reason, I have stolen her from her mother. The Queen of the Night intends to break down the foundations of our temple, but she will not succeed. Now, let Tamino and his companion be brought into the outer temple."

The circle of priests moved into a white, shining arc around the altar, raising their arms in praise to the gods. Sarastro said, "O Isis and Osiris, we ask you to bring the spirit of wisdom to this new pair! Bring them patience when danger is near. If death should take them, we ask you to lead them to your abode!" (Aria "O Isis und Osiris.")

The majestic chant rang through the temple, and lingered long after the priests had followed Sarastro out.

(SCENE 2) While waiting for the initiation to begin, Tamino and Papageno stood silently watching the blue sky and the columns that rose into the

THE MAGIC FLUTE

white clouds. The sound of a priest's voice made them realize that the ordeal was to start. "What do you want and what do you ask of us?"

"I want friendship and love," Tamino answered promptly.

"Are you prepared to die for them?"

"I am."

At the very mention of death, Papageno began to shake. Soon he was a mass of fluttering feathers.

"Are you, too," asked another priest, "prepared?"

"I'm not a hero," Papageno replied. "And, furthermore, I don't care to become one. All I want is food and drink and a nice wife. If that's possible."

"If you follow our laws and do not turn away from death," the priest informed him, "you shall have a pretty wife who will be just like you."

"And her name?" Papageno asked distrustingly.

"Papagena."

"May I see her now?" the birdman asked, wanting immediate proof.

"You will see her soon. But you cannot speak to her until the appointed hour."

The priest turned to Tamino. "On you, also, royal Prince, the gods impose this same silence. You shall see Pamina. Yet you may not speak to her. This is the first stage of your probation."

The priests departed. Tamino noticed that the sky was drained of all its blue. He and Papageno were enveloped in a weird darkness.

"Let's have some light!" Papageno shouted.

"Be patient," Tamino said quietly, "it's the will of the gods."

Almost at once, the path leading up to the portico of the temple was bathed in light. They could see the Three Ladies running toward them, brandishing flaming torches. "You cannot stay in this horrible place," they cried. "You are lost if you do."

"This is too confusing," Papageno said, hiding behind the Prince. "Perhaps we should go with them?"

"Be still, Papageno, and don't break your oath. Remember that you are not to speak to any woman here," Tamino said, pulling him back. "Just be still."

"The Queen is close by," the Ladies went on. "She has told us that all who join this group of men are doomed for life!"

Tamino stood firm. "A wise man does not pay attention to the vulgar crowd," he said coolly to Papageno.

"Papageno is so quiet," the Ladies teased. "Speak."

"Be still," Tamino commanded the birdman.

"It seems that no one can speak his own mind here," the Ladies cajoled, moving closer to Tamino and Papageno.

"This sacred place has been defiled by these women!" the priests shouted as they came out of the temple. "Away with them!"

There was a crash of thunder that threatened to shake the foundations of the shimmering white columns, and the Three Ladies ran screaming into the forest. Papageno fell quivering with fright at Tamino's feet. But the young Prince stood fearlessly watching the blue streaks of sky as they forced the black clouds out beyond the horizon.

(SCENE 3) That night, Monostatos came upon Pamina sleeping in her garden. The white moonlight on the roses that grew around her couch added immeasurably to the evil Moor's romantic feelings for the beautiful Princess. He could not resist the temptation to kiss her before she wakened. (Aria "Alles fühlt der Liebe Freuden.") But just as the moon slipped behind a cloud, the Queen of the Night appeared, seething with rage. Monostatos fell back.

Pamina awoke as the Queen swept past the startled man. "My heart is full of vengeance," she shouted at Pamina. "If you do not destroy Sarastro, you will no longer be my daughter!

"Now that Tamino is being sworn into the temple," the Queen told her, "he is lost to you forever. But you can save us all. Take this dagger and kill Sarastro, and I will rule again."

"But, Mother . . ."

"Not another word!" the Queen said, placing the dagger in Pamina's hand. (Air "Der Hölle Rache kocht in meinem Herzen.") There was a flash of lightning and the Queen vanished.

"But I cannot murder," Pamina cried, looking to the Moor for help or advice.

"Give the weapon to me and trust me. There's only one way to save yourself and your mother," said the Moor.

Pamina shuddered as he took the dagger from her. "Love me or die," he roared. The Moor reached out for the girl, but Sarastro stepped out from the bower of roses and wrenched the sharp blade from the slave's hand.

Pamina and the High Priest watched the angry Moor as he ran from the garden.

"I beg you not to punish my mother," Pamina whispered, kneeling at Sarastro's feet.

"I know everything," the wise old man said, helping her up. "Did you know, Pamina, that within our sacred temple, vengeance is unknown? Within its holy walls traitors are not allowed. All men are brothers, and our enemies are forgiven. If our teachings do not make a man happy . . . then he does not deserve to be a man." (Aria "In diesem heil'gen Hallen.") Pamina smiled at the great ruler as he put his arm around her and they walked out of the garden.

(SCENE 4) Tamino and Papageno were led into a room and told again to maintain silence. Papageno whined that they didn't even have any water. Whereupon an old woman appeared holding a cup.

"Do you have a sweetheart?" Papageno asked jokingly.

"Yes," she replied.

"What is his name?" he asked.

"Papageno," the old woman answered.

Papageno was flabbergasted. As the old woman was about to tell him her name, there was loud thunder and she scurried away.

The sun was rising over the silver lake when the Three Spirits escorted Tamino and Papageno down the path bordered by silver rose trees. "For the second time, you are welcome in Sarastro's kingdom," they told the young men. "He returns your magic flute and your chimes which were taken from you."

At a wave of their hands, a magnificent table unfolded from the ground, heavy with delicate cakes and wine. "Eat freely," they continued, "and when we meet for the third time you will be rewarded." Tamino took the flute and Papageno took his chimes, and the Spirits vanished.

At the very moment that Tamino began to play on the silver flute, Pamina ran into the garden. However, even though they were excited to see her, neither the Prince nor Papageno would break their oath of silence. Not understanding their reasons, the poor girl began to weep.

"I feel that everything has vanished," she said, looking sadly at Tamino. "All of our love has flown." Tears flowed down her cheeks and spotted her silver dress, but the Prince stood silent.

"If you do not feel as I do, Tamino, then there is nothing left but death." (Aria "Ach, ich fühl's es ist verschwunden.") She waited in vain for him to speak, but he refused to say a word. Pamina turned and slowly walked away.

The sound of trumpets rang out, calling Papageno and Tamino. They followed the sound, which was the signal that the tribunal was about to be held in the Temple of Isis and Osiris.

(SCENE 5) Walking down the long corridors, Papageno and Tamino were genuinely impressed by the solemn pagaentry. Sarastro and the priests stood regally in their white robes before a blazing sunburst of gold on the wall.

Sarastro said, "Prince, your behavior up until now has been manly and controlled. Let Pamina be brought in." At a sign from the High Priest, two of the brotherhood left the hall and returned with Pamina. She was covered from head to toe by a flowing white veil.

"Where am I?" she asked. "Where is Tamino?"

"Here," said Sarastro, removing Tamino's veil.

The young girl cried out in happiness. But Tamino motioned for her to stand back.

"Will I *never* see you again?" she wept.

"You will surely see each other again," Sarastro said. "It is time to say 'good-by,'" Sarastro signaled two of the priests. "But we will all meet again."

The Prince and Pamina were led away, and the temple was empty save for Papageno and the Speaker. Fearful of being alone and away from his friends, the birdman ran to the door to follow them, but he was driven back by tongues of flame. He ran to the door through which they had come into the temple, but there, too, he was forced back by deafening sounds of thunder.

"I can't go forward and I can't go backward," he wailed. "I should never have come here at all!"

"Do not be afraid," the Speaker said sympathetically. "Although you cannot be admitted into the brotherhood, because of the earthiness of your character, your appetite will be satisfied."

"Then I'd enjoy a glass of wine."

The Speaker merely pointed his finger, and magically a silver goblet of wine appeared through the marble floor. Amazed and happy, Papageno did not even notice that the Speaker had disappeared. The first drink from the goblet made the birdman feel delightfully strange. He began to play a tune on his silver chimes. He was quietly singing to himself about his longing for a beautiful girl who would be his wife when an old woman, tottering and trying to dance to the sounds of the chimes, hobbled into the temple. (Aria "Ein Mädchen oder Weibchen.")

"Here I am," she cackled. "Give me your hand as your pledge of our union."

"Not so fast!" Papageno said, looking at her dirty rags and her wrinkled skin.

"I advise you not to hesitate, Papageno," the old woman croaked. "If you do, you will be imprisoned here forever, and live only on bread and water."

"Bread and water? Give up the world?" Papageno cried. "Here is my hand!"

"Do you swear to that?"

"I do," answered Papageno, hiding his eyes with his other hand. When he peeked out he saw a radiant young girl standing before him. She was dressed as he was, in colorful feathers that fluttered and danced as she moved. She smiled at him.

"Pa- pa- Papagena!" he shouted with joy and ran to embrace her.

"Not yet," growled the Speaker, appearing from nowhere and stepping between them. "He is not worthy of you so soon, Papagena."

The old man led her away, leaving Papageno in despair.

(SCENE 6) Separated once again from Tamino, Pamina ran wildly into the garden of the silver

palms, carrying the dagger that her mother had given her.

"There is no other way," she sobbed as she leaned against one of the slender trees. "I will kill myself. At least we will meet in death."

As she raised the dagger, the Three Spirits stepped out from behind the trees. They snatched the dagger from her hand. "Wait and listen to us. If Tamino were to see this, he would die of sorrow. He loves only you."

"But he turned away from me. He wouldn't speak to me!"

"We must not tell you the reasons for that, but if you will follow us now we will show you Tamino. You will be surprised to see that not only has he given his heart to you, he is willing to give his life."

"Take me to him," Pamina begged, and wiping her eyes she followed the Spirits through the silver gate.

(SCENE 7) As twilight was falling over Egypt, Tamino found himself in a wild, mountainous place. The two priests with him observed him quietly as he gazed in wonder at two massive iron gates barring their way. Between the two gates were two men in armor. Through one gate Tamino could see a dashing torrent of silver water racing down, and through another, roaring flames tipped with silver tongues.

"If you pursue this path, Tamino," the armored men said, "you will find it full of danger. But if you can overcome the fear of death, you will be able to rise to heaven and understand the mystery of Isis."

"I'm not afraid of death," Tamino replied. "Open the gate for me."

"Wait for me, Tamino," Pamina cried from the distance. "Wait for me."

Pamina ran into the Prince's arms. "I will always be your companion, Tamino. Our love will show us the way through the fire and the water."

"It will be very dangerous," Tamino warned.

"But we will have your magic flute to protect us. Let us go." (Quartet "Ihr wandelt durch des Tones Macht.")

The gates swung wide and Pamina placed her hand confidently on Tamino's shoulder. Joyfully accompanied by the sound of the silver flute, they walked unscathed through the snapping flames and the flood of water to the Temple of Isis. It loomed ahead of them, white and shining. They could hear the voices of Sarastro and the priests calling to them.

"You have triumphed over the dangers and we consecrate you to Isis. Walk freely now within the temple gate."

The young lovers ran up the road to the blazing light that beckoned to them.

(SCENE 8) Papageno stood alone in a small garden, contemplating the branch of a silver tree. "Everyone is gone. I will never see Papagena again. I think that I shall die like a hero, hanging from the branch of this tree."

The birdman foolishly started to climb up into the highest branches, but he was quickly stopped by the sudden appearance of the Three Spirits.

"Stop, Papageno," they cried. "Man only lives once. Let this be enough for you."

"Your jokes and words are very fine," Papageno said sadly, swinging by one hand from the branch, "but if your hearts were burning like mine, you, too, would do the same."

"Then play on your silver chimes." They laughed, and said, "They might bring Papagena to you."

"What a fool I am," the little man said, jumping to the ground. "I forgot those magic things."

As the chimes tinkled in the air, the three youths called out to him, "Turn around, Papageno. Look what we have brought you!"

"Pa-pa-Pa-Papagena!"

"Pa-pa-Pa-Papageno!"

(SCENE 9) While the birdpeople were dancing and singing together over their new-found happiness, the Queen of the Night was plotting her horrible revenge with Monostatos, who was now anxious to destroy the power of Sarastro.

"We had better be quiet," the Moor warned the Queen and her entourage as they stumbled up the path. "We are nearing the temple," he said ominously. "Don't forget that you have given me your word that your daughter will be my wife."

"I have not forgotten," the Queen snarled. "I will keep my word."

"Be still," Monostatos whispered. "I hear a strange noise of thunder and rushing water. Can we already be in the main hall?"

"We will surprise them all," the Queen said, leaning against the Three Ladies for support in the dark. "We will kill them all!"

A storm of rain and lightning swept down the rocky pass, and in a flash of blue and silver the earth opened beneath them. In a torrent of raging water they were swallowed up and never seen again.

At the top of the hill, in the temple of the sun, Sarastro greeted Pamina and Tamino with outstretched arms. "The rays of the sun have destroyed the night and all its evil powers. Join us, Royal Prince and your bride, in giving thanks to Isis and Osiris."

The young lovers joined hands, smiling at the chorus of priests that welcomed them.

Above the temple, the sky was very blue and the sound of a silver flute hovered quietly in the air for a moment and then disappeared.

MANON

✦ By JULES MASSENET ✦

1842 - 1912

Libretto by Henri Meilhac and Philippe Gille

Based on the story "Les Aventures du Chevalier
des Grieux et Manon Lescaut," by Abbé Prévost

CAST OF CHARACTERS

POUSETTE	SOPRANO
JAVOTTE	SOPRANO
ROSETTE	SOPRANO
DE BRETIGNY	BARITONE
GUILLOT MORFONTAINE	BASS
INNKEEPER	BASS
LESCAUT	BARITONE
MANON LESCAUT	SOPRANO
CHEVALIER DES GRIEUX	TENOR
COUNT DES GRIEUX	BASS

TIME: 1720's   PLACE: PARIS, AMIENS, AND LE HAVRE

✦ First Performance: ✦

Opéra-Comique, Paris; • January 19, 1884

Massenet told a story in his memoirs about how he wrote *Manon*. He had already started to work on the opera, when one day he went for a walk. He passed a florist's shop and saw a young girl who was vital and delicate, and seemed to him to be dreaming of a life of luxury. He said to himself, "There she is. That is Manon." For the rest of the time that he worked on the opera, he kept the picture of the florist's assistant in his mind. He never saw her again, but to him she was Manon.

ACT I

AN ATMOSPHERE of fragility hung over the courtyard of the inn at Amiens. The sunlight that sifted through the willow trees was not golden, but a pale, soft yellow. Even the laughter of Pousette, Javotte, and Rosette, three frivolous coquettes who were looking out the window of the inn, was muted, happy but quiet.

Guillot Morfontaine and Bretigny, two wealthy Parisians, were standing idly on the steps to a tiny pavilion. They knew that the coach from Arras was due and they were wondering what new faces it would bring. Perhaps it would be bringing someone who was prettier than the fashionably dressed girls behind them in the window.

The three young ladies called out to the owner of the inn, and begged him to save them from hunger and thirst. Morfontaine and Bretigny joined the girls in calling out to the innkeeper. Bretigny sighed with relief as the deaf old man finally appeared, followed by several servants, all bearing food to the pavilion. Pousette, Javotte, and Rosette squealed with delight and ran out of the inn to join their hosts.

The innkeeper, remembering that he had promised to reserve a place on the coach for the young Chevalier des Grieux, hurried back into the inn, leaving his guests to enjoy their dinner.

Among the growing crowd of sightseers gathering in the courtyard were three soldiers, one of whom was named Lescaut.

"My young cousin, Manon, is arriving on the coach," he said. "I shall wait for her here and meet you later in the tavern." His companions nodded in approval and moved on through the crowd into the inn.

The coach soon arrived. The tiny clouds that it left in its wake were more like puffs of perfumed powder than dust from the country road, and as the horses stopped before the inn the fragile clouds curled up and blended into the twilight sky. Manon descended from the coach, wide-eyed with amazement. The pushing crowd was made up of unsophisticated country folk who found great excitement in the simple pleasure of watching the arrival of a coach. She had never seen so many people before.

She was on her way to a convent and this first trip away from home, plus this first taste of humanity in such a large mass, rather overwhelmed her. Lescaut caught sight of her pretty face immediately and quickly helped her through the crowd.

"Your looks do great credit to the family," he said with open admiration.

Manon curtsied. Her pale green eyes left the gaze of her cousin's to glance at the activity around her.

"I apologize, Cousin, for being such a country girl. But this is my first journey and everything on the road to Amiens has been so exciting and wonderful, I thought that I would weep." (Aria "Je suis encore tout étourdie.") Taking off her yellow bonnet she sat down on a gray stone bench, quietly folded her hands in her lap, and waited as her cousin went in search of her luggage.

Manon pushed a wisp of yellow hair from her forehead and looked up into the trees. Even the bird's song sounded different here, freer and happier. She heard the door to the pavilion opening. It was Guillot Morfontaine, ordering more wine. As Manon's pale eyes caught his, the elderly Morfontaine knew that he had never seen anyone so lovely, not in all of Paris, and he was determined to speak with her. She found his declarations of love-at-first-sight very funny, and she laughed. The tinkling sound amused his companions, who had come out of the pavilion to participate in the little scene.

"Come back, Guillot, before you burn your fingers," they chided. But before returning he whispered to Manon, "There will be a coach waiting for you. My money, anything you wish, is yours if you will run away with me." Manon nervously tied and untied the yellow ribbons of her handbag, and was relieved and happy when Lescaut came back and demanded of the stranger what he was saying to his cousin. Guillot ambled back to the pavilion accompanied by the ironic laughter of his friends.

Lescaut was preparing to have a serious discussion with Manon, concerning just such conversations, when one of his soldier friends reminded him that they were waiting for him in the tavern. "I must leave you, Manon, for a few moments." Manon patted him on the cheek.

Alone, Manon decided that she must really give up all her dreams and thoughts of frivolity. Once she was at the door to the convent, she would have to leave her fancies behind. "But," she thought wistfully and with a little envy, "how beautiful those girls look in their Paris dresses. Oh, enough of these silly dreams, Manon." She turned her back again to the pavilion. (Aria "Voyons, Manon, plus de chimères.")

A young man, who was by his dress surely a seminarian, came into the courtyard. His quiet dignity and his somber brown eyes attracted Manon and she smiled at him. He was the Chevalier des Grieux, who had just missed his coach. He respectfully introduced himself and sat down beside her.

"I am Manon," she said shyly but directly. He nodded. He was unable to take his eyes from hers, and he was unable to rid himself of the strange feeling that he was now confronted with a crisis in his life.

"I am a poor girl," she continued, tilting her head slightly to avoid a ray of sunlight that drifted through the trees. "Not bad at heart," she added coquettishly, "but my parents are putting me in a convent because they fear that I am too fond of pleasure. That is the story of Manon Lescaut."

"How barbaric to lock such beauty and charm up in a convent," the young boy said with great sincerity. Manon laughed and shook her head in approval. It was certainly not difficult for him to convince her that his way of thinking was right.

From the corner of her eye she caught sight of the driver of the carriage that the infatuated Guillot had promised her, and the brilliant idea of running away with Des Grieux danced through her mind. "That old gallant who is dining in the pavilion has offered me a carriage. How wonderful it would be if *we* could run away to Paris together."

Des Grieux watched her and knew that he was in love with her. "We *will* run away, and we will live in Paris!"

Manon could not mistake the serious tone of his voice, nor could she deny that she, too, had fallen in love with him. "Together," she said. "Always the two of us." (Duet "Nous vivions à Paris.")

Taking the young girl's hand in his, Des Grieux led Manon out of the courtyard. A burst of merry laughter spilled out of the pavilion and floated around Manon. She looked back. "How wonderful! Oh, how wonderful it must be to amuse oneself all of one's life." Des Grieux kissed her gently and they ran away.

The sound of their horses brought Lescaut, drunk, from the tavern. Guillot and his friends also appeared. Noticing that Manon was gone, Lescaut accused Guillot of having had her abducted. Guillot's anger was obvious to the gathering crowd, and

the innkeeper's announcement only added fuel to the fire: "The lovely child who was here has run away with a young man in Monsieur Guillot's carriage!"

"I will be avenged," the old man roared.

ACT II

IN PARIS, Manon was free. Free, she hoped, to live a life of glittering luxury. But for the time, she and Des Grieux were satisfied to live in a tiny apartment in the Rue Vivienne.

Their continuing lack of money annoyed Manon, who in a few short weeks grew from a daydreaming country girl into a glamorous young Parisienne. However, her genuine love, so she thought, for Des Grieux often surmounted her hunger for wealth, and she contrived to remain happy.

One late afternoon, she looked over Des Grieux' shoulder, watching him as he wrote his father a letter. His words of praise about her beauty and charm pleased her. He kissed her hand and questioned her about the bouquet of flowers near the window. The sight of them troubled him.

"Poor Chevalier, I have told you again and again. They were tossed in the window by a stranger." Manon laughed teasingly, and Des Grieux believed her. Why shouldn't he? After all, they were soon to be married.

Answering a knock at the door, Manon brought her cousin Lescaut and Bretigny into the apartment. Des Grieux was surprised to see them and Lescaut's angry accusations annoyed him. He also wished that Manon were not so friendly with Bretigny. Supposedly, she had not seen him since the day of their meeting in Amiens.

"Dear Chevalier," Lescaut said in a quieter tone, "Manon *is* my cousin, and I have merely come to ask whether or not you intend to marry her."

"This letter that I have just written should answer all your questions," said the young man. "Come nearer the window and I will read it to you." As he read to Lescaut, he could see Manon quietly chatting with Bretigny.

"Manon," whispered the nobleman, "I have been in touch with the boy's father. He is planning to take the Chevalier away from Paris tonight, by force."

"I refuse to listen to any of your schemes, Bretigny. I am in love with him."

"Perhaps, Manon, you prefer a life of poverty with him to one of wealth with me?"

The sound of Pousette's laughter and the memory of glittering gowns and jewels welled up in Manon's mind. "I cannot live or be happy if I am poor," she thought.

By the time Lescaut had assured himself that Des Grieux' letter would take care of all the marriage plans, the young Chevalier's destiny had been planned. Manon's desperate need for wealth would eventually take her into Bretigny's fashionable world.

After the departure of Lescaut and Bretigny, the young couple sat down for supper. Suddenly Des Grieux realized that he had not posted the letter to his father.

"I must do it now, Manon, or it will be too late." He reached across the table and took her hand. "But I cannot leave, even for a few moments, unless you assure me that you love only me."

A sad smile crept across her face. "You know that I do. We will be together always."

Manon watched as the door closed behind him. The lavender shadows of evening and the reflection of her face in the crystal goblet filled her with melancholy. "Good-by, little table," she said quietly, pushing her plate aside. "Good-by to all the happiness we have known. Why am I so weak that I cannot be happy with what we have shared together? It should be enough to remember that Des Grieux and I were happy in our poverty." But it was not enough, she knew. (Aria "Adieu notre petite table.")

When the young man returned, he began to tell her of the dream he'd had.

"I dreamed, Manon, about a tiny house in the woods. The song of the birds was everywhere, and small though it is I will make it paradise with you!" (Aria "Le Rêve.")

There was knocking at the door and Manon started. Now she was frightened. Without knowing why, the word "Good-by" slipped from her lips. "Do not answer, Chevalier. I don't want to leave you!"

Des Grieux laughed. "I will simply tell the visitor to leave." He touched her hand. "I will be back in a minute and we will laugh over your fear."

Manon gripped the edge of the table and wept as she listened to the scuffling noise in the hallway. Then the rolling sound of carriage wheels in the street made her run to the window. Flinging it wide, she looked out and cried, "My poor Chevalier."

ACT III

THE poet who described Paris as the place "where the air was filled with the quiver of fleeting things" could have been painting a picture of Cours-la-Reine, a favorite gathering spot of the fashionable world, as it came to life in a blaze of lights. All Paris seemed to be roaming up and down before the stalls and boutiques. The cries of shopkeepers selling their wares, and the conversations of the passers-by punctuated the night. Everyone was in a frivolous mood, and Pousette, Javotte, and Rosette were busy flirting with the young men on the promenade.

Lescaut, whose skill at dice and cards had recently netted him a small fortune, laughed and talked with his friends, advising them never to economize. "Why should one, when he has a set of dice in his pocket and knows the way to the Hotel de Transylvanie, the most famous gambling resort in all Paris!"

Bretigny came out of the theater in a joking frame of mind, and refused to let his former friend Guillot escape any of his barbed remarks. "Please, dear Guillot, you have so much, do not try to take Manon away from me."

"Away? Me?" asked Guillot ironically.

"Yes. You know she has a passion for money. Her latest fantastic whim is that I bring the entire opera here to perform tonight! But I had to refuse."

Guillot smiled quietly. Now he knew how to get even with Bretigny. He pulled at his white gloves gleefully and walked away.

Bretigny glowed with pride when Manon arrived. He had never seen her so resplendent. A powdered wig, so popular in the elegant courts of the eighteenth century, covered her yellow hair, and tiny butterflies of silver and gold sparkled and nestled in its curls. Envious women marveled at the fortune of jewels that hung about her swanlike throat. As Bretigny assisted her from her sedan chair, Manon greeted the crowd with poise and charm. She was no longer little Manon from the country, she was the Queen of Paris! Bretigny remained in the background and listened as she told her admirers that now she had everything that a woman could desire: beauty, power, wealth, and many admirers. "I am the happiest creature on earth," she said. (Aria "Gavotte.")

When the music ended Manon withdrew to talk with some of her new-found friends, and Bretigny turned to talk with a very old one, Chevalier des Grieux' father!

"I have just come up from the country," the old man said, "for a visit with my son. He is now the Abbé des Grieux, you know. He's going to preach his first sermon at Saint Sulpice this evening." Bretigny congratulated him and pointed to Manon. "There she is—the one who was once the object of your son's affection."

"I can see," said the boy's father, "why you were so concerned with his involvement."

"Weren't we right, Count des Grieux?" Bretigny asked.

At the name Des Grieux, Manon felt a cool breeze sweep across her. She immediately contrived to have Bretigny run an errand for her and began to ask the old Count for news of the Abbé des Grieux. "He was once in love with a friend of mine . . . a dear friend," she said, almost shyly. "Does he ever repeat her name?"

The elder Des Grieux watched her young eyes, sparkling with eagerness, and he answered, "He has, my dear, borne all his suffering silently. He has done what all men should do. He has forgotten."

"Forgotten!" said Manon sadly. "Forgotten?" She barely noticed the old man's departure or the sound of voices as the crowd surrounded her again. Guillot stepped forward grandly to announce that he had brought the ballet of the opera to perform just for Manon's pleasure. The ballet music seemed endless to her and she could hardly wait for the last notes to be played. Finally, the last white tutu faded into the wings and the conductor put down his baton. Guillot turned to Manon expecting some small "Thank you" for his expensive tribute, but her green eyes stared coldly through him and he heard her say, "But I have seen nothing." Indeed, she had seen none of the dancers and heard none of the music, really, for her thoughts had been with Des Grieux. With a sweep of her hand she called for her sedan chair and set out for Saint Sulpice.

(SCENE 2) The parlor of the seminary at Saint Sulpice was filled with the devout members of the church, and the sounds of the organ wove majestically in and out of their conversation.

"How eloquent the young man was," exclaimed one. "And only his first sermon," added another. They smiled warmly and affectionately as the young Abbé came in to greet his father.

"We are all proud of you, my son," said the Count des Grieux. "But I do wish and ask you to think twice before you adopt the priesthood as your ultimate way of life."

"Until now I have experienced nothing but bitterness and loathing," the boy said sadly. "This is what I wish to do."

"You are very young, my child, and you will see that life has much to give you." The Count embraced his son. "I must bid you farewell now, but I do want you to know that you will be receiving thirty thousand gold pieces as part of your mother's estate. Take care."

Des Grieux stood alone and confused. Visions of Manon appeared in every corner, and he could not thrust the image of her from his mind.

"I have tried to forget you, Manon! I have tried to find peace in the church," he cried, hiding his face in his hands. "Oh, go away! Disappear and let me rest!" (Aria "Ah! fuyez, douce image.") Disturbed by the many faces of memory that danced around him, he sadly turned and went into the church to attend the service that was about to begin.

As the door quietly clicked shut, Manon came in from the street, bribing her escort to allow her to stay until the Abbé returned again. The sound of the Magnificat in the distance and the soft religious peace of Saint Sulpice erased, momentarily, all her dreams of wealth and a life of pleasure. Manon knelt to pray for forgiveness.

When Des Grieux returned and saw her pale eyes and heard her pleas, he knew that this was no vision of Manon. She was real and he was caught again in the net of her charm. There was no ring of truth in his words when he told her that he had forgotten her. Manon pushed back the hood of her gold cape and looked into his eyes. "I love only you, Chevalier. Come, take my hand. Is it not the same hand that held yours long ago? Am I not the same Manon?"

"These words are blasphemous here, Manon," Des Grieux said, turning away. But her white hands were on his shoulders, and he knew that blasphemous or not they were the words that he had wanted to hear.

No matter what she had done or would do, life without her was impossible. The gray peace of Saint Sulpice would never compare with the yellow sunlight that was life with Manon. They were together again, hand in hand, and they ran out into the night.

ACT IV

MANON'S repent mood vanished as quickly as Des Grieux' thirty thousand gold pieces, and her need for luxury drove him to the gambling tables of the famous Hotel de Transylvanie. His obsession with her, and her consuming need of gold and jewels, made him hate her as well as love her. However, it took only a few words from Manon's cousin, "Remember, how she hates poverty," to make him accept Guillot's challenge of a game at the tables.

Observing her happiness in the plush surroundings quickly reminded him of all the tricks at cards that Lescaut had taught him months ago. Time and time again he cheated at the game, until Manon's former suitor stormed from the room in a rage, swearing revenge on them all. Not many chips had been pushed across the boards before the police had arrived.

"My regrets, Mademoiselle," Guillot said to Manon. "And you see, young man," he turned to Des Grieux, "I have trumped your card!"

"I will begin consoling myself," Des Grieux answered, "by throwing you out!"

"And will you throw me out, too?" asked his father, appearing suddenly from the anxious crowd around the table. His son hung his head in shame.

"I have only come to save you from this madness and to save the family name," the old man said quietly. Des Grieux could not even look at his father.

Guillot gloated over his revenge and smiled as he saw Manon lean against the table. All the crystal chandeliers were spinning above her, she thought. "It is all over now," she murmured.

"We will let justice decide what is to be done with them," the Count said. "Take them away."

Tears of anger and surprise filled Des Grieux' eyes as he heard his father say to him, "I will arrange for your release, later."

"And Manon?"

"She will be sent to a prison colony—where she belongs!"

"Never!" screamed the young boy. "I will defend her myself . . . now!"

Manon was seized by the guards and one of the diamond clips from her hair fell to the floor. "I am dying," she sobbed. "It is the end of everything . . . the end of life."

Guillot laughed, and ground the brilliant jewels under his shoe as the lovers were taken away.

ACT V

AN ATMOSPHERE of doom and desperation hung about the young Chevalier des Grieux as he sat along the side of the road to Le Havre, waiting for Manon's cousin to appear. Together they hoped to save Manon from being shipped to a prison colony in America. Shading his eyes, he scanned the horizon for a sign of Lescaut or even the prison van that would be carrying Manon. Lescaut finally appeared and told Des Grieux that the men hired to help in the escape had run away at the sight of the heavy prison guard.

Des Grieux could see the soldiers as they came into sight on the hillock. "I will fight them alone!"

"No, my friend, we will hide and bide our time."

The soldiers drew nearer and Des Grieux heard one of them mention Manon's name. Should he believe his ears? Was Manon really desperately ill?

Throwing caution to the winds, Lescaut stepped out and bribed the sergeant, asking if they might see Manon, alone.

"Impossible," the sergeant replied, but he had a quick change of heart when he saw the gold pieces in Lescaut's hand. "I will leave one man here to watch you," he warned them. Counting his gold, he ordered the rest of the soldiers to move on. A few remaining coins enabled Lescaut to lead the single guard away, and Des Grieux was alone on the road.

A dry wind swept across the plain and blew the dirt up into brownish-gray clouds of dust. Stumbling through it was Manon! Her yellow curls were dirty and disheveled, and her clothes were rags. With a cry of joy she ran into Des Grieux' arms.

"Manon! Manon, you're crying," he said, wiping the tears from her dirty cheek. "This is only the beginning . . . we are going to escape from Le Havre. We'll have a new life together."

Manon wearily sat down on the side of the road and smiled weakly. "How wrong I have been! I have never really known how good you were for me. It is too late now." She rubbed her eyes and stared into the distance. Beyond was only the gray sea. But she could see the coach at Amiens, and the little table, and Des Grieux in his clerical robes of Saint Sulpice. She touched Des Grieux' cheek.

"The soldiers have gone. We can escape now," Des Grieux urged, but Manon was too weak.

A cool gray mist fell on everything, forcing back the blazing sun until only pale-yellow rays fell on her parched lips like a gentle caress. She smiled and whispered, "That is the story of Manon Lescaut." (Duet "Manon! Tu pleures!") Her hand reached out for Des Grieux', grew cold, and slipped away.

Now Des Grieux knew that no one could ever take her away again. Through all the years to come, Manon's hand would be clasped in his.

THE MEDIUM

BY GIAN-CARLO MENOTTI (1911–   )
Libretto by Gian-Carlo Menotti

Monica, Madame Flora's daughter: Soprano

Madame Flora (Baba), a fake medium: Contralto

Mrs. Gobineau: Soprano   Mr. Gobineau: Baritone

Mrs. Nolan: Mezzo-soprano   Toby, a mute

TIME: THE PRESENT   PLACE: A CITY IN EUROPE

**FIRST PERFORMANCE: BRANDER MATTHEWS THEATRE,
COLUMBIA UNIVERSITY, NEW YORK CITY; MAY 8, 1946**

Gian-Carlo Menotti wrote about *The Medium*, ". . . in 1936 in the little Austrian town of St. Wolfgang. . . . I had been invited by my neighbors to attended a seance in their house. I readily accepted their invitation, but, I must confess, with my tongue in my cheek. . . . It gradually came clear to me that my hosts, in their pathetic desire to believe, actually saw and heard their dead daughter. . . . The creative power of their faith and conviction made me . . . wonder at the multiple texture of reality."

The Medium has had over a thousand performances in Europe and America.

ACT I

To TOBY, Madame Flora's apartment was a dark and frightening place, and Madame Flora, the medium, was a mysterious and frightening woman.

Toby took a string of purple and red beads from an old trunk and pressed them against his cheek. They were cheap, glass beads, but, with the flickering candlelight reflecting in them, one could imagine them to be the priceless jewels of a Maharaja . . . or a King! The long, cool strands tickled him as they fell over his coffee-colored skin. He laughed. There was a flashing smile of white teeth. But there was no sound. Toby was a mute.

This mattered little to him and Monica, Madame Flora's daughter, for they had a language all their own. Their fingers and their eyes were better than all the words in the world. The boy could read Monica's lips so clearly that not a single word escaped him.

Toby dropped the colored beads on the floor. Pulling some shining pieces of silk, bits of orange and red and green, from the trunk, he started to fashion them all into a strange costume.

Monica, watching him, leaned against the dingy couch. She no longer even commented to her mother about its gaping holes. Tonight, the ragged holes were partially concealed by a white, organdy party dress and a soft veil. She began to sing her favorite song. Its haunting melody and its fairy-tale words about a very regal queen, an evil little gnome, and a lost spindle and thread always made her happy in a melancholy sort of way.

Combing her hair, she caught Toby's image in the little glass in her hand. His reflection made her realize that Baba—for some strange, forgotten reason she called her mother Baba—would be coming home soon.

Forgetting her song, Monica called out to Toby. "Nothing is ready, Toby, and if Baba catches you playing with the things in the trunk, she'll beat you again." She had to smile at the boy and his strange clothes. The brilliant colors made him look like the King of Babylon.

Monica laughed. "You must realize, Toby, that I am *really* a princess from a land across the sky." She smiled. "And one day . . . that princess is going to be your bride."

The boy began to dance and made a sweeping bow before her. Monica threw her arms around Toby. He was the one thing that made her life happy in the rundown place that was her home. She hated the cracks in the wall that allowed the cold damp of the European winters to ooze into the dark rooms. She hated the candles and the multicolored shade of the huge lamp that hung ominously over the big, round table in the center of the room. Most of all, she hated the things that happened in Madame Flora's apartment, and the strange, sad people who came there.

The door downstairs that led to the dirty street slammed shut. Monica was all hands and fingers, trying to help Toby untangle himself from the silks and the beads. They caught on his belt and in his dark, curly hair. It was too late, and before Toby could even think of closing the lid of the trunk, Baba was staring at them from the staircase.

"I thought I told you not to touch my things!" she screamed. "You dirty little gypsy!"

Toby cowered behind the couch. The sight of Madame Flora's heavily rouged cheeks, accentuating the red rims of her tired eyes, frightened him.

Unloosening a bedraggled piece of fur that clung to her shoulders, Madame Flora continued to find fault with everything. "*Nothing* is ready! The clients will be here any minute. The séance will be ruined!" Madame Flora staggered up the stairs and lunged at the boy.

"Stop it, Baba," Monica said, pulling at her mother's torn, purple sweater. "Everything will be ready. Please tell us where you have been."

Baba grunted and raised a threatening hand to Toby. She opened her handbag, pulled out a wad of bills, and tossed it on the table. "I finally got this," she laughed, "by sitting in front of Mrs. Campi's door all night. She owed it to me," she shouted.

"But . . . Mrs. Campi is terribly poor," Monica said.

115

Madame Flora ignored the remark, screaming that the two of them should get things set for the séance. The old medium pushed the jungle of gold bracelets back from her wrists and started to help Monica into the white dress and veil.

Toby dashed to the little puppet theater at the back of the room. He immediately began to test all the wires and levers that were hidden in a tangled mess behind the white curtains. As he pulled at one of them, the big, round table seemed to raise itself from the floor. Another lever lowered the great lamp.

The doorbell rang. Like a flash, Monica ran from the room. Toby jumped into the puppet theater, drawing the curtains behind him. Flora pushed the buzzer to the downstairs door and then sat at the table. She began to deal a game of solitaire. For moments she ignored her callers. Eventually she spoke to them. "Mrs. Nolan . . . Mr. and Mrs. Gobineau."

They nodded. They had met downstairs and hardly needed the introduction. Madame Flora continued, looking at the cards on the table. "You will have to wait for the other clients."

The three visitors began to talk among themselves. "I only come to these séances," Mrs. Nolan remarked, "because it is a way of speaking with my daughter, Doody. She died a year ago . . . when she was sixteen. Do you think that I *will* be able to speak to her?"

Mrs. Gobineau smiled, pulling her dull, lavender hat down on her head. "You will *see* her," she said firmly.

"I wonder . . ." mused Mrs. Nolan.

Flora gave her a withering glance and left the room.

"Have you known Madame Flora long?" Mrs. Nolan asked.

"We've been coming here every week for two years," Mr. Gobineau said quietly. "Our little boy died when he was just a baby. Naturally, he can't talk to us, but we can hear his laughter."

Mrs. Gobineau straightened the cushion at her back and dabbed at her eyes with her lavender handkerchief. "It all happened while we were living in France. We had a beautiful garden there . . . with a fountain." She wiped her eyes. "On our little boy's second birthday, we gave him a sailboat . . . I don't remember *what* happened. But, when I looked in the fountain . . ." (Aria "It happened long ago.") She put her wrinkled handkerchief to her mouth to stifle sobs that rose up in her throat.

"There, there, my dear," Mr. Gobineau said, taking her hand, "our little baby is happier now."

Baba rushed in, announcing loudly that it was time for the séance to begin. After locking the doors, Baba switched off the lights. Except for the

tiny candle burning at the feet of the statue of the Virgin on the wall, the room was plunged into darkness. Baba looked around the table, making certain that all of her clients' hands were resting on its edge. Then she threw back her head and began to moan.

A dim, misty light illumined the signs of the zodiac on the wall. From behind them, Monica's figure appeared. "Mother, Mother, are you there?" her frail, childlike voice called out.

"Doody? Doody? Is that you?" Mrs. Nolan asked. "Can you see your father?"

"He's very near," Monica's voice answered. "Please don't cry, Mother."

Mrs. Nolan tried to stop crying.

"You must go home," the voice continued, "and give all your belongings away. You are to keep only the little gold locket." (Aria "Mummy, Mummy dear.")

"But I have no gold locket," wept Mrs. Nolan.

The image faded away.

Screaming loudly, Mrs. Nolan ran toward the wall where the vision had appeared, but the Gobineau couple held her back. They begged her to be quiet so that they might talk with their little son.

Baba waved her heavy arms about her head and began to wail and growl. She seemed to be mysteriously communicating with other lost spirits.

"Send me my son," Gobineau pleaded.

Tittering, childish laughter floated into the room and faded away.

Baba jumped up from the table, crying out in terror. Her hands, with their long red nails, reached for the lamp and switched it on. She ran to the stairs and then back to the table.

"Someone touched me!" Baba screamed. "Someone touched me!"

"Why be afraid?" her clients asked. "It's happened to us."

In a fit of panic, Baba swept the cards from the table. She hid her face in her hands. "Get out! Get out! All of you!"

Amazed, but not daring to defy her or argue with her, Mrs. Nolan and the Gobineaus silently put on their coats and descended the stairs.

"Why be afraid of the dead?" they asked, calling back over their shoulders. "Why be afraid of the dead?"

The door creaked shut, and when the catch fell into place Monica came running into the room. Baba was hysterical with fright. "These séances have got to stop," the medium said. "We will give them all their money back! While I was pretending that I was in a trance . . . I felt an icy hand around my throat."

Baba staggered to the puppet stage and pulled back the curtains. "It was you!" she shouted at

Toby. "You played this ugly trick on me. You see things that no one else can see."

"Oh, Baba," Monica said, pulling her mother away from Toby, "come, sit here with me. I'll sing to you."

Monica cradled her mother's head in her lap. She began to hum. Rocking slowly back and forth, she began to sing. Her sad song about a young bride who had lost her lover seemed to calm the frightened old woman. (Aria "The sun has fallen.")

Baba turned her head, listening to a voice that no one else could hear. The voice kept calling, "Mother, Mother, are you there?"

"Someone is hiding in the other room," Madame Flora whispered frantically. "Toby . . . go and see who it is."

He returned, shaking his head. He had seen no one.

Baba knelt sobbing at the feet of the Virgin, chanting, "Ave Maria . . . Ave Maria." Baba's eyes widened with fright and her trembling, ringed fingers touched her throat. Now she heard the faint, rippling sound of a boy's laughter.

With a horrible cry, she ran to Monica's side and began to weep.

ACT II

A FEW days after that black night, Toby play-acted in the puppet theater. Monica applauded happily as the young boy took a bow.

"There will be waltzing and a little supper by candlelight," Monica said, whirling about the room. "Monica, Monica is dancing the waltz . . . dancing to the tune of trombones and guitars . . ."

Toby watched her tenderly. Suddenly, he threw his arms around her. Monica could understand his desperate attempts at telling her he loved her. So she asked him to "sing" his role of her suitor—she would be the Queen of Arundel. Together, they danced and sang a fairy-tale story of their love for each other. (Aria "Up in the sky.") Silently, Toby cried out his adoration for Monica and then began to sob.

"Oh, Toby, Toby," Monica whispered, "if I were to listen to all the voices in the world, I would never hear one as lovely as yours."

The wind beating the shutters against the dirty panes prepared them for the loud bang of the downstairs door. Baba was back. Instantly, Monica ran into her room and Toby scurried behind the couch.

Madame Flora staggered up the creaking stairs. She was gripping a half-empty bottle as though it were her life. Her carrot-red hair, looking as though it had been powdered with rouge, was matted and wet from the rain. "Where is Monica?" she shouted at Toby.

He pointed to the door.

The medium pushed the myriad pillows from one of the chairs. She slumped down, exhausted, at the table. "Come here, Toby," she croaked, trying to appear friendly. "You know that I have always loved you. You are like my own son."

Trustingly, he put his head in her lap. She smoothed his dark curls with her dirty fingers. "Haven't I always been good to you? Ever since the day I found you wandering hopelessly in the black streets of Budapest? Now, we must be friends again." Toby could not look at her.

"I will never punish you again," she went on. "I'm even going to buy you a beautiful red silk shirt . . . and a golden scarf." A threatening tone colored her voice. "Was it you who touched my throat during the séance?"

Toby didn't move.

"Tell me all you know," Baba begged. "I will give you the beads that are in the trunk and *all* the red silk."

The mute boy remained motionless.

"Perhaps it was not you who touched me . . . but you know who it was."

Toby tried to crawl away, but Baba's hand darted out and grabbed him by his shirt. Screaming with rage, she tore it off his back.

Controlling her anger, she decided to try other tactics. "You'd like to marry Monica, wouldn't you? Well, if you tell me what you did the night of the séance . . ."

Toby hid his face in his hands, cringing before her.

"I'll make you tell!" Baba screamed, running to the cupboard.

The demanding sound of the doorbell brought her to her senses, making her drop the whip with which she had been wildly beating the defenseless boy. Monica ran into the room and took the bleeding Toby in her arms.

Baba looked around and stared in drunken amazement at the Gobineaus, with Mrs. Nolan, as they slowly walked up the stairs. "Why have you come?" Baba asked, pushing her matted hair from her eyes.

"It is time for the séance, isn't it?" they asked.

"I will have no more séances here," Baba replied, throwing some crinkled bills on the table. "Take them. There will never be another séance. It's all a fake!"

"That just isn't true," Mrs. Nolan said, moving into the room. "Why, I saw Doody."

"And we heard Micky's laughter," the Gobineaus insisted, watching Baba as she walked over to the puppet theater. She ripped the curtains aside.

"It was a fraud. Here are the wires . . . and here is a hidden microphone."

Her visitors shook their heads in disbelief.

"*There* is your daughter," Baba screamed, showing Mrs. Nolan Monica's silk scarf. "And, *there* . . . is your voice," she laughed, switching on the microphone.

"Mother, Mother, are you there?" the tremulous mechanical voice wailed.

"Why, it's not even the same," the Gobineaus said, "and even if you thought you were faking, we have not been cheated. Without your marvelous help, we would be without our loved ones forever. You must allow us to have another séance now."

In her rage, Baba violently forced them down the stairs. Hanging over the railing, she listened for the sound of the closing door.

"And you," she shouted at Toby, "must go, too. I can't stand that ghostly look in your eyes."

"If you send him away," Monica wept, "I'll go with him. He is helpless by himself."

Madame Flora raised her arm in a gesture of terrible warning and Toby ran down the stairs, clutching at Monica's hand over the railing. Tears filled Monica's eyes.

"Get to your room, Monica," Baba screamed and the girl obeyed.

The medium silently watched the raindrops slithering down the windowpane.

"Mother, Mother, are you there?" Baba heard a voice sing. She drew back in terror, looking at Monica's door; ran to it and locked it. She walked across the creaking floor to the cupboard, and took several comforting drinks from the bottle inside. Momentarily calmed, she sat down at the table. "Can it be," she mumbled to herself, "that *I* am afraid?"

A cold wind whistled in through the broken pane in the window, and Baba pulled her tattered sweater tight around her shoulders. "I have seen so many terrible things . . . women being slaughtered . . . men's blood-stained hands, and little children dying, covered with filth . . ."

As her fear mounted, Baba pushed back the sleeves of her sweater and tore frantically at the gold bracelets on her arms. "I'm sick and old," she wept. "I want peace. I want to be free of these ghosts that come to frighten me." She laughed, trying to reassure herself. "There's nothing to fear. We must all laugh at nothingness." (Aria "Afraid, am I afraid?") Baba threw her head back, roaring with hysterical laughter. Then she fell face down on the table in a drunken sleep.

Behind her, Toby pulled himself up the stairs. He crawled to Monica's door and fell against it like some tired, wet animal. He crossed over to the trunk. As he was looking through its contents, the lid accidentally fell down with a crash! Baba jumped up, failing to see the boy as he vanished behind the curtains of the puppet theater.

"Monica?" Baba called out. "Monica?" The medium pulled the drawer in the table open quickly and removed a revolver.

The wind tossed the colored shade of the lamp. The slivers of light escaping through the dirty shade sent red and purple shadows dancing against the wall and the curtains of the little theater. Baba gasped in terror as the curtains rustled slightly and then fell still.

"Answer me! Answer, or I'll shoot!"

Pulling herself away from the table, Baba fired the gun, time and time again, into the white silk.

Everything was quiet. The medium stood motionless, watching a tiny spot of brilliant red blood slowly oozing through the curtains. "I've killed a ghost," Baba screamed triumphantly. "I've killed a ghost!"

Toby's slender, brown hand reached through the silken panels, clutching them against his smooth skin as he fell onto the dirty carpet.

"Let me out!" Monica cried from her room. "Let me out!"

As if hypnotized, Baba unlocked the door. Monica took a frightened look at Toby's dead body and ran into the rain, calling for help.

The medium squinted in the darkening shadows. "Was it you?" she asked, kneeling beside him. "Was it you?"

Her only answer was a crash of thunder and the cold, wet wind beating against the jagged glass pane. Baba clutched her throat, and the candle at the Virgin's feet sputtered out.

Die Meistersinger von Nürnberg

THE MASTERSINGERS OF NUREMBERG

BY

RICHARD WAGNER

(1813-1883)

Libretto by Richard Wagner

CHARACTERS

WALTHER VON STOLZING	Tenor
EVA	Soprano
DAVID	Tenor
HANS SACHS	Bass
POGNER	Bass
BECKMESSER	Bass
MAGDALENE	Mezzo-soprano

TIME: 1500's

PLACE: NUREMBERG, GERMANY

First Performance:
National Theatre, Munich;
June 21, 1868

In Germany, the successors to the minstrels were the Mastersingers. These were craftsmen who formed musicians' guilds similar to the usual craftsmen's guilds. The Mastersingers had song contests with strict rules and regulations concerning rhythm, meter, and construction. Among the most famous of the Mastersingers was Hans Sachs, who lived from 1494 to 1576. He wrote several thousand songs and was a well-known poet.

ACT I

IT WAS a perfect day. The sky was a perfect blue and the clouds a perfect white—the dazzling blue and white that were the heraldic colors of Bavaria. The Pegnitz River sang as it flowed through the city of Nürnberg.

Walther von Stolzing, a young Franconian knight, entered St. Katherine's church and waited as the choir sang the final chorale of the service. He watched Eva. She was so young and so fair. When her blue eyes caught his he knew that there was no one in all of Nürnberg as beautiful as she. Magdalene, Eva's nurse, who was not too many years older than her charge, caught his eye, too, and urged Eva to pay attention to the service. When it was over, Walther walked over to them. He was determined to speak to Eva before she left the church.

"Eva, you must give me an answer," Walther said, gently touching her arm. Eva lowered her eyes and gazed at the white prayerbook in her hands.

She toyed with the blue ribbon that marked the service of the day. Then she looked up. "Walther, it has already been determined that I am to be the bride of the winner of the contest tomorrow." He turned his back on her dejectedly.

David, Hans Sachs' apprentice, a jovial young man of about twenty-five, was already drawing the curtain that partitioned off the church—part of the preparations for the preliminary song trials that would select the contestants for the festival day. Magdalene smiled at him as Eva turned to her. "Oh Magdalene, I'm going to need your help," she said, looking at Walther, "to get the right man for me."

"Let David teach you all the rules of the contest, Walther. As a contestant you would have a better chance to win Eva," Magdalene said.

"Shall I see you soon?" Eva asked Walther.

"Tonight!" he replied hastily, as Magdalene gently but firmly escorted her charge out of the church.

The apprentices arrived and David put them all to work arranging the long wooden benches and building a platform for the auditions. At the same time he tried to explain the many and varied rules of the important musical event to Walther. The young knight pretended to listen, but his thoughts were outside, on the sunny street with Eva.

"To be a Mastersinger," David said very seriously, "one must be a poet as well as a singer. Hans Sachs is teaching me!"

"I will enter the contest," Walther said, jumping up from the great oaken chair in which he had been sitting.

"That's wonderful!" David exclaimed.

As the Mastersingers filed into the sunlit church, Pogner, the goldsmith, was the first to pass the young knight. As they moved along, Walther could clearly hear Beckmesser, the town clerk, begging Pogner to please remind Eva of his devotion to her. Walther interrupted them and greeted Eva's father.

"What! Another rival, at this crucial moment?" Beckmesser muttered. The goldsmith only smiled and proceeded to introduce Walther to the others. They were quick to give him their permission to sing at the preliminary trial. After the roll had been called and all the Masters had seated themselves, Pogner took up the business of the day.

"For many years now I have traveled all over our beautiful Germany and it has become more and more obvious to me that the burghers of this city are not admired by our fellow Germans. They believe that we are not really interested in culture or art." He raised a bushy eyebrow. "So, to prove to the world that we burghers of Nürnberg are not such material dullards, I am making a very special contribution to this year's song festival. My daughter, Eva, will be the bride of the winner!" (Pogner's Address "Das schöne Fest.")

Hans Sachs was the only one to speak up against the general approval. "I rather think," he said quietly, "that the bride should have some little vote in this important matter. Our fellow citizens, too, should have the right to raise their voices concerning our singers' qualifications!"

His colleagues listened to his words carefully, for kindly Master Sachs was their most respected citizen. After all, he had composed some 4,300 master songs and about 300 plays, in addition to being a wise friend to them all. His reputation all over Europe was not only as a master shoemaker; he was the backbone of the much-respected Mastersinger contests. He was also known as a great human being who believed that the arts were a very necessary expression in every man's life. Many of the guild Masters were rather doubtful of the masses' sound judgment concerning any artistic ventures. The Masters were also stubborn.

"May I suggest a compromise?" Eva's father asked. "We will allow Eva to refuse the winner, but with the stipulation that the only eligible bridegroom *must* be one who has been voted a Mastersinger at one time or another." After no little arguing, his plan was agreed to.

He introduced Walther as a contestant, and, as was the custom, several of the Masters began to question him. "Where did you learn the art of singing?"

The knight replied, "I studied singing from the book of an ancient minstrel, Walther von der Vogelweide. And nature taught me, too. I listened to the quiet fields, and to the silver streams, even the birds."

Sachs expressed his admiration, but some of the less imaginative Masters had to argue about this very unorthodox method of learning singing.

"What will be the theme of your song?" one asked.

"Love," answered Walther, seating himself in the proud, oaken, singer's chair. (Aria "Am stillen Herd.")

Beckmesser, already appointed as one of the men who would tabulate all the contestant's errors, marched grandly up to the platform. "Each entrant is allowed seven, no more, mistakes," he warned Walther in a whining tone, reminding the young man that the Masters were very strict in their adherence to certain rules of meter, rhyme, and content.

Walther's song about love and a spring that enfolded the entire world managed to break all the rules. His bright, young voice rang out loud and clear. Unfortunately, not loud enough to drown out Beckmesser's angry scratches on his black slate. (Aria "Fanget an!") The self-styled critic had covered his marker with chalk marks before Walther had even finished his song.

Beckmesser interrupted him, commenting, "Are you finished? The slate is full of faults."

"But," Walther said angrily, "isn't someone going to hear the end of my song?"

"It's all wrong," Beckmesser said. "There is no Bible text. Metrically it's wrong. There are no rhymes and there is no beat to it!"

"And," said Kothner, the baker, "the singer rose from his seat while he was singing! Inexcusable!"

Hans Sachs protested strongly against such a narrow, military judgment, but he was shouted down by Beckmesser.

"There are songs of golden birds that soar and sing despite the hoots and cries of owls and ravens," Walther said, thinking how much he hated old and unbreakable rules. The young man looked at Hans Sachs, turned, and walked angrily out of St. Katherine's.

"He has talent and courage," Sachs said approvingly. But he stood alone. Walther was rejected.

The wise old cobbler watched his friends as they left the church, violently discussing the events of the morning. He watched sadly as the apprentices removed the oaken, singer's chair. Sachs smiled and his beautiful, time-worn hands made a gesture of resignation.

It was very quiet in St. Katherine's.

ACT II

THE beautiful blue-and-white day turned into a beautiful evening. Magdalene closed the door to Pogner's house and looked across the cobblestone street to Hans Sachs' home. She smiled at David, who was helping the apprentices as they put up the shutters of the houses.

"How did the trials go this morning?" she asked, lifting the blue cloth from the basket of food she had over her arm.

"Badly, I'm afraid," the boy said. He looked hungrily at the rolls and sausage. "He was rejected."

"Rejected? Then you'll have none of this for supper!" Magdalene slapped his hand and ran back into the house. David's friends began to tease him, but Sachs appeared and ordered the boy into the house.

Pogner and Eva walked slowly down the alleyway that led into the square. They had planned to sit quietly for a while, discussing the festival that was to take place the next day, but Eva saw Magdalene waving frantically at her from the door.

"Let's go in, Father," she said, suspecting that something was wrong. "It's time for supper." Magdalene curtsied to Pogner, and cleverly managed to detain Eva at the threshold.

"David says that your knight is finished."

Eva sighed and looked back across the street at Sachs' house with its solid brown beams. "I will have to go to Master Sachs for advice," she said calmly. "Surely the wise shoemaker will know what to do." She closed the door.

Sachs came out of his house and looked up at the sky. He sat down at his bench and tried to work, but the heavy scent of lilac on the air and the memory of Walther's beautiful song disturbed and distracted him. (Monologue "Wie duftet doch der Flieder.")

He was glad to hear Eva's "Good evening, Mas-

ter," as she walked gracefully across the square. He had a deep affection for this daughter of his close friend, and he hoped that the outcome of tomorrow's contest would bring her happiness.

He smiled. "Tomorrow you may be a bride."

"And I wonder who the groom will be. Beckmesser is always tormenting me, but he won't do. Somehow I thought that I had attracted your fancy."

Sachs laughed quietly. "You are but a child, Eva."

"Your mind is elsewhere, anyway," Eva said. "How did the trials go today? Was there anyone that you especially approved of?"

Sachs could easily tell what direction the conversation was taking and he willingly played her game. "There was a knight. But he has no chance now." He playfully attacked the knight with words and watched the girl's anger rise. Her flashing eyes proved that she really loved Walther.

"Magdalene is calling me. I'd better go now," she said.

At the door, Magdalene scolded her for not answering her father's call. "And Beckmesser has just informed me that he is going to sing to you tonight."

Walther was just turning the corner. Running to meet him, Eva cried, "Oh, Walther, I've heard."

"The Masters will never choose me, Eva. And you will never be able to choose me. I'm tired of all these judges and these hustling crowds. Come away with me tonight."

Hans Sachs watched the two lovers from the upper half of his door. From the shadows he could see and hear all the plans that were being discussed. As the nightwatchman approached, the cobbler pushed his door open a little more. It was ten o'clock.

Eva ran into her house, leaving Walther alone in the flickering, disappearing rays of the watchman's lantern. When the young girl returned, she was in Magdalene's clothes. Sachs knew that now or never he must keep Walther and Eva from doing anything foolish.

He opened the shutter to his window and held his lantern up. The young lovers were caught in its rays! Eva pulled Walther back into the shadows. "Let's not get in the shoemaker's way," she said petulantly. "He's no friend of yours. Look."

Beckmesser was leaning against Sachs' house, tuning his lute. His eyes looked up squintingly at Eva's window. He was completely unaware that the lovely fraulein was Magdalene in Eva's dress. Sachs smiled and placed his workbench in his doorway. He put a shoe on the last and began to hammer away.

Beckmesser began to lose his temper. After all, he was here to serenade Eva and he was deserving of an atmosphere of peace and quiet.

Sachs began to sing to himself. (Song "Jerum! Jerum!")

"What is this new trick of yours?" screamed Beckmesser, nervously tapping his foot on the cobblestones.

"You'll need these shoes tomorrow. I have to finish my work, that's all."

"Well, if you have to work, you can mark my new song. Try to hammer only if you hear a mistake." Beckmesser's shaking voice proved that his song was made up of nothing but mistakes. And Sachs' hammer verified it.

Sachs laughed heartily as he held the finished shoe aloft. "I'll call this my good marker's shoe!"

Beckmesser's sallow face grew red with anger. The off-pitch notes of his serenade continued to cackle through the night, and suddenly, as all the irate villagers were awakened, windows and doors flew open, enveloping the square with light.

David, too, looked out of his window and saw Beckmesser rapturously serenading Magdalene. The impetuous apprentice dashed out into the street wildly swinging a club, several blows of which landed on Beckmesser. The fight was on! In moments, the cobblestone street of Nürnberg was a mass of screaming, jostling humanity. Women, men, children, dogs, and cats—they all joined in the free-for-all.

The sheer madness of the uproar gave Walther and Eva a chance to escape from their prison of shadows. The knight, hand on his sword, tried to push Eva through the angry mob. Sachs ran over to the young couple and with the strength of a man half his age he took Walther's arm. At the same time he quickly pushed Eva into the protection of her own house, grabbed David by his ear, and then shoved the two startled young men into his house.

When the nightwatchman returned to announce that it was now eleven o'clock, he found the street deserted, as it had been just an hour ago.

The watchman chuckled as he looked up at the full moon that hung over the rooftops. Somewhere across the Pegnitz, in the cool, blue fields, a nightingale was singing.

ACT III

THE glorious Bavarian sun followed the moon into the city. Hans Sachs sat in his great armchair absorbed in the contents of a large folio on his lap. David was examining the contents of a basket on the table. He smiled at the ribbons and flowers, at the sausage and cake that nestled together beneath them. Sachs looked up and scowled.

"I'm here, Master," David said, hiding the food. "I've taken the shoes to Beckmesser and I ask your forgiveness for my behavior last night. It was all for Magdalene."

Sachs continued to read and suddenly closed his folio with such a smack that its sound frightened David. He stumbled and fell at the shoemaker's feet.

"Don't forget that today is St. John's day. Do you know your verses?"

David proved that he did by singing a song about John the Baptist. Somehow he attached the words to the melody of Beckmesser's silly serenade of the night before. The shoemaker was rather startled by the odd combination of words and music, and he was glad when David stopped singing the irritating song. "Now, away with you, David. Get ready for the festival."

David was genuinely touched by his master's quiet understanding. He kissed his hand and left the room.

Sachs was glad to be alone. His fingers moved slowly over the blue leather binding of his book.

"A madness is everywhere," he thought. "Men are always fighting! Why even here in Nürnberg, this peaceful place, men and children blindly go wild and fight one another." He looked at the gilt-edged pages of his folio. They were warm in the sun. Sachs set the book on the arm of the chair and rubbed his hands on his leather apron. "Well, it's Midsummer's Day, and I must be the one to weave a new spell. A spell that will bring something of value from all this madness." (Aria "Wahn! Wahn!")

Looking up, he saw Walther coming into the room. "I hope you slept well," he said, greeting him affectionately.

"My sleep was good," Walther smiled. "I had a wonderful dream."

"That's a good omen. Tell me about it."

"I'm afraid to speak of it," Walther said. "The magic of it might fade away."

"Our dreams have been known to show us great truths," the Master said, urging the young man on.

As Walther spoke, Sachs wrote down every line. As the words spilled out, Sachs realized that the words would be the core of the song that would win the competition. His interruptions were few and constructive, intended only to help the boy, and to keep him from angering the judges again.

"Even though our youth tells us not to, we must obey the rules. They have meaning. They were established with the best of intentions, Walther."

Walther sat on the workbench near Sachs and began to sing, "A glorious garden lay bathed in sunlight at the dawn of day."

Sachs listened to the end. "That meets one rule—that was a 'stanza.' Now, we need another."

In a few moments Walther had divulged all his dream and that its source of inspiration could be no one but Eva. (Aria "Morgenlich leuchtend.")

"We will have courage, my boy, and try for the prize today," Sachs said, placing his arm about the knight. "Go and dress yourself in the clothes that you intended for your wedding!"

As they left the study, arm in arm, Beckmesser limped in. Remembering the night before, he winced in pain and rubbed his back. His cunning eyes roamed the room. His glance followed a ray of sunlight coming through the leaded-glass panes. The golden shaft fell on the oaken table. The light made it easier to discover the paper that contained the words to Walther's song.

"That devil, Sachs!" Beckmesser said, carefully reading the words. "He's going to enter the contest himself!" When he heard the door behind him open, Beckmesser crumpled the sheets and stuffed them into his pocket.

"Greetings, Beckmesser."

"Enough of your jokes, friend Sachs. I see through your tricks! I can see what you are trying to do. Here is my proof." He began to fumble in his pocket for the song. Sachs looked at the table and smiled.

"You took it, eh? Well, rather than have people call you a thief, I give the song to you as a present."

Beckmesser's sick look changed to one of joy. "If this is really for me, it seals our friendship for all time. All our quarrels are forgotten."

"It is yours, Beckmesser, on my oath. But be aware that it is not a simple song. It will demand everything of you to perform it."

Beckmesser danced about the room and gratefully embraced Hans Sachs. Then, suddenly reminded of his pains from the night before, he limped out the door.

For several moments, Sachs watched the sunlight as it danced across the wide, shining boards of the floor. Then he looked up and saw Eva standing in the doorway. "Good day, Ev'chen."

She looked away from him. "I'm dressed for the festival, Master Sachs, but one of my shoes feels very uncomfortable."

"Well, put your foot on this stool and we'll have a look." Her blue eyes still evaded his. Sachs knew that the shoe was a perfect fit, and when Eva almost lost her balance and placed her hand on his shoulder to support herself, he looked up. (Duet "Sieh, Ev'chen!") Then he knew her reason for coming to his shop.

Walther stood in the doorway from the inner room.

"I recently heard a beautiful song. I wish that someone would sing me the third verse of it," Sachs said, looking from Walther to Eva.

The cobbler took Eva's white shoe and began to work on it at his bench.

Walther sang:

"The stars danced down to make a shimmering crown,

For her sparkling hair and the blue of her eyes."

Sachs looked at Eva. "That is a mastersong, child."

The blood rose in Eva's white cheeks and tears filled her eyes. Carried away by the happiness of the moment she threw herself into Sachs' arms and wept. "O, Sachs, my dearest friend," she cried, holding him tightly, "I owe you everything. I was nothing until you . . . your spirit is mine." (Aria "O Sachs, mein Freund!")

"Dear child," Sachs replied, "I know the story of Tristan and Isolde very well. I am wiser than King Marke."

As David and Magdalene came in to break the spell, Sachs laughed. "The witnesses are here. We're ready for the christening."

The four young people were bewildered.

"A new mastersong has just been born." Sachs rubbed his hands together. "But since no apprentice can be a legal witness, I shall have to make David a journeyman! On your knees, boy!"

The shoemaker gave him a friendly box on the ear, the age-old custom for bestowing this new rank, and bade him get up. David beamed with pride.

Eva took Walther's hand and looked at Sachs.

"The song that was whispered here this morning will soar and sing at the festival."

"It will win me the greatest prize," Walther said, feeling the soft coolness of Eva's hand in his.

Sachs nodded approval. "Eva really belongs to another now," he thought, "but I am happy for them and the prize they will gain when the poet wins." (Quintet "Selig, wie die Sonne.")

The wise shoemaker looked out of the window and over the red geraniums at the people scurrying by on their way to the contest. A sound of a fanfare of trumpets sang in the square. Opening his arms to the two happy couples, he bade them all hurry.

(SCENE 2) The golden meadow where the song competition was to be held was almost white in the sunlight. The Pegnitz flowed blue in the distance, blending with the brilliant blue flags of the draped platform that had been set up for the judges of the contest. The entire meadow became a riot of color as the various guilds paraded in, waving their great banners of green, yellow, and red. When the Masters had taken their places on the platform, the apprentices silenced the crowd and Hans Sachs stepped forward. He was greeted with a tumultuous cry of proud approval from his friends.

"Your praise is far beyond my worth," he said warmly. He looked at Eva. "The prize of the day and the fate of this beautiful girl depend on your judgment. Think on that and then let the voice of Nürnberg be raised in praise of art and her Mastersingers!"

Beckmesser wiped the sweat from his forehead as Sachs turned to him. "You are the first contestant," Sachs said, watching the poor man as he nervously scanned the words of Walther's song.

Beckmesser looked up at Eva in her white dress, and as he bowed low before her he noticed, even in his state of nervous excitement, that the blue ribbons in her hair were a perfect match for the blue of her eyes. With a silly flourish he began to sing. Somehow, the words of Walther's song combined with the music of his own serenade of the night before had disastrous results. The crowd began to nudge one another and their titterings and snickers unnerved him even more. But he ranted on. The song was nothing but a reckless confusion of meaningless words, and his last off-pitch note brought a roar of laughter from the townspeople.

"This was your trick, Sachs!" Beckmesser yelled with his last ounce of breath. Furiously shaking his fists, he ran wildly into the crowd and disappeared.

Sachs shook his head. "He is right and yet he is wrong. I merely put the words of this song on a piece of paper. The true poet is the one who can bring their magic forth. If the one to prove my words is here, let him step forth!"

The Nürnbergers looked with anticipation toward Walther as Sachs extended his hand. "Walther von Stolzing! You will sing now."

Walther remembered the day so recently when he had walked up the winding road to Nürnberg. As he had come through the great gate, he had thought that that was his day. But today the sky was even bluer and the clouds whiter. He was not just singing today. It was happening to him. There before him was a magic garden. Everything was drenched in the rosy glow of early morning. The trees were really enchanted trees and the beautiful girl before him was his Muse. She is Eva. Eva of the yellow hair and the blue eyes. She will carry us both, us all, to Paradise. (Aria "Preislied" [Prize Song].)

The crowd was spellbound. The breeze swept down from the mountains into the meadow. As it poured through the tall grass it magnified Walther's song, and the townspeople were caught up in the beauty and wonder of the music. With a spontaneous roar of approval, they awarded Walther the prize. Eva lovingly placed the victory wreath of laurel and myrtle on Walther's head. Hand in hand, they knelt before her father.

Pogner held a golden chain in his hand. The three Masterguild medals hanging from it gleamed in the sun. "I give this to you, Walther von Stolzing."

But Walther, remembering with some bitterness his experience in St. Katherine's just a short time ago, refused it. Sachs understood the young man's feelings, but his wisdom also allowed him to understand why the Masters had treated the knight as they had. His kind, sympathetic eyes looked into Walther's.

"Don't disdain the Masters, my friend. They have preserved the standards of art with truth and right." He placed his strong but gentle hands on Walther's shoulders. "Beware of the bad times that face us all. *If* we Germans should ever be conquered, we must know that our art is safe." (Aria "Verachtet mir die Meister nicht.")

Walther knew that the great man was right and so did the townspeople. With a joyous rush of acclaim, they echoed his words. Eva smiled and took the wreath from Walther's head. She placed it on Sachs' head. He kissed her tenderly on the cheek and, taking the chain from Pogner, placed it around the young knight's neck.

In homage to the great man, their beloved Hans Sachs, Pogner knelt before the master shoemaker, and all the people of Nürnberg rushed toward the flower-decked platform, shouting, "Hail, Sachs! Hail, Sachs!"

He looked at Walther and Eva, and at David and Magdalene. Everyone—every tree, every bird—was alive and singing, "I am glad that I am alive today!"

PAGLIACCI

⊰ The Clowns ⊱

BY

RUGGIERO LEONCAVALLO

(1858–1919)

Libretto by Ruggiero Leoncavallo

CHARACTERS

CANIO (*Pagliaccio in play*)	. . . . .	TENOR
NEDDA (*Columbine in play*)	. . . . .	SOPRANO
TONIO (*Taddeo in play*)	. . . . .	BARITONE
BEPPE (*Harlequin in play*)	. . . . .	TENOR
SILVIO	. . . .	BARITONE

Time – 1860's   Place – Montalto, Province of Calabria, Italy

FIRST PERFORMANCE - - TEATRO DAL VERME, MILAN; MAY 21, 1892

When Leoncavallo was a boy in Montalto, which is where *Pagliacci* takes place, a jealous actor killed his wife after a performance. Leoncavallo's father was the judge at the trial. The murder made such an impression on the boy that many years later he used it as the theme of *Pagliacci*.

Pagliacci and *Cavalleria Rusticana* are often played together on the same bill. Both are comparatively short; both are products of the *verisimo,* or realistic, style of opera; and both are the only operas written by Leoncavallo and Mascagni that have remained popular.

PROLOGUE

CALABRIA is a province in southern Italy where the hot sun beats down on the earth, baking it a reddish, rusty brown. The white flowers, growing wild everywhere, accentuate the black, gnarled trees of the landscape. The people of Calabria are hot-blooded and quick to lose their tempers, and their black eyes are quick to shine with love or hate.

In a sunlit street of Montalto, an ancient, little town in Calabria, the small theater had been set up for the performance that the traveling players would give there that night as part of the festivities for the Feast of the Assumption. The white curtain and the tiny rust-and-black flags about the stage fluttered in the warm breeze, and from the distance the sound of a trumpet and the beating of a drum broke into the stillness of the afternoon.

Tonio, a hunchbacked clown, sat near the steps leading up to the theater, thinking about all the actors and all the plays that had been performed on this stage. "Life is like a stage;" he mused, "a place where plays take place—but real plays with real people. And perhaps I, even I, am a sort of Prologue to something exciting. I wish the play would begin!"

ACT I

HE WAS awakened from his dreaming as some villagers ran by, shouting that the players were arriving. "Pagliaccio is here!"

"Simple fools," he snarled, "they even believe that that silly clown is real!" Looking about, he saw Canio, Nedda, and Beppe arriving in their little donkey cart. The young and beautiful Nedda, with slender arms covered with red-and-gold bracelets, was waving to the people. And Canio, with flashing black eyes, was beating on the great drum. How jealous Tonio was of them both!

"I invite you all to attend the play tonight," said Canio. "It is all about the great Pagliaccio!"

Tonio limped over to assist Nedda as she stepped out of the cart, but he was pushed aside by her husband. The force of the blow knocked the hunchback to the ground, and the villagers, thinking it was all part of the play, began to laugh.

Tonio spit at the urchins who had started to tease him and then hobbled on into the theater, quietly muttering threats against them all.

Canio, throwing his whip down on the steps of the stage, dashed inside to change from his costume into something more appropriate for drinking at the village inn.

"Tonio? Are you coming to the inn with me?" Canio asked moments later.

"No," answered Tonio, who was following him, "I must stay and take care of the donkey."

"Ha, ha," laughed one of the crowd. "He's only staying here so he can make love to Nedda!"

"Oh, no, my friends," Canio said, looking at Tonio. "If I, like Pagliaccio, were on a stage and found my sweetheart with a rival, I would either thrash them both or just calm down. But if I were to find Nedda, in *real life,* in the same kind of scene," he sneered, "the end of our play would be much different."

Nedda, astonished by his remark, whipped around in surprise. Canio, anxious to assure the villagers of his love and trust, walked over to his wife and kissed her. The men left for the tavern as the vesper bells called the rest of the crowd to their prayers. Nedda was left alone in the square.

"I wonder if old Tonio suspects me," she thought as she watched the birds whirling and soaring in the sunlight. "How wonderful it must be, flying free and happy in the sky!" (Aria "O che bel sole.") Noticing the whip on the steps, she picked it up and casually tapped it against the red poster of the clown that was pasted to the side of the theater.

"Nedda," said Tonio, coming up behind her, "I had to stay here with you. I love you!"

As he reached out to touch her, Nedda slashed

him across the face with the whip. "Save your embraces for the stage, you fool!"

Tonio drew his hand across his face. "You'll regret that, Nedda. I may have my revenge some day," he threatened.

Nedda leaned against the wall at the back of the theater, watching him limp away. She quivered with rage.

"Weeping, Nedda?" asked a young man as he climbed over the wall.

"Oh, Silvio, how glad I am to see you! While I was waiting for you, that ugly, crippled Tonio tried to make love to me."

"When are you going to come away with me? You are not in love with Canio. Let me take you away from Montalto and we can start a new life together. Nedda, tell me you love me."

As they talked, Tonio silently crept out from the theater, in time to hear Nedda say, "Silvio, I do love you, and we will run away tonight, as soon as the play is over." (Duet "Silvio! a quest'ora.") Already plotting his revenge, Tonio went on to the tavern in search of Canio.

Traveling into evening, the sun cast reddish-brown shadows against the clay-colored houses, and Canio and Tonio, hurrying back from the inn, could see the disappearing figure of a strange man. They could also hear Nedda's voice calling after him, "I will be yours, tonight and forever . . ." Her last words, possibly the stranger's name, thought Canio, vanished on the wind.

Rushing at his wife, knife in hand, Canio shouted, "Tell me his name, Nedda! Tell me his name!" When she refused, he raised the knife to strike her. But Beppe, rushing from the stage, jumped in front of him. "Canio, control yourself! The villagers are already returning from church. The play has to go on!"

Tonio laughed to himself. Already his revenge was taking its course. "Bide your time, Canio," he said. "Perhaps the fool will come to see the play tonight, and you can catch him then."

"Put on your costume," advised Beppe, as he and Tonio went into the theater.

"That's right," thought Canio, "Put on your costume and laugh. Put on your make-up! The people pay their coins to laugh. Make them laugh! Laugh, even if tricky Harlequin takes your Columbine away! Laugh and win applause! I want to cry, but I must laugh!" Canio staggered up the steps and hid his face, sobbing into the white curtains. (Aria "Vesti la giubba.")

ACT II

THE warm, red sun sank completely out of sight, and the cool evening settled over Montalto. Moving among the excited villagers as they seated themselves on their wooden benches, Silvio looked anxiously around for Nedda. She passed by him as she was collecting the admissions for the play, pausing a moment to whisper, "I will meet you tonight at our usual place. Remember me, Silvio." She moved on through the audience, turned to wave, and went into the theater.

Silvio fidgeted nervously and stared at the rust-colored dust on his shoes. He looked at the white lanterns swinging in the breeze. Then he saw the curtain rise.

There was Nedda, dressed as Columbine. How beautiful she looked in her fluffy costume. And how the spangles on her bodice sparkled in the light of the candles at the foot of the stage. Silvio settled back and listened to the play.

"Oh, why does my husband Pagliaccio have to be late tonight? And where is my servant, Taddeo? He was due back from the market hours ago!" Columbine danced around, then stopped to listen to the serenade that drifted in through the window. It was Harlequin singing of his love for her.

Silvio looked carefully. Was that Tonio he saw coming on the stage? It was. He was playing Taddeo, the faithful servant.

"Where is the little chicken for my supper?" Columbine asked, straightening the red bow in her hair. Taddeo bowed before her and opened the lid of the wicker basket he was carrying.

Columbine ignored him and turned again to the window, enchanted by the music of the serenade.

"Oh, Columbine, you are more beautiful and more pure than the whitest snow," said Taddeo.

Harlequin, taking this opportunity to crawl over the window ledge, skipped up behind Taddeo. "Away with you, you fool," he said, kicking him

soundly in the seat of the pants. The audience roared with laughter.

Taddeo looked at Columbine and winked. "I'll keep watch for you." Meekly, he turned and walked off.

Columbine and Harlequin clinked their glasses of wine together and laughed as they pulled the bits of chicken apart. With supper finished, Harlequin gave Columbine a sleeping drug for her husband, Pagliaccio.

Taddeo rushed in, shouting, "Pagliaccio is coming! Pagliaccio is coming."

Immediately, Harlequin jumped out of the window as Columbine whispered after him, "I will be yours tonight and forever."

The words seemed very familiar to Silvio as he nervously wiped the little beads of perspiration from his forehead with his black handkerchief.

Pagliaccio was on the stage and furiously angry! Everyone in the audience could tell. His eyes were glaring brighter than the black pompons on his white costume. "You must believe Columbine," Taddeo called out. "She would never tell a lie, great Pagliaccio!"

Pagliaccio demanded that Columbine tell him her lover's name. Suddenly, Silvio saw it all! The character was really Canio!

"I claim my honor!" Pagliaccio raged—or was it Canio? "This woman doesn't deserve my grief. She has no shame!" (Aria "No, Pagliaccio non son.")

Columbine—or was it Nedda?—seemed to be enjoying it all. She danced about the tiny stage, saying, "If that is the way you want to judge me, then send me away."

"You will stay until you tell me your lover's name," shouted Canio, beating his fists on the table.

"Oh, Pagliaccio," cajoled Nedda, trying to continue the play, "don't try to be so terrifying. Nothing tragic is happening here."

The villagers talked among themselves, perplexed by the happenings on stage. It seemed too real, even for their favorite strolling players.

Canio, maddened by jealousy, cried, "His name, or you will die!"

Then, as Nedda pirouetted in front of him, he drew a knife from his sleeve and stabbed her in the heart. Silvio jumped up and rushed to the stage as Nedda, dying, breathed his name. But as he leaped over the candles at the edge of the stage, Canio whirled about and plunged his knife into Silvio's chest.

Seeing the two lovers murdered before their very eyes, the audience screamed, and Canio dropped his knife and began to sob.

"The comedy is over," he cried, and fell against the white curtain, pulling it down over the dead bodies.

DER ROSENKAVALIER

THE CAVALIER OF THE ROSE

By

RICHARD STRAUSS

(1864–1949)

Libretto by Hugo von Hofmannsthal

CHARACTERS

OCTAVIAN	MEZZO-SOPRANO
THE MARSCHALLIN	SOPRANO
BARON OCHS	BASS
ITALIAN SINGER	TENOR
VALZACCHI	TENOR
ANNINA	ALTO
MOHAMED	ACTOR
LEOPOLD	ACTOR
HERR VON FANINAL	BARITONE
MARIANNE	SOPRANO
SOPHIE	SOPRANO
INNKEEPER	TENOR

TIME: *The eighteenth century,*
during the reign of Maria Theresa

PLACE: *Vienna*

First performance: Hofoper, Dresden; January 26, 1911

After the grim *Elektra*, Richard Strauss wanted to write an opera in the Mozartian style. *Der Rosenkavalier* was the result, a witty comedy. Strauss wrote about it, "The spirit of Mozart was there before me, but I remained myself."

If *Der Rosenkavalier* were performed in its entirety, uncut, it would run almost four hours. It is said that when Strauss conducted the opera himself for the first time, he whispered to the first violinist, "Isn't this awfully long?" The musician answered, "Why, Maestro, you composed it yourself." Supposedly, Strauss answered, "I know, but I never thought I'd have to conduct it."

ACT I

THE sun broke through the mists of the Vienna woods and sent its shafts of light up onto the spire of St. Stephen's, down onto the cool water in the beautiful fountain in the market, in and out of the chestnut trees on the Prater, and down again on the road to Grinzing. It flowed through the windows of the Princess von Werdenberg's palace and danced across the black-and-white marble floors. Then it rested for a while, shining a moment on the ornate Chinese screen that stood near the Princess' bed.

The beautiful Princess sat quietly in a great chair, listening to the sound of the birds and watching Octavian Rofrano, who was kneeling at her feet. She smiled at his young face and answered his exaggerated declarations of devotion with words of mingled affection and amusement. By now the sunlight had filled the room, and the gold cherubs and the mirrors, even the pale frescoes on the ceiling, seemed to come alive in its warmth.

Octavian jumped up. "Why does there have to be daylight? I hate the day. It means that everyone can see you!" He rushed to the window and drew the heavy curtains. They were a forest of blue scattered with silver roses.

The Princess laughed to herself and begged Octavian to be quiet, for the tinkling sound of tiny bells in the hallway made her realize that Mohamed, her servant, was on his way with breakfast.

"Go and hide yourself! Quickly, behind the screen." Seeing Octavian's sword on the floor, the Princess added, "And hide your sword, foolish boy!"

The little Negro servant bowed as he entered the room and carefully set the Princess' morning chocolate on a silver table. Smiling at his mistress, he backed out of the room. The Princess drew her dressing gown about her and laughingly called to Octavian.

The young nobleman sat next to the Princess and decided that he was a very fortunate man indeed, for he was in love with the most beautiful woman in Vienna and she was in love with him.

"Why should there be so much noise in the hallway so early in the morning?" the Princess thought, placing her fragile white cup and saucer on the table. Could it be her husband, the Field Marshal, returning from his hunting trip? Listening intently and then turning to Octavian, she said, "There is someone forcing the footmen to make way. It must be my husband!"

Octavian drew his sword and ran to the door, thinking he should at least try to escape.

"No! Not there!" the Princess cried. "There are too many people waiting there." Octavian ran to a smaller door that led to a private passageway.

"Too late! They've already reached the private passage. You'll have to hide!"

"I will not let them pass!" the young boy said gallantly. "I will stay with you."

"No, no, Octavian. Get behind the curtains and don't move. I'm not really afraid because my footmen will not allow anyone to get too near."

The noise grew increasingly louder, and above the bedlam the Princess tried to recognize that single raucous voice. It was not her husband's. Its coarse accent was familiar now. It was Baron Ochs!

The Princess laughed when she turned and saw Octavian. He stepped out from behind the curtains dressed in a skirt and a short jacket. His hair was wrapped in a kerchief and tied with a ribbon, like a cap. He smiled coyly, and made a curtsey.

"Are you pleased, your Highness? I haven't been in your household very long."

The Princess kissed the boy quickly. "The Baron is about to break the door down. We must let him in. Now, as quickly as you can, walk past everyone disguised as you are; no one will notice. You may come back later . . . in your own clothes."

The white doors were flung open with such force that the painted silver cherubs in the panels with their garlands of silver roses seemed to quiver in fright. The Marschallin's footmen made a brave effort to keep the Baron from entering her room. But Ochs, who was obviously a man of the world, pushed them aside, greeting his cousin with all the grand gestures of the French court his mind was able to recall. His alert eyes also made a quick note of Octavian's presence. "I was sure," he said, giving the Princess his hand, "that your Highness would receive me, even if it is very early in the day. People of *our* rank do not have to pay attention to the hours in the day."

The Marschallin sighed and motioned for the footmen to leave the room.

"You will forgive them, Cousin," she smiled at the Baron. "They were only obeying me. I have had a terrible headache for days, and visitors were the last thing I wished to have disturbing me." She noticed that the Baron was obviously distracted by Octavian in his disguise. "I trust that the rough ways of my new maid, Mariandel, will not displease you, Baron."

"Don't think of it. She's charming," he replied, clearing his throat. "By the way, were you surprised by the news of my marriage?"

"Marriage?" the Princess asked, turning to Octavian.

"Of course, I wrote you all about it in my last letter."

The Princess remembered the letter but not its contents. She began to toy nervously with the little silver box on the table, and then discreetly motioned to Octavian to leave the room. But he refused.

"Oh, yes, I remember the letter. And who is the fortunate girl? The name was on the tip of my tongue just a moment ago . . ."

"Sophie von Faninal. Her Majesty was responsible for raising the Faninal family to the nobility. The girl is charming, fresh from the convent, *and* her father owns twelve houses and a castle in Vienna!" He caught the Princess signaling again to Mariandel, and now he was determined that the charming country bumpkin should stay in the room.

The young nobleman in disguise was backing toward the door with the silver tray in hand when the Baron cunningly asked, "Are we going to leave all that chocolate unfinished? And with me so hungry!"

"Mariandel, bring back the tray and wait upon his Lordship," the Princess ordered. She hoped that the Baron would leave soon. But instead he told her that, as was the custom in all noble families, he was going to send his betrothed a silver rose as a promise of his eternal love. "Will you recommend a messenger to deliver this pledge?" he asked.

"Tomorrow, Cousin. I will think of it tomorrow."

The major-domo announced that the usual morning visitors were waiting in the anteroom. The Princess' attorney, cook, hairdresser, and many others were patiently biding their time and anticipating the early morning ritual of discussing the plans of the day with their mistress.

The Princess dismissed the major-domo and then asked Mariandel to go to her dressing room and bring a medallion to her. Opening it and showing the Baron the portrait of Octavian inside, she asked, "Would you choose *this* young gentlemen, Count Rofrano, to take the silver rose to your young lady?" The Baron agreed eagerly he would, and mentioned the resemblance between Octavian and Mariandel. Smiling, the Princess dismissed the maid and watched as Mariandel closed the door in the Baron's face.

She could not muse long on the humor of the situation for suddenly the doors swung wide again and pandemonium broke out. From the crowd three orphans dressed in deep mourning stepped out to kneel at the Princess' feet, begging her to recall their noble father and his great deeds; her milliner deluged her with new hats; an animal vendor was trying to display his collection of yapping little dogs and screaming birds. The Princess' hairdresser and his assistants elbowed their way through the mob and began arranging her coiffure. Over all the hubbub she could hear a silver-voiced tenor pouring out all his heart and breath in a passionate, Italian aria, and in her mirror she could see three foolish-looking young men entering the room. The tallest of them was carrying a red jewel case and they all seemed to be arguing violently. They caught the Baron's eye and he nodded for them to wait for him. Valzacchi and his companion, Annina, brought a scandal sheet to the Princess, which she refused.

The Princess looked at her new coiffure in the mirror. "Hypolyte, this simply will not do. You've made me look like an old woman!" Her hairdresser looked at the sad expression on his mistress' face and frantically began to rearrange her coiffure. The crowd was thinning out and she could hear Valzacchi and Annina offering their services to the Baron. They were always involved in some intrigue. This time it was to spy on the Baron's bride-to-be, but he was more interested in their finding out some information about Mariandel. "Try your hand at that," he said, and turned to the Princess.

"Tell them all that they are dismissed!" the Marschallin commanded her major-domo, looking up wearily.

"Leopold! The leather case!" the Baron barked to one of his men. "I have the silver rose here, Cousin," he went on.

"Leave it in its case and put it on my table. I'll look at it later, Baron. I will also make your wishes known to young Rofrano." The Princess began to powder her nose. "Now, Baron, I must go, or I shall be late for Mass. You must excuse me."

Everyone ceremoniously took their leave of the Princess and she was left alone. The quiet was a relief from the clamor and the Baron's doltish, vulgar ways. As she sat pensively gazing into the mirror of her dressing table, a quiet, haunting melancholy filled the room. The Princess turned away and looked at the silver roses at the window. "I remember when I was a girl like Sophie. I also was forced into a loveless marriage with an older man," she thought, looking down at her hands. "Where is she now . . . that young girl? Soon they will be calling me 'The old Princess! The old Field Marshall's lady!' "

The Princess picked up a tiny hand-mirror with smiling silver cherubs encircling the glass, and looked closely at her face. A wan smile flitted across her lips and she sighed. "How does it happen so soon? How?" Her melancholy thoughts were interrupted by the return of Octavian. (Aria "Kann ich mich auch en ein Mädel erinnern.")

"You are so pensive. Why?" Octavian said.

"You know that my moods change rapidly, Octavian. Already this one has passed away."

The young nobleman tried to embrace her, but she pushed him away. Seeing that she had offended him, the Princess tried to explain her feelings of sadness. "The things we treasure most are fleeting, Octavian, like clouds . . . like dreams."

Octavian turned away. "You only want to tell me that you do not love me." He began to weep.

"The time will come, dear one, when you will leave me," the Princess said, softly stroking his hair. "Time is a very strange thing, Octavian. First, we pay no attention to it at all, and then suddenly we feel nothing but time. I see it in my mirror and I see it here, between you and me. Sometimes I arise in the dead of night and stop all the clocks so I will not hear the sounds of time." (Aria "Die Zeit im Grunde.")

Octavian smiled tenderly. "But I am here with you now. Who cares about time?"

"There is always time. Tomorrow, or maybe the next day, you will find someone and leave me. Someone younger and perhaps more beautiful than I." The Princess smiled sadly.

"You must go now, Octavian. It is time for me to go to church. Later today, perhaps, I will ride in the park and you can join me there. Please do what I ask."

Dejected and forlorn, the young Count turned and left the room without looking back.

The Princess watched him go and heard the door close. Suddenly realizing that she had forgotten to give Octavian the silver rose, she called for Mohamed. "Take this case to Count Octavian and tell him he will find the silver rose inside. He will know all the rest."

After Mohamed had gone, the Princess von Werdenberg sat staring into her mirror. The sun disappeared behind the tall trees in the garden, draining her room of all its color.

ACT II

THE day of the silver rose arrived. Just thinking that she was about to be the wife of the great Baron Ochs was almost too much for Sophie von Faninal. The fact that he had made such a match for his beautiful daughter was almost too much for her father; and the whole thing was surely too much for Marianne, Sophie's duenna. Why, just the sight of the new family carriage drawing up to the house made her feel faint. It was indeed a day for rejoicing.

The major-domo glanced approvingly at the highly polished rosewood panels, the glistening silver sconces, and the sparkling chandeliers in the great hall. He came into the grand drawing room to remind Master von Faninal that etiquette did not prescribe finding the bride's father in the house when the emissary arrived with the silver rose.

"When I come back," Faninal said, kissing his daughter, "I will bring your bridegroom!" Sophie smiled and waved good-by. As her father walked up the great staircase and out the door, she said a little prayer, asking God to prepare her for this wedding.

Great shouts of "Rofrano! Rofrano!" came up from the street below and Sophie took a last quick glance at herself in the mirror above the fireplace. The reflection of a lovely fifteen-year-old, radiantly happy, with every blonde curl and every pink ribbon in place, gave her courage. There was an aura of untouched purity about the girl, combined with a graceful charm that would have made her appealing to any man.

Marianne was beside herself. She had never been a part of such splendor. From the window she could see Octavian as he stepped from his silver carriage. "He is dressed entirely in cloth of silver. He looks like an angel!"

Sophie's heart was beating faster now. Certainly the bridegroom would be even more handsome than his messenger, she thought. "How can I wait any longer?" She turned and looked through the huge glass doors that led to the entrance stairway, and there he was at the top. Octavian stood glittering and dazzling in his suit of silver and white. Then, as he slowly proceeded down the stairway, silver rose in hand, Sophie caught her breath. She had never seen anyone so handsome! Their eyes met and Octavian knew then that he had never seen anyone so beautiful!

He handed the silver rose to the young girl. It was studded with diamonds that glistened like the dew on the chestnut trees in the park. "I am very honored by this mission," the young Count said, bowing before her. "This rose is a token of love from Baron Ochs von Lerchenau."

"But I am in love with *you*," Sophie thought, never taking her eyes from Octavian.

Realizing that he had fallen instantaneously in love with her and not knowing what to say, Octavian tried to compose himself by lightly commenting, "Some drops of oil from the fragrant roses of Persia have been poured on it." He smiled.

Marianne took the rose from Sophie and instructed all the servants to withdraw. She sat near the window and watched the two young people as they talked together.

"I know all about you," Sophie said demurely. "I know that you are seventeen and that you are called 'Quinquin' by many of the ladies of the court." Ocatavian laughed with boyish pride.

"I'm very glad that I'm to be married soon," the girl continued, "I often worry about all you lonely bachelors." Octavian listened, enchanted. Sophie seemed little more than a child to him, but he enjoyed her shallow nonsense of conversation. It was so different from the Princess' serious, intellectual words. Sophie made him feel like a man, not just a boy. Yes, he was in love with her.

Moments later Faninal returned with the Baron,

and Sophie was desolate. He was so vulgar and so ugly, she thought. Not what she had expected at all! Octavian was angered by Baron Ochs' uncouth remarks to Sophie and enraged that her father could have planned such an impossible marriage. He decided that he would have to protect her from the terrible fate of becoming the wife of this horrible man.

They were all drinking to the bride's health when Octavian saw the Baron roughly take Sophie in his arms. She squealed in anger. In a blaze of temper, the young Count broke the wine glass in his hand and threw the pieces against the marble stairs. Marianne was delighted with all this added excitement, but Sophie was in tears.

"You will discover, little one," the Baron said mockingly, "that I will be everything to you. Time will pass slowly when I am not around to amuse you." He laughed as Sophie pushed him away.

"I must spend some time with the attorney, discussing the legal aspects of this marriage," the Baron continued, turning to Octavian. "Meanwhile, Sophie, you will be entertained by my cousin here."

The Baron was followed out of the room by Sophie's father and his attorney, and seconds later a loud rumpus among the servants in the hallway attracted Marianne's attention. With her departure the young people were alone.

"I entreat you to help me," Sophie cried.

"And I will," Octavian declared, "if you will have courage. We will be together always. It is as though we had loved before. We can never be parted now." Sophie beamed and wiped her eyes. Why weep when one was safe in Octavian's embrace? (Duet "Mit Ihren Augen voll Thränen.")

Suddenly and unexpectedly, Valzacchi and Annina appeared from the fireplace. Annina quickly folded her black fan and placed it under her belt. Then she grabbed Sophie. Valzacchi was close behind her, and in seconds he had pulled Octavian's arms behind his back. When the spies started to call for the Baron, Octavian realized that these two Italians were employed by Ochs to spy on him and Sophie. He was furious.

The Baron came storming into the room. "Very well, young lady. What are you going to tell me?"

"What could I tell you that you would understand?" Sophie said quietly.

Octavian stepped forward. "I demand that you give up this marriage. Why, your fiancée doesn't even like you."

"I congratulate you, young man. For a boy of seventeen, you have a lot of courage. I was just like you when I was young. But I cannot give up this marriage!" The Baron took Sophie's hand and tried to pull her away. He had to get the marriage papers signed. However, Octavian complicated things by standing directly in front of him. The tip of his sil-

ver sword touched the Baron's fat belly. Awkwardly trying to defend himself, Ochs was wounded, very superficially. "I've been murdered," he screamed, flouncing down in a chair.

Sophie's father was shaking with rage and indignation over Octavian's behavior, and ordered him to leave the house. "And you," he roared at Sophie, "shall go back to the convent if you do not marry the Baron!"

Looking at Octavian, Sophie smiled saucily and replied, "Then I shall jump from the coach that takes me there!" The tumult and confusion grew. The Baron was roaring and waving his arms, and Faninal was ordering her to her room, but all Sophie could see was Octavian. "He is my silver rose. He will save me from all this."

Octavian whispered that he would see her soon and then disappeared through the glass doors and up the great staircase. At the top, he motioned to Annina and Valzacchi. They winked at each other and ran up the stairs.

After the doctor had dressed Ochs' wound and everyone had left the room, the Baron relaxed over another glass of wine. He laughed a little over Octavian's youthful daring and Sophie's temperamental defiance. Life was not bad. In fact, the future looked very rosy. He started up as Annina cautiously came into the drawing room and handed him a letter. The Baron opened the letter with his good hand and held it several inches from his eyes. The words were only black curlicues. He needed ·his glasses.

"Are my glasses in my pocket?" he asked. Annina glided over to him, smiling. "Never mind," the Bar-

on said suspiciously, preferring that she not go through his pockets. "Read it to me, if you are scholar enough."

It was from Mariandel. The charming country servant of the Princess would be free for dinner the following evening. Perhaps she and the Baron could meet at that little inn on the outskirts of the city?

Indeed the Baron's future was going to be rosy! He would have this rendezvous with Mariandel, marry the wealthy Faninal girl, and have his revenge on the youthful Octavian.

Dismissing Annina, he filled his wine glass again and waltzed around the room. There was music coming from some distant café. It was beautiful in Vienna. He would relax and enjoy life. Sinking into a pleasant slumber, for he was slightly tipsy now, he sang quietly to himself, "With me—no night is too long for you . . . With me . . ." Things were very quiet in the Faninal house, except for the ticking of a clock somewhere beyond the great staircase.

ACT III

THE marvelous idea of arranging a plot against the wily Baron Ochs had come to Octavian during all the tumult at the Faninal home. And at precisely the same time, clever Annina and Valzacchi had decided to switch allegiance from the Baron to the young Count. After all, Counts do have more money than Barons do. With their help, the plan would be a spectacular success.

It was early evening and Octavian glanced up at the sign at the inn. He had on his Mariandel costume with his riding boots peering out from the long skirt. He laughed and walked into the inn, thinking, "What a night this will be!"

Annina and Valzacchi were already there. Everything was all arranged. People were concealed everywhere and at a designated time and signal would peer out of the windows, chests, and from under the table to confuse the Baron. He would eventually, they hoped, call for help and expose himself. The great Baron, on the eve of his wedding, involved with a simple country girl! Then, to finish it all off, Annina would arrive dressed as a widow, accompanied by a whole row of children who would all say that the Baron was their father! A splendid plan, they all agreed, and Octavian showed his delight by tossing a bag of gold coins to Valzacchi. Then, as Mariandel, he left the room to meet the Baron.

When the Baron and Mariandel came back into the room, all was silent. The Baron angrily extinguished some of the candles with his fat hand. "And what is all that music?" he roared at the innkeeper. "I didn't ask for it and I don't want it!" He turned and smiled at Mariandel. "But let them play on. However, the rest of you get out! My men will serve the roast and I can pour the wine."

The innkeeper smiled knowingly, and departed. The Baron and Mariandel then sat at a table. But every romantic declaration of the Baron's was interrupted by disheveled heads eyeing him from every corner. "I am surely seeing things," the Baron thought. It was getting very warm in the room and the Baron decided to remove his wig.

Now he was confronted by Annina, crying that he was her husband! Four children followed her into the room, shouting, "Papa! Papa!" The Baron groaned and tried to beat the children off with his napkin.

Octavian was quick to seize the chance of conferring with Valzacchi. "Is Faninal going to come?"

"He will soon be here," Valzacchi replied with amusement, and turned to Baron Ochs. "I warn you to be more careful, for the police of this community are very harsh with men like you!" Snorting contemptuously at Valzacchi, the Baron rushed to the window and called for help. And it arrived in the form of the Police Commissioner.

He addressed the innkeeper first: "These goings-on do not speak well for you. I want the whole truth of what is happening here."

The blustering innkeeper tried to reply by pointing to Ochs. "His Lordship, there . . ."

"That fat old man?" the Commissioner asked. Looking at the Baron's shiny bald head, he continued, "Pray, where have you put your wig?"

"His Lordship is the Baron von Lerchenau," added the innkeeper.

"Humph! He'll have to prove it. Do you have any witnesses?"

The Baron thought he was safe now. Valzacchi would be his witness. But the crafty Italian denied even knowing him. "They are liars, all of them!" the Baron bellowed.

By now, Mariandel was running aimlessly around the room wailing, "I wish the earth would open up and swallow me."

"Who is that?" demanded the Commissioner. "I'll count to three and then you must answer. *Who* is that girl?"

The Baron was trapped. But he would try to wiggle out. "Is there anything wrong with a gentleman dining with his fiancée? She is young Miss Faninal. Sophie Anna Barbara, the daughter of Lord Faninal."

At the sound of his name, Faninal swept into the room. He was shocked indeed to find his future son-in-law embroiled in such a situation, and as things became more clear he decided that he could never allow Sophie to marry such a wicked man. He called for his daughter who was outside, and loudly bemoaned the scandal they were all involved in.

"I'm actually very happy," Sophie smiled. "I never thought of him as belonging to me." Von Faninal's angry blood was throbbing at his temples as he clenched his fists and swung out at the Baron. He collapsed at the Baron's feet and had to be carried from the room, attended by Sophie and the innkeeper. The scandal was not over yet, for Octavian stepped behind the curtains to change into his own clothes just as the frantic innkeeper announced that the Princess von Werdenberg was coming into the inn!

Momentarily, the tumult subsided and all eyes focused on the door. The Princess stood for a few seconds in the doorway, looking about with disdainful eyes. The Baron was stupid enough to think that she had come to help him, so he spoke to her. "I am overwhelmed by this indication of your friendship, your Highness."

Ignoring the Baron, the Princess spoke quietly to the Commissioner. "A long time ago, weren't you the Field Marshal's orderly?"

"Yes, your Highness. I am at your command."

Sophie was coming into the room, and Octavian appeared in his own clothes from behind the curtains. The Princess smiled casually. "Baron, I suggest that you leave well enough alone. Before I count to two, I would like you to depart." Raising her hand in reproach, she added, "Think of your dignity."

Looking at the Commissioner, the Princess commented, "I believe that this entire evening was just a pleasant diversion, Commissioner. Shall we all regard it as such?" The officer agreed, and bowing low, left the room.

"I do not know what to think," the perplexed Baron said, rubbing his head. "Octavian, Mariandel, your Highness? It is all too confusing."

"It then befits a real cavalier to refrain from thinking at all, Cousin," the Princess said. "That is what I expect from you."

"In the presence of such charming finesse, what can I say?"

"You may say, dear Baron, that you renounce forever this alliance with Sophie von Faninal." Their conversation was over. Like a burst of fireworks the noisy participants in the whole masquerade appeared—the screaming children, Annina, Valzacchi, everyone—and the contrite but noisy Baron followed them out of the door, now realizing how he had been fooled.

The Princess was left alone with Sophie and Octavian, and it was at that moment that she knew she had lost the young Count. But being a great lady, she decided to allow Octavian to take control of the situation. Embarrassed, he stammered, "I am surprised to see you, Marie Therese." He wanted to throw himself at her feet and beg her forgiveness.

She had been so right. The time had come, as she had said it would, when he loved another.

The Princess turned and looked out of the window, knowing in her heart that Octavian was a world away from her. Confronted with the loneliness of being without him, she still had to give her blessing to Sophie and Octavian and bury her own feelings. "Go quickly, Octavian, and do as your heart tells you." But the young man was caught between the two women, not knowing what to do. "You're a fine picture of a man. Go to her," the Princess said sharply, and Octavian turned to Sophie.

Sophie thought, "Why am I feeling ashamed in front of the Princess? Her somber eyes keep looking at me, and Octavian does nothing to help me."

With a friendly glance the Princess looked into Sophie's puzzled eyes and asked, "Have you fallen in love with him so quickly?"

"I don't know what your Highness means."

The older woman gently touched the girl's face with her fan. "The paleness of your face tells me."

Octavian was deeply touched and he approached her tenderly. "How good you are, Marie Therese. I don't know at all . . ."

The Princess wanted it all to be finished now, and she answered, "I also know nothing, nothing at all."

The music from the outer room drifted in and carried them away in the dream world of their own thoughts. The Princess smiled at their disturbed young faces. She had known that this time would come. Octavian would be happy now, and he belonged to this girl. Octavian looked at them both and wanted to ask the Princess about this new love. But he did not. He knew that there could be no one but Sophie. Sophie was happy and perplexed. She felt honestly that the Princess was giving her Octavian as a wonderful gift, and yet she was also keeping a part of him. (Trio "Hab' mir's gelobt.")

The Princess left the room. The candles, all save one, sputtered and died, casting long shadows across the room as Sophie and Octavian pledged their undying love. (Duet "Ist ein Traum.")

When the Princess returned with Faninal, they saw the two lovers in each other's arms. She heard Faninal say, "That's the way it is. Love like that is for the very, very young."

"Yes. Yes," she answered resignedly, and extended her hand to Octavian. The warm, loving gesture seemed to say, "I understand and forgive." The young man kissed her hand and she left the inn.

Sophie and Octavian slowly walked out into the night. The waltz music was playing softly when Mohamed ran into the room. He was searching for something. There it was—Sophie's handkerchief, lying on the floor. He picked it up and danced out. The silver bells on his shoes tinkled on the night air.

TOSCA

BY

GIACOMO PUCCINI

(1858—1924)

LIBRETTO BY LUIGI ILLICA

AND GIUSEPPE GIACOSA

BASED ON THE DRAMA

LA TOSCA

BY VICTORIEN SARDOU

CHARACTERS

Angelotti	Bass
A Sacristan	Baritone
Mario Cavaradossi	Tenor
Floria Tosca	Soprano
Baron Scarpia	Baritone
Spoletta	Tenor
Sciarrone	Bass

Time: Early 1800's   *Place: Rome*

First performance: Teatro Constanzi, Rome;

January 14, 1900

Puccini saw the great actress Sarah Bernhardt perform Sardou's play *La Tosca* in Paris, and thought that it would make an exciting opera. Some critics felt that the plot was too dramatic to make a good opera, but *Tosca* was a tremendous success when it was first performed, and is still a favorite.

At the time that *Tosca* takes place, Roman supporters of Napoleon and republicanism are waiting for him to advance from northern Italy, and Roman officials are daily searching for and imprisoning Napoleon's adherents.

ACT I

AT the beginning of the nineteenth century, Floria Tosca was one of the most beautiful women in Rome. She was the reigning prima donna of the opera and adored by musicians and public alike. Audiences at the Argentine Theater wildly threw flowers upon the stage following her every performance, and artists clamored to paint her. She was a favorite of the Queen of Naples and admired by the Chief of the Roman Police, Baron Scarpia, who was hated and feared by everyone. But Floria, or "La Tosca" as she was spoken of in Rome, was in love with Mario Cavaradossi, a young painter.

Events which would change these peoples' lives began in a church. It was the church of Sant' Dandrea della Valle, and the month was June. The nave of the church near the Attavanti Chapel was quiet, and the afternoon sun played gently among the delicately twisted columns, illuminated with tiny mosaics. They glistened in the light. A dirty, frightened man, mumbling about his recent and narrow escape from some prison, was searching frantically for something. He found hidden at the base of a statue of the Madonna a key that opened the door of the chapel. He went in and closed the door just as the chubby Sacristan came through the grilled gates and jerkily walked over to a platform and easel that stood quietly waiting for some artist to return and finish his work.

The Sacristan poked at the dirty paintbrushes and grumbled. "I wonder why Mario isn't here?" Looking in a food hamper nearby and realizing it had not been touched, he concluded that Mario would return soon. He blew his nose on a huge red handkerchief and quickly dropped to his knees as the Angelus bells sounded.

Mario walked in, glanced at the old Sacristan, and immediately began to study his new painting. He looked at the canvas, a portrait of a beautiful blonde woman as the Magdalene. The Sacristan got up, brushed off his red cassock, and exclaimed, "She reminds me of the lady who prays here every day at the shrine of the Madonna."

Mario smiled. "You see well. Her lovely face did inspire me. But she cannot compare with Floria. Tosca's eyes are black, like the night, and the eyes of the portrait are blue. And anyway, I love Tosca. There is a strange, eternal music about her. Tosca is the one!" (Aria "Recondita armonia.")

The Sacristan looked at Mario, putting his pudgy hands against his fat ears in a mock attempt to block out such unchurchly ideas about women and love. Shaking his head in dismay, he left the painter alone and walked into the main part of the church.

At the sound of the chapel door opening behind him, Mario put down his brush and turned around. He was surprised to see his old friend Angelotti. "What are you doing here?" he asked, as he leapt down from the platform and embraced the terror-stricken man. Then he quickly locked the gates that were the only entrance to that part of the church.

"I have just escaped from Castle Sant' Angelo," Angelotti told him. "I need help desperately."

"And you shall have it!" said Mario, eager to assist his friend in the bitter fight against the factions who supported the likes of Baron Scarpia. He and Angelotti hated the Monarchists who had long kept most of Italy and all Rome torn apart with their battles against the Bonapartists.

Floria's voice calling, "Mario! Mario!" made him realize that he would have to see her and placate her before he could help his friend.

"Take this basket of food, Angelotti, and stay here in the chapel. Be very quiet, and I will find a place to hide you as soon as Tosca is gone."

Angelotti made his way into the chapel just in time, for Tosca was impatient and she pouted as Mario unlocked the grilled gates and let her in. Her purple dress and bonnet accented her big, dark eyes, and the bouquet of acacia blossoms that she had brought as an offering to the Virgin made her marblelike skin more radiant than ever. Mario could not help being in love with her.

Yes, he was in love with her, and she was the reason he stayed in Rome. Although, upon occasion, her jealous tantrums made him wonder why.

Floria arranged the flowers at the feet of the

Madonna, prayed with great devotion, and blessed herself. Now it was Mario who was impatient and showed signs of wanting to get on with his work.

"The opera I am singing tonight is a short one, Mario, so if you will wait for me at the stage door, we can go straight to your villa."

"Tonight?" Mario asked, wondering what he would do with Angelotti.

"Aren't you pleased?"

"Of course," he replied, looking over his shoulder at the chapel door. Tosca described the happiness they would have. (Duet "Non la sospiri lia nostra casetta.")

Then she cried, catching sight of the picture on the easel, "Who is this with the blond hair and the blue eyes?" She kicked at the long train of her dress

as she recognized who it was. It was the Marchesa Attavanti. "It was she who was with you!" she cried jealously. "When the gate was locked, I *knew* you were not alone!"

Mario ignored her remark. "It was pure accident that I happened to paint her face, Floria. She comes to pray here. There are no eyes in the world to compare with yours."

She turned the amethyst ring on her finger and smiled. "I will leave now, if you will promise to paint the Magdalene's eyes black like mine instead of blue." Mario agreed, and Floria, happy again, left him to finish his work.

As the sound of her heels disappeared, echoing among the columns, Mario locked the gate and called to Angelotti. Looking anxiously about to make sure that no one was within hearing distance, the escaped man told his friend of the events that had brought him here. "My sister, the Marchesa Attavanti, has hidden some clothes under the altar. Women's clothes—even a fan to hide my face—to disguise me and help me escape from Scarpia."

"Scarpia! That evil killer?" Mario exclaimed. "I will save you if it costs me my own life! Here, take this key to my villa. If danger threatens you there, run to the well in the garden. There is still water in it, but halfway down there is a secret opening that leads to a cave. You will be safe there." The words were hardly out of his mouth when the sound of a cannon rumbled through Rome and reverberated in the church.

"They have discovered my escape," Angelotti said, frozen to the spot.

"Come, I will show you the way myself," Mario said, and they both rushed out of the church.

The Sacristan ambled in, expecting to find Mario still at work. He looked up at the cold, blue eyes of the portrait and shrugged his shoulders. The old man was soon surrounded by a noisy group of choir boys and clerics. "Bonaparte has been defeated," the Sacristan told them, "and tonight there will be a great torchlight procession and festival at the Farnese Palace. A new cantata composed for the occasion will be sung by Floria Tosca!"

There were loud cries of "Long live the Queen!" "Te Deum!" "Gloria!" and the boys joined hands and danced around the Sacristan. Their gaiety was short-lived, however, for the Baron Scarpia's menacing figure stood hovering behind them. His huge black cape lined in purple reminded them all of some great bird of prey.

"What is this scandalous uproar in church?" he shouted. "Go! Prepare for the service." The boys scurried silently around him, almost bumping into his ratlike assistant, Spoletta, and his other henchmen. Then they disappeared. The Sacristan trembled and mopped his shiny bald head. Scarpia raised his lorgnette to peer at the old man. From behind the thick glass and the ornate gold stem, his beady eyes took in every object in the church.

"We are tracking down a fool who has escaped from the prison," he said, smiling cruelly. "We are aware that he has come *here.*"

The old man bowed before him and mumbled. Scarpia brushed past him and went into the chapel. In seconds he returned, carrying a tiny ivory fan which he opened and closed stealthily. "This fan bears the crest of the Marchesa Attavanti, and the painting there is oddly like the Marchesa. Who painted it?"

"Mario Cavaradossi," answered the Sacristan. Scarpia sneered. He knew the names of all the chief Bonapartists well.

One of the Baron's men came out of the chapel carrying the empty food hamper. The fat, little Sacristan blinked his eyes and swallowed hard as he foolishly blurted out, "Young Cavaradossi doesn't have a key to the chapel, so he could not have possibly eaten there!"

Scarpia was quick to deduce that it could be no one but Angelotti who had eaten the food. He could be sure that Mario was actually involved in the escape. Seeing Tosca returning, Scarpia hid behind a pillar. He advised the Sacristan not to move.

"Where is Mario?" Floria asked impatiently.

"The painter? Who knows?" the Sacristan stuttered and hurried out.

Scarpia approached Tosca with a great flourish and offered her some holy water from the font. "I must compliment you, Floria Tosca, on your devoutness. There are people who would profane this quiet spot by using it as a romantic trysting place." He casually looked at the fan he had found. "Some lady dropped this in haste when she was surprised here." He watched Tosca's eyes as they were drawn to the golden crest.

"So it was La Attavanti!" she sobbed. "I came here to tell him that I have been commanded to sing at the royal celebration tonight, and now I discover this!" Tears of rage filled her eyes. Glaring at the painting, she ran up the steps to the easel. "I will have my revenge, Attavanti!"

"My dear lady," Scarpia said with an oily, accusing tone, "you must not give way to your earthly rage in this consecrated place. And, anyway, cheeks as beautiful as yours should not be disturbed by tears."

"Traitors!" she cried, "I will surprise them both." Scarpia looked at her. Now she was not only jealous, she was humiliated. Weeping, she begged God's pardon and turned to leave. Scarpia followed her with his eyes. Her purple figure and the purple plumes on her bonnet swept through the open bronze doors and into the street.

"Follow her, Spoletta," he ordered, "and report to me at the Farnese Palace!"

Scarpia stood alone in the nave, flipping the little fan open and closed. Swiss guards entered in the cortege of the Cardinal, and Scarpia knelt in mock prayer. The sounds of the organ rose in the great *Te Deum*.

"Go, Tosca! Scarpia has already wormed his way into your heart! Go to Cavaradossi," he mused. "I shall have the double triumph. I will have you *and* the defeat of Cavaradossi!"

The thundering sound of *"Te aeternum Patrem omnis terra veneratur"* rose and sang on the evening air.

ACT II

SCARPIA had been in Rome only a week, and the events of the day, especially Angelotti's escape, weighed heavily on his mind. The implications disturbed him. They might ruin his career as the chief of the Roman Police and cut short his period of residence in the magnificent Farnese Palace. It was fitting that he should be there; after all, it had been completed by the great Michelangelo.

His dining table had been placed near the huge windows that looked out over the courtyard and its three rows of large arcades. Here he could also conveniently watch the cantata and celebration that would honor General Melas' reported victory over Napoleon. Scarpia tipped the wine in his glass back and forth. "Well, it won't be long," he thought, bringing the goblet to his lips, "until both Mario and Angelotti are hanging by their stupid necks! Tosca is a good hawk. Surely by this time she has led my men to the traitors' hideout."

Sciarrone, one of his henchmen, came into the room with the news that Tosca had arrived at the palace.

"Tell Tosca that I shall expect to see her after the cantata," the Baron ordered. "Take her this note." He tapped his wine glass with the silver knife that lay next to it. The crystal rang clearly against its sharp edge. He laughed to himself. "She will come because she loves Mario. These insipid love affairs are not for me . . . these turtle-dove cooings and songs by moonlight. Violence and hatred are more exciting." He sipped some more of his wine, savoring its aroma. "God has created many varieties of beauty—just as there are varieties of wine. I would like to taste them all. Love, bah!" (Aria "Ha più forte sapore.")

His philosophy of evil was rudely interrupted by Spoletta, who rushed into the room trembling with fear. "We have reached Cavaradossi's villa and there is no sign of Angelotti!"

"How dare you let him escape!" Scarpia roared.

"But we have brought Cavaradossi with us," Spoletta added, watching Scarpia's rage subside.

"Well, bring him in!" Scarpia ordered, glancing out of the window as the sound of Tosca's voice soared up from the courtyard.

The young painter was pushed into the room and the Chief of Police, with elaborate courtesy, asked him to join him at the table. "You no doubt know that a prisoner today escaped from Sant' Angelo?"

"I did not know that," Mario answered.

"It is said that you met him in the church and gave him food. It is also said that you took him to your villa. But the police found no one there."

Mario laughed.

Scarpia got up from the table angrily. "This is more a matter for tears!" The cantata was getting on his nerves and he quickly drew the drapes. "Where is Angelotti?"

Mario denied that he knew anything at all. "Come, now, Mario Cavaradossi—reflect a while. A confession will save you much suffering," Scarpia said.

Tosca entered breathlessly, and the Baron rose gallantly to assist her in removing her ermine cape. The famous Tosca diamonds flashed against her white skin, and her purple, brocaded gown, encrusted from bodice to hem with tiny pearls, shimmered in the candlelight. Ignoring the Baron, she ran to Mario. "Say nothing of what you saw at the villa," Mario whispered to her. "If you do, you will be my death."

Scarpia placed the prima donna's cape on a gold-backed chair. "The judge is prepared to hear your confession in the next room, Cavaradossi!" he said.

Tosca did not know that the room referred to was the Baron's torture chamber, but she and Mario were soon to find out. "Proceed in the usual way, Roberti," Scarpia called out to one of his men, and Mario was dragged away. The door to the chamber was closed and Sciarrone was left standing guard.

Tosca seated herself on the couch, watching Scarpia as he picked at a bunch of grapes with a silver knife. She turned away as he spoke to her.

"Let us have a little talk, like good friends. Do not be frightened. Tell me about the fan." He leaned over the couch.

"Mere jealousy on my part," Tosca said indifferently.

"The Marchesa was not at the villa?" Scarpia asked.

"No. He was alone." Tosca replied.

"Insist that Cavaradossi tells the truth, Sciarrone," Scarpia said, motioning to his henchmen to proceed with the torture.

"Then to please you, one has to lie?" Floria asked ironically. "Questioning him is useless, Baron." Tosca frivolously removed her long, white gloves and tossed them over the back of the couch.

"An honest answer from you might save your lover more pain," Scarpia said, returning to the table and placing the knife on a lace napkin near a decanter of wine. "At this instant, your painter's head is in a steel band that has the grip of a vice. We can tighten it a little more," he said, sipping his wine. "As Mario continues to deny . . . the blood will continue to flow from his beautiful head!"

Tosca cringed in horror as a groan from the inner room gave proof to Scarpia's words. She moved to the door and listened. "Mario?" she called.

"Do not speak a word, Tosca. Not a word," Mario's muffled voice called back.

Wild with rage, Tosca screamed at the Chief of Police, denouncing his mad brutality.

"Brava, Tosca! Your performance is worthy of the great stages of the world," Scarpia replied. "Open the door, Spoletta!"

Tosca could look into the torture chamber, and she had to lean against the frame of the door, as she recoiled in terror. Scarpia was standing behind her. "Where is Angelotti, Tosca?" he asked.

"Let me speak to Mario. Please let me speak," Tosca begged.

"What could you say? What do you know?" Mario answered bravely.

Floria turned to Scarpia. "It is I whom you are torturing." Mario's screams tore through her, and suddenly and uncontrollably the words came forth. "Angelotti is in the well in the garden," she whispered.

A gesture of Scarpia's leathery hand stopped the torture. Mario was dragged into the room. His first words to her were, "Did I reveal the secret, Tosca?"

"No, beloved Mario," she wept, gently putting his bleeding head against the purple cushions of the couch.

Scarpia roared, "To the well in the garden, Spoletta!"

Mario turned violently on Tosca. "You have betrayed me!" Her sobbing exclamations were interrupted by Sciarrone's appearance on the scene. His news that the celebration for General Melas was a mistake—Bonaparte had defeated *him* at Malengo—sent Scarpia into a fit of rage.

"Victory! Victory! You hangman!" Mario shouted exultantly at Scarpia.

"Throw the traitor in a cell," Scarpia shouted back to his men, as Tosca fought with the guards to keep Mario from being taken away. It was useless. The door closed and she was alone with Scarpia again.

He smiled suavely. "Come, Tosca, join me in a glass of wine. We can discuss things now."

She removed her gloves from the couch and placed them on the chair with her cape. Years of experience in the theater allowed her to remain calm, never once removing her eyes from Scarpia's.

She thought, "There is a price for everything."

"What is your price?" she asked.

Scarpia answered, "People who hate me and are jealous of me call me depraved and calculating, Tosca. But one thing I never do is degrade myself as far as beautiful women are concerned. I never speak of them in foul terms of money. I have waited a long time for you. Why, even the hate in your eyes makes you more beautiful." (Aria "Mi dicon venal.") He reached across the table to grasp her hand, and to escape she moved toward the door.

"You are free to go, Tosca, but your hopes are for nothing. You think that you will find the Queen and that she will pardon Cavaradossi. Her grace would be bestowed on a corpse." Tosca turned to the window, pushed back the purple velvet and looked out into the quiet night.

"Cavaradossi will be dead," Scarpia said, pouring another glass of wine, "before another hour ticks away."

Floria fixed her eyes on the gold crucifix that hung on the wall. "What have I done?" she thought. "I have lived only for my singing and my art. I have given everything to them and those I love. Haven't I decked the altar with flowers, and given my jewels for the mantle of the Madonna? Haven't I helped the poor and sung for God? Why has He deserted me now?" In the candlelight the crucifix seemed unmoved, and Floria fell to her knees sobbing, begging Scarpia to hear her prayer and let her go. (Aria "Vissi d'arte.")

"My price for Mario's life is still the same, Tosca," Scarpia said, offering his hand to her. As he helped her from the floor, Spoletta came in.

"Just as we reached out to capture Angelotti, he took poison. He's dead," the henchman said, lowering his eyes.

"Hang him anyway!" Scarpia roared.

"And Cavaradossi?"

"Well?" asked Scarpia, looking at Floria. She nodded her consent and buried her face in the pillows on the couch.

"Good! The Cavaradossi execution will be a mock one. Just as we did with Palmieri. Remember, Spoletta?"

"I understand completely," Spoletta replied, as he left the room and closed the door.

"You, Tosca, will even be allowed to come to the execution and inform Cavaradossi of his reprieve," Scarpia said consolingly. "I have kept my promise."

"Not yet, Baron. I want a paper of safe conduct out of the Roman states for Mario and myself . . . by the way of Via Vecchia."

"Agreed," said Scarpia, seating himself at his

writing table. Tosca watched his gnarled hands as they filled in the necessary papers. The scratching noise of his pen and his hawklike features in the candlelight frightened her even more now. She walked to the table. Perhaps a glass of wine would calm her nerves. The candle burning under the crucifix sputtered out, but its last flicker of light, like an inspiration, glistened on the silver knife. Her eyes were drawn to its sharp edge, and almost spontaneously she grasped its cold handle. Hearing Scarpia stamping the passports, she quickly hid the knife behind her back. As he walked toward her she leaned against the table to steady herself. As he moved to kiss her, she thrust the blade in his heart.

"Here is your kiss from Tosca," she said, almost spitting the words out.

The Baron fell backward to the floor, gasping and crying out for help. Floria could not bear to look at his eyes, and turned her head as she stooped over him to pry the passports out of his hand. She quietly placed the two great candelabra on either side of his head, and removed the crucifix from the wall. Standing at his feet, she looked down at the Chief of Police for the last time.

"To think that before *him*, all Rome trembled," she murmured. A roll of the drums, sharp as a stiletto, cracked through the night. She placed the crucifix on Scarpia's chest and left the room silently.

ACT III

As SHE was hurrying down the empty streets to the bridge, in the prison of Sant' Angelo, Mario was being led onto a parapet. The air was clear and the early morning sky was still filled with stars. He stopped and listened to the sounds of morning. The cow bells and the song of a shepherd trembled on the air as dawn began to break. Rome, the city of churches, was beginning to awaken.

The sergeant with Mario pushed him before the old jailer who was in charge of the prisoners. "You have an hour to live, Mario Cavaradossi. A priest is at your service if you wish one."

"I have no need of a priest," Mario said, "but I do have one last request." He handed the old man his ring. "Will you deliver a last message to one I dearly love?" The man hesitated, then agreed.

Mario sat down at the jailer's table and began to write. He dropped his pen, for thoughts of Tosca overwhelmed him and more words would not come. He remembered their happy times together. Now, everything was gone. "I am not afraid to die," he sighed, "but to die unhappy." Mario hid his face in his hands and sobbed. (Aria "E lucevan le stelle.")

The gray dawn was now tinged with purple and pink as Floria came up the staircase and ran to the astonished Mario. She kissed him and showed him the safe-conduct papers. Mario glanced at the signature suspiciously. "This is certainly Scarpia's first act of grace."

"And his last," Floria answered. "I killed him after getting these papers."

Mario took her white hands in his and kissed them tenderly. "These little hands," he smiled, "that were meant for holding roses and children? You've bloodied them for me?" (Aria "O dolci mani.")

Tosca put her head on Mario's shoulder and told him the details of the false execution that was to take place. The guns of the soldiers would be loaded with blanks. "And," she said, "you must fall to the ground and pretend that you are dead as soon as you hear the sounds from the rifles. Think that it is nothing but a play in the theater. And remember, Mario, you must fall without hurting yourself. Just as I do on the stage."

As the firing squad approached from the stairway, Mario smiled and kissed her gently. He would not allow the sergeant to blindfold him. Instead, he motioned him away, and looked at Floria as he repeated, "Just like Tosca on the stage!"

Floria watched him standing against the wall and grew impatient. "I know it is all a comedy, but why the delay?"

In answer, a volley of shots rang out and Mario fell to the floor. She watched nervously as the sergeant examined his body and prepared to give him the *coup de grâce*. But Spoletta restrained him, and he and the soldiers turned and marched away.

Floria looked cautiously over the parapet, warning Mario not to move yet. She looked up at the fading stars—time was running out. They must get away.

"Come, Mario, come quickly!" But Mario did not move. Touching him, she realized that the execution had not been a mockery. It had been real! Scarpia had won! She cradled Mario's head in her arms and called his name, but there was no answer. From below, she could hear the voices of Spoletta and Sciarrone, calling out for her. Scarpia's murder had been discovered.

Spoletta bounded up the winding stairs and tried to seize the prima donna, but Floria pushed him aside and stepped onto the edge of the fortress parapet.

Spoletta and the soldiers heard her last words, "We will meet before God, Scarpia!" just as she went hurtling through the air to the courtyard below.

Floria Tosca's body was motionless on the pavement. The purple dawn was enveloping all of Rome. It was a new day in June. June in Rome. The city of fountains. The city of churches. The city of romance.

LA TRAVIATA

BY

GIUSEPPE VERDI

(1813-1901)

Libretto by Francesco Maria Piave

Based on the play *La Dame aux Camélias (Camille)*

BY ALEXANDER DUMAS

Violetta Valery	. .	SOPRANO	Gastone	. . . . . TENOR
Flora Bervoix	. .	MEZZO-SOPRANO	Alfredo Germont	. TENOR
Marquis d'Obigny	.	BASS	Alfredo's father	. BARITONE
Baron Douphol	. .	BARITONE	Dr. Grenvil	. . . BASS
		Annina . . . . . MEZZO-SOPRANO		

TIME: About 1700   PLACE: In and near Paris

FIRST PERFORMANCE: LA FELICE THEATER,

VENICE; MARCH 6, 1853

La Traviata, written by Verdi in four weeks, was a horrible failure at its first performance. One of the reasons given for this is that the opera was played in contemporary dress, which the Italian opera-goer did not like. Also, the soprano who played Violetta was a fat, healthy-looking woman. When the doctor proclaimed that Violetta was dying of consumption, the audience thought this was extremely funny and laughed loudly.

A year later *La Traviata* was presented again, and the time at which the opera took place was set at 1700. The audience could enjoy lavish costumes and sets. The opera was a tremendous success and has been since. Today, the opera is performed in a period setting of the 1840's.

ACT I

Paris in the 1840's was a wonderful place to be. Life was a round of parties and gaiety. Even if one were ill, as Violetta Valery, the Lady of the Camellias, was, one danced and laughed and was happy.

Violetta sat on a dark-green sofa in her drawing room, talking with her doctor and several friends. Her thoughts strayed as she glanced at the richly laid table in the center of the room. She saw her pale face and her black hair reflected in the great gold mirror over the fireplace. She placed her slender white hand against her cheek and sighed. The soft glow of the camellias she was holding accentuated the pallor of her skin. She was too young to be so ill, she thought, but quickly smiled as she saw Flora, her friend, entering the room.

"Flora, dear Flora," she said, as she rose, "how glad I am to see you. I want you to help me make this a particularly festive party tonight. I am always happier when my friends are here."

Flora kissed Violetta, and arranging the many diamond bracelets that sparkled against her long velvet gloves inquired, "But, chérie, are you feeling well enough to be entertaining tonight?"

"Yes, I want to," Violetta answered. "It's the best medicine for my illness."

The elegant Marquis d'Obigny, who had arrived with Flora, agreed. "You are indeed right, Mademoiselle. Life is made for pleasure." Violetta smiled as the gallant Marquis kissed her hand and she excused herself to greet some new arrivals. As she moved across the room she brought her bouquet of camellias close to her face. Their fragile aroma somehow made her wistfully happy, even when she was not.

Two handsomely dressed young men came into the room and paused, looking about.

"Gastone, you are here at last!" Violetta said teasingly, as one might to a very dear friend.

"Yes, dear lady, and I have brought an admirer of yours. May I present Alfredo Germont?"

Their eyes met and they were both at a loss for words, but Violetta, withdrawing her gloved hand from his, quickly remarked, "Thank you, cher Gastone. Now, come let us dine. The wine and food will banish our secret cares."

As he helped her into her chair at the table, Gastone leaned close to her, whispering, "Alfredo is always talking of you. Nothing but you."

"You must be joking."

"No, I am not. When you were ill these past few weeks, he hurried here every day to see if you were better."

The Baron Douphol with his deep-set hawk eyes looked across the table at Alfredo, and turning to Flora remarked, "I've taken a dislike to that young man."

"But, why?" asked Flora coquettishly. "I think he's very handsome."

The Baron grunted, touching his nose with his green silk handkerchief. He was obviously jealous.

Violetta's pallor seemed to take on a warmer hue in the candlelight, and at her suggestion Alfredo proposed a toast. Lifting his glass, he said, "Let us drink to love and this fleeting hour!" Violetta joined him in the spirit of the occasion.

"I will share my times of happiness with all of you. We know that everything in this world is folly and that everything is fleeting . . . like my camellias, they blossom and then die. So, let us be happy tonight!" Turning to Alfredo, she said, "There *is* nothing in life but pleasure, you know." (Drinking Song "Libiamo.")

"Only for one who is not in love," he replied, placing his glass on the table.

"I don't know the meaning of the word, dear friend," said Violetta, lowering her eyes, "so do not speak to me about it."

The guests chatted among themselves, and the wine glasses tinkled in harmony with the sound of music that wafted in from the adjoining room. Violetta looked up, as though awakening from a trance, and urged everyone to dance. Flora, the Baron, and all the guests agreed and rose from the table. Suddenly, Violetta's face was drained of all its color and she clutched at the back of her chair, dropping her camellias to the floor. Flora was quick to notice and rushed to her side.

"What is the matter?" she asked, and the urgency in her voice brought everyone back into the room.

"Nothing, nothing. Come, let us dance!" Violetta took a few steps and stopped, murmuring, "Oh, dear Lord."

Alfredo gripped her arm and helped her to a chair. "You must be in pain. What can I do for you?"

"It is nothing, really," she said, breathing heavily. "I feel a bit chilly. You go ahead and I will join you in a while." But Alfredo lingered in the shadow of the doorway.

Violetta walked to the great mirror over the mantlepiece and gazed silently at her face. "How pale I am," she sighed, and, turning, saw the young Germont. "You're still here?"

"This life you're leading will kill you," Alfredo gently admonished. "You must take care of yourself. If you were mine, I would spend my life watching over you."

Violetta walked over to a little gold-legged table that stood near the sofa. Several camellias were nestled in a bowl that sat on the green fringed cloth. She took one of the flowers and caressed its petals. "Have you loved me a long time?" asked Violetta with a curious smile.

Alfredo told her of the first time he had seen her and how he had loved her since that day.

"If that is true, Alfredo, you should avoid me. I don't know what love is. If you were to leave me now, you would not find it so difficult to forget me."

Violetta's casual air disturbed Alfredo, and he turned to go. "I will obey you and forget you, Mademoiselle. Good night."

Violetta removed the camellia from her hair. "Please take this flower. You can bring it back when it is faded. Tomorrow, perhaps." (Duet "Un di felice.")

Within moments he was gone, as were all the guests. The music had stopped, and the maid had put out all the candles. The first signs of dawn were appearing through the windows. More than an hour had passed, but Violetta Valery, the beautiful Lady of the Camellias, the most sought-after young woman in all of Paris, could not sleep. She quietly roamed through her apartment, glancing at a book here, a portrait of an old friend there, an empty wine glass, and the camellias, fading as the cool air of morning came in the windows. She thought of the opera and the ballet, of Flora and Gastone, of the old Baron, of many things, but always her mind came back to the intense young man, Alfredo, who had spoken of his love for her. Perhaps it was he

whose presence she had felt during those days of her last illness. Maybe he was the future she was hoping for, that strange mixture of sadness and happiness that love brought. (Aria "Ah, fors' è lui.")

"No! Thinking of him is madness," she said. "I want to live the rest of my life dancing and laughing! No mysteries, no heartaches." (Aria "Sempre libera.")

She pushed back the great lace curtains at the windows, and looked out into the gray-green dawn. She could see Alfredo, standing beneath her balcony, his eyes clear and bright in the shadows of the chestnut tree. He lifted the camellia she had given him in a gesture of tenderness, and walked away.

"I will think of him no more," Violetta decided, and she let the folds of the curtain fall back into place.

ACT II

BUT she did think of him and she did see him, again and again. And the more she saw of him the more she realized that her past life had been an empty one. Together they moved to a beautiful house, miles away from the din of Paris. They roamed through the fields and gardens, and the color came back to Violetta's cheeks.

Alfredo never forgot that she had given up all her wealthy admirers and her lavish parties to be with him, but since the day she had told him, "I want to live for you alone." he, too, had forgotten the rest of the world. (Aria "De' miei bollenti spiriti.")

He stood, now, thinking these thoughts. He was awakened from his reverie by the sound of footsteps coming into the room. It was Annina, Violetta's maid.

"Bonjour, Annina. Where have you been this beautiful day?"

"I have just come from Paris on an errand for my mistress."

Alfredo looked at her questioningly. "But why in Paris?"

The maid fumbled with the ribbon of her bonnet, and looked up. "I was disposing of all my mistresses' belongings. Her horses and carriages and her jewels." Alfredo was silent. "It is very expensive for the two of you to live here," she continued.

"How much is needed?" asked Alfredo.

"A thousand louis," said Annina.

"I am going to Paris myself!" said Alfredo. "I will take care of everything, and I want you to promise that you will not tell your mistress of our conversation." Annina nodded and Alfredo ran down the path, just as Violetta stepped out of the house.

Annina saw her watching his disappearing figure.

"The young master has left for Paris, and he asked me to tell you that he will return this evening."

How strange, thought Violetta. Why should he go to Paris today? She was interrupted by the gardener bringing her a letter from Flora. "So, Flora has discovered our hiding place." She laughed as she opened her letter. It was an invitation to a party at her house for this evening. Tossing the scented note on the white table, she smiled. "Flora will wait in vain for me to appear!"

"Mademoiselle Valery?" Violetta turned to see a stately, dignified man. He looked very serious behind his gray beard.

"I am she," she replied.

"And I am Alfredo's father."

Violetta motioned for him to be seated.

"Yes," he said, removing his gloves and placing them neatly on the table, "the father of that reckless young man who is headed for ruin—if he stays with you!"

"Allow me to leave you, Monsieur. This is my home   "

The elder Germont continued calmly. "He wants to give you all he owns."

"I would refuse it."

"But the luxury of this house . . ." said the old gentleman, looking about him. "It must take a fortune to keep up!"

"I am forfeiting all my possessions in Paris to keep this," Violetta answered. "My past life is no more. Now that I have Alfredo, it no longer exists."

"I ask you to do me a favor, Mademoiselle, a favor that you will understand."

Violetta sat in silence as he begged her to leave his son and never see him again. He told her the day would come when Alfredo would leave her. And he told her of Alfredo's younger sister, who could never marry while her brother was in the company of the famous Lady of the Camellias.

Violetta wept, because she knew that everything he said was true. Life was folly, after all. The beautiful courtesan wiped the tears from her eyes. "If you will embrace me as your daughter, I can be strong and do as you ask."

Touched by her generous spirit, Alfredo's father took her in his arms. "Your noble sacrifice will be rewarded some day." (Duet "Madamigella Valery?")

"You had better leave now," Violetta cautioned him, drawing away. "I hear someone coming."

"Farewell, dear lady," said the old man as he bowed low and kissed her hand. "I wish you great happiness, and I thank you for what you are about to do." He strode solemnly away. Hastily, Violetta wrote a note, then rang a tiny bell which brought Annina from the house.

"Go this instant, Annina, and deliver this message yourself. Hurry, or it will be too late." Violetta

had barely enough time to finish writing another letter when she saw Alfredo coming through the garden. Smiling bravely, she gave him the envelope, making him promise to read it, not now, but later. Violetta said, "I will always be near you, Alfredo. So always love me as I love you." She turned and ran away, leaving Alfredo silent and perplexed. The events that had occurred—Annina's trip to Paris, then a message from his father, who had evidently been here and gone, and now Violetta acting this way—had made it a strange day.

As he reached to pick up a camellia Violetta had left on the table, a voice asked, "Monsieur Germont?" A stranger quietly handed him a letter, saying, "A lady in a carriage gave me this message for you."

"Why should I tremble?" Alfredo thought, when he saw that the handwriting was Violetta's. But the contents verified his feelings of fright. She had gone away forever. He turned to find himself face to face with his father, who had returned. Alfredo embraced the white-haired old man and sat down, burying his face in his hands.

"Oh, Father, she has gone away."

"My son, do not weep," the elder Germont said. "Come back to Provence with me. You were happy there and will be again. We have all suffered since you went to Paris. Please come back to Provence." (Aria "Di Provenza il mar.")

Alfredo looked up and saw Flora's scented letter. So that was where Violetta had gone! Back to her green-and-gold salon and the pleasures of Paris! Ignoring his father's pleas, Alfredo rushed wildly back to the city.

ACT III

FLORA BERVOIX' apartment reflected her lighthearted, shallow personality. Everything was overdone; there was too much gold and there were too many candles. The air was thick with the smoke from her tiny black cigars, and heavy with the aroma of her very expensive perfume.

The Marquis, who frequented all Flora's parties, told her that Violetta and Alfredo had separated. This was surprising news, for just an hour ago Violetta had informed her that she would attend the party. Would she arrive with the Baron? Probably, said Flora to herself, as she walked toward the gaming table. When she saw Alfredo approaching her, she said, "You're quite free now, I see. Good, let us gamble for a while." Alfredo sat down and cut the cards.

Voices on the stairway made Flora turn around. Violetta was entering the room, and she was with the Baron! Flora went to greet them. "How nice that you have come, Violetta. I'm grateful to you, Baron, for bringing her," she said slyly.

Seeing Alfredo at the table angered the Baron and he gripped Violetta's arm tightly, whispering, "Not a word to that man, you understand?"

"I was foolish to have come," Violetta thought as she sat down beside Flora, who was already busily telling her all the latest gossip. Talking together, both of them could easily see what was going on at the gaming table. Alfredo was winning, time and time again. And he was also aware of Violetta's presence, for all his conversation was directed to her side of the room.

"Lucky at cards, unlucky in love," he remarked, putting up another stake. "I shall win again and return to the country."

"Alone?" asked Flora, tossing the words over her shoulder.

"No," answered Alfredo curtly, "with the one who ran away from me!"

The Baron, angered by the remark, walked over to the table and said sardonically, "You are in such good luck tonight, you tempt me to play."

"Please do, Baron. I accept your challenge," answered Alfredo without looking away from his cards. Lady Luck was kind and stayed with him, and in only minutes he had won many hundreds of louis from the Baron. Flora, however, broke into their game to announce that supper was about to be served in the dining room.

Minutes later Violetta re-entered the room, hoping that Alfredo would heed her invitation to follow her and talk with her while the others were dining. The sound of the closing door assured her that he had. She turned to see his young face, now filled with hatred.

"I am here. What do you want?"

"You must leave this place, Alfredo. You are in danger."

"Do you think I am a coward?" He looked at her, coldly observing everything—the emeralds in her hair and at her throat, and the camellias at her waist. "Any quarrel with the Baron could only end in a duel . . . in his death or in mine. And what do you care?"

"Listen to me, Alfredo. You must go!"

"I will go only if you follow me," he said, gently touching her arm.

"I cannot, dear Alfredo, for I have sworn an oath to stay away from you."

"Who could have forced you to do that?"

Violetta lowered her eyes and answered, "One who has the right to do so." Forcing her lips to continue, she listened to the words as they took shape, "It was the Baron."

Alfredo strode to the great French doors. Swinging them wide, he called everyone to come into the gaming room. As Flora and her guests listened in shocked surprise, Alfredo pointed to Violetta and told them that he was ready to repay her for all the wealth she had squandered on him. With tears of anger in his eyes, he flung a purse of gold coins at her feet. They clinked and rolled; then, like so many diamonds in the grass, they lay quietly around her pale, satin shoes. Trembling with fear and embarrassment, Violetta clutched at her throat and fell fainting into Flora's arms.

Alfredo, shocked by his own actions, could not move. Somewhere in all the confusion and noise he could hear voices. Was that the Baron's, challenging him to a duel? Was that his father's, saying, "Where is my son? I no longer see him in *this* man!" Was it Violetta's, sobbing, "You will never understand, Alfredo, that I have really loved you. Even when I am dead, I shall love you." The gold coins twisted and danced before his eyes. Then, blinded with tears, he left the room.

ACT IV

THE Lady of the Camellias grew increasingly ill after the events of that night. Each day, her illness was taking its toll of her great beauty. One by one, her shallow friends, who now saw her without money, deserted her. She was left alone with only her faithful Annina to care for her and to see that her beloved camellias were always on the table beside her bed. Piece by piece, the magnificent furnishings of Violetta's green-and-gold apartment were sold. The beautiful mirror that had reflected so many happy faces was gone, and the green velvet sofa had been sold just this morning.

"Let in some light, Annina. It is so dark in here," Violetta said, trying to get up. Obeying her mistress, Annina opened the shutters, and in doing so saw the doctor stepping from his carriage.

"Doctor Grenvil is here and, since you insist upon getting out of bed, at least let me help you to the couch." The doctor came into the green room just in time to assist the maid, for Violetta had no strength at all. Taking her pulse, he assured her that she was recovering and before long would be walking in the park. But to Annina he spoke more honestly. "She has only a few hours left. There is nothing more I can do."

Trying to hide her tears, Annina bid the doctor good day and turned to her mistress. "It is such a beautiful day, Mademoiselle. Listen to the sounds of laughter from the street. It's carnival time and there are harlequins and clowns dancing everywhere. Soon you will be able to join them."

"Dear, faithful Annina, heaven knows how many people are suffering in this world while it is carnival time in Paris. How much money is left in the bureau drawer?"

"Twenty louis, Mademoiselle," Annina answered.

"Give ten to the poor," Violetta said. "Nothing will happen to me while you're gone." When Annina left the room, Violetta opened a letter that she had kept hidden in the folds of her lace negligee and began to read. It was from Alfredo's father, telling her of the duel between the Baron and Alfredo and of his son's subsequent trip abroad. The elder Germont had also told his son that it was he who had made Violetta run away and that now Alfredo was returning to beg her forgiveness. "Too late," thought Violetta, as the sound of revelry rang up from the street. "Too late for me to be happy again. Everything is ended." (Aria "Addio! del passato.")

Annina rushed into the room, and with her words, "Alfredo is in Paris! He's on his way to see you!" Violetta's spirits soared. She struggled to rise to her feet, but fell into Annina's arms, weeping, "My camellias, bring some camellias for my hair. He cannot see me like this. I am so ugly."

A sudden, new feeling of life engulfed her as Alfredo dashed into the room, begging her to forgive him and telling her that soon they would leave Paris and spend the rest of their lives together.

"I am stronger. See, Alfredo, I am smiling again. Annina, help me to dress, for we are leaving Paris now." (Duet "Parigi, O cara.") But a sharp pain shot through her and she fell back upon the couch, gasping for air.

"Dear God, I cannot. I cannot move," she sobbed. "Oh, Alfredo, I am too young to die." She was still weeping in his arms when Alfredo's father appeared. The contrite old man knew now that he had misjudged the Lady of the Camellias and he, too, begged her to forgive him.

Violetta smiled and took a tiny portrait from the jewel box on the table. "Take this, Alfredo . . . it is of me as I used to be. Let it always remind you of me."

"No, you must not talk like that. You are going to live!"

"It is strange, but all my pain is gone," said Violetta as she tried to raise herself from the couch. With the false strength of one who is dying, she stood up, a radiant smile on her face. But as her arms reached out for Alfredo, she fell dead.

The sound of voices floated up from the street below, and as Alfredo lifted her frail body he saw a fragrant camellia with its green, waxen leaves clutched in her hand. Its tiny petals, crushed of life, fell on the floor.

Tristan and Isolde

BY

RICHARD WAGNER

(1813-1883)

LIBRETTO BY RICHARD WAGNER

Based on a Medieval Legend

CHARACTERS

Isolde .... *Soprano*
Brangäne .... *Mezzo-soprano*
Tristan .... *Tenor*
Kurvenal .... *Baritone*
King Marke .... *Bass*
Melot .... *Tenor*

Time: Middle Ages
Place: A ship; Cornwall; Brittany

First performance:

ROYAL COURT THEATRE

Munich

June 10, 1865

Tristan and Isolde was completed in 1859, but was not performed until 1865. Between 1862 and 1863 an attempt was made to produce it. It had at least fifty-four rehearsals in Vienna, but then it was abandoned. The reason given was that it was too difficult to do. Finally, with the help of King Ludwig II of Bavaria, Wagner's patron, it was performed in 1865 in Munich and was an artistic success.

The main source Wagner used for *Tristan and Isolde* was the thirteenth-century epic poem by Gottfried of Strassburg, which was based on an old, probably Celtic, legend.

ACT I

TRISTAN'S ship held its course on the calm sea. The mild, soft winds filled the sails until they were the shapes of huge, billowing clouds. The water was not so much blue as it was gray—probably because, even miles away from shore, it reflected the gray slate of the land and the majestic cliffs of Cornwall. The gray sea also reflected the orange of the sun. This warm color, combined with the gentleness of the winds, seemed strange indeed when compared to the cold and imperious coast line.

The song of a young sailor drifted to Isolde, the Princess of Ireland, who sat on a great oak bench in a pavilion near the bow of the ship. She listened to the words of the sailor's song about an Irish girl he had left at home, and she was angry. She was also angry with the sound of the waves against the side of the ship and the sound of the wind that speeded her journey to Cornwall and her husband-to-be, King Marke.

Her green eyes flashed like the gold rings around her long braids of red-orange hair. She turned to her lady-in-waiting, Brangäne, who was gazing at the sea, and impatiently asked, "Where are we, Brangäne?"

"Bands of purple and orange are rising in the western sky and the ship is forging ahead swiftly. By evening we will surely be in Cornwall."

"I will never put foot on that land!" said Isolde. "I would rather use the magic powers my mother gave me, and summon a great storm to shatter this ship and all of us!"

"Dearest mistress, why must you be strange and angry with me, your friend? Tell me about this fear that makes you rage and call upon the sea to destroy us all."

Isolde haughtily pushed the heavy fur rugs from the bench and ordered Brangäne to open the huge curtain that cut off the view of the ship from the pavilion. She gazed silently down the whole length of the ship. About the mainmast she could see the sailors busy with the ropes, and she could see the young knight Tristan, staring at the sea.

Turning to Brangäne, Isolde laughed as she asked, "What do you think of *him?* The hero who turns his eyes away from mine and looks at the sea."

"Are you speaking of Tristan, dear lady?"

"Yes. The great hero," Isolde answered scornfully. "Go, tell him to come to me. Tell him it is an order."

Brangäne obediently walked up the steps to the deck and hesitatingly made her way past the sailors to the stern. She spoke to Tristan as Isolde watched. Above the sound of the wind and the water and the creaking of the boards as they strained against the sea, Isolde could hear the conversation. Then Kurvenal, Tristan's faithful servant, joined his master and told Brangäne that Tristan did not obey a woman. Tristan, Kurneval continued, was the hero who killed the Irish lord Morold, who was Isolde's fiancé, when Morold came to Cornwall to collect taxes. Then Tristan sent Morold's head back to Ireland. Isolde could see that her wish to talk with Tristan was not to be granted. Enraged, she threw herself on the couch and waited for Brangäne's return. Brangäne drew the curtain behind her as she entered the pavilion and knelt at her mistress' side.

"Tristan says he cannot leave the helm. If he should, how could he pilot the ship and you in safety to King Marke?"

"Tell me no more, Brangäne," Isolde said. "I have heard all the words myself." Like a caged animal, she walked about the pavilion, looking at the rich tapestries hanging on the walls. The scenes of court life, the silver swords and orange mantles of the nobility, and the blue eyes of all the figures did not please her. Their vivid colors and stormy scenes reminded her of Tristan and the day she had first seen him.

She had found him just a year ago wounded and dying, in a little skiff by the seashore. She had tended him faithfully and brought him back to life.

"Brangäne," Isolde said, speaking as in a dream, "you do not know the story of Tristan, do you? He said that he was a harper and that his name was

'Tantris,' but I discovered that he was Tristan, the knight who had murdered my betrothed."

Brangäne looked at her mistress questioningly. Isolde continued, "How did I discover his true identity? While the knight was sleeping, I picked up his sword and saw that the nick in it fitted evenly with the sliver of metal I had found in Morold's head when he was mortally wounded. A voice within me told me to avenge Morold's death and to kill Tristan!" Isolde turned away and hid her face in her hands. In the tapestry behind Brangäne she saw Tristan's eyes as she had that first day, blue and helpless. Unable to kill him, she had dropped his sword and prayed that when he was fully recovered he would leave Ireland and never trouble her again.

Brangäne interrupted her thoughts. "How blind I have been, dear lady, not to have seen your reason for being angered."

"And now, Brangäne," said Isolde, weeping, "after all his promises and oaths of gratitude, he has come back to take me to his uncle, to be the old man's wife!"

Raising her arm in Tristan's direction, she cursed him wildly. She cursed the day he had killed Morold, for, by killing him, Cornwall was free forever from Ireland. Her rage mounted as she realized again that now she was being brought as tribute from Ireland to Cornwall's king. "Death to us all!" she sobbed, as she violently pulled one of the heavy tapestries from the wall. It lay on the floor like a shattered dream, a mass of haunted figures in red and orange and gold.

Brangäne drew Isolde to the couch. "Dear lady," she said, "this is false anger. Sir Tristan pays you a great compliment by making you the Queen of Cornwall. King Marke is a fine and noble man, and you should be happy with this marriage."

She bent over her mistress, whispering, "Remember that your mother has taken care of everything." She went to the trunk near the couch and returned with a small golden box. "Your mother prepared all the magic potions in here. There is a balm for pain, one for wounds, and there are antidotes for great poisons. And here," she picked out a tiny vial and held it up, "here is the greatest potion of them all, the magic potion of love."

"No, Brangäne, you are wrong. I have marked the greatest one myself!" Isolde seized another vial and held it close to Brangäne's face.

"But, lady, that is the poison of death!" she said, recoiling in horror. Isolde dropped the vial into the box, for the sound of seamen's voices aloft made her realize that they were nearing Cornwall.

Kurvenal blustered down the steps and announced that the women should prepare to disembark. His crude manner offended the Princess Isolde, but she spoke to him with great dignity.

"Mark me well, Kurvenal, and tell your master my words as I speak them to you. Tell him that I will not leave this ship until he has come to me so I may forgive him for all his past offenses. He must have my pardon before he escorts me to the King."

Kurvenal lumbered up the stairs, and Isolde went to the gold casket and removed the bottle she had marked. "Brangäne, take this and pour it into the golden goblet. I shall drink a pledge of truce with Sir Tristan. My mother has remembered me well by sending these draughts with us."

Obeying her mistress, Brangäne took the vial and walked to the back of the pavilion just as Kurvenal was heard announcing the arrival of Tristan. The Princess moved slowly toward the couch and leaned against the head of it. Its four massive pillars had been carved to represent four angry and forbidding lions' heads, whose eyes stared coldly at the entrance to the pavilion. Their eyes were blank and oaken, but Isolde's were green and vengeful as she watched the curtain swing back and she heard Tristan's voice.

"What is your command?" he asked.

"You know, Tristan, that I have sworn vengeance for Morold, and at his death I vowed if no man would clear his name and honor, I would."

"If Morold was so dear to you," Tristan said calmly, "then take my sword and kill me now."

Isolde smiled and answered, "What would the great King Marke think of me if I were to kill his most trusted knight? In me you are bringing the greatest pledge of truce possible between our countries. Sheathe your sword, and we shall drink a pledge of truce!"

Isolde signaled impatiently to Brangäne to bring the golden goblet. Believing that it held the deathly poison, Isolde offered the goblet to Tristan. He looked at her and spoke. His words voiced none of his suspicions. "My oath of truce between us I swear to you, Isolde. I drink to peace and to the end of haunted dreams and endless sorrow."

The Princess wrested the goblet from his hand, saying, "And half is for me, dear Tristan. Betrayer, I drink to you!"

Each had expected the drink to be poison, but the liquid did not course through their veins with fiery devastation. Instead, the warm sweet brew engulfed them both in a rapturous feeling of radiant joy. Isolde felt all her hatred slip away, fade and die. And she saw Tristan's eyes, full of love, just as they were on that day when he lay wounded, the day she had really fallen in love with him. Isolde placed her hand in his and said, "I have won you now, Tristan."

"And I have won Isolde the Fair," Tristan answered.

They stood motionless and oblivious to the

sounds from the shore. The curtains of the pavilion swung wide, disclosing the knights of the court, and looming ominously ahead, the cold gray castle of Tintagel!

Brangäne placed Isolde's flaming orange cape about her mistress' shoulders, urging her to hurry, for the King was coming.

Tristan stared dazedly at the shore, saying, "The King? What King?"

"Brangäne, why are they cheering?" Isolde asked. "Am I alive?"

"Yes, dear child. I gave you the draught of love—not the poison."

Isolde turned in terror to Tristan, as the people of Cornwall swarmed on board and surrounded them. In the confusion, the gold goblet that Isolde had thrown to the floor rolled across the polished planks and rested in the folds of her cape. It blazed and shimmered as the sun set behind the gray cliffs.

ACT II

ISOLDE was married to King Marke, but his kind and gentle ways and his deep devotion to her could never erase the great love she felt for Tristan. The magic potion had been their doom.

One night when the mists had lifted and the stars were looking down at Tintagel for the first time in many months, the courtier Melot and the King decided to go into the forest to hunt wild boar.

"Can you hear the sounds of the hunting horns?" Isolde asked Brangäne.

"They are still very near," Brangäne answered.

"Fear makes you hear strange sounds, Brangäne. It is not the sound of the horns. It is only the laughing of the branches in the wind." Isolde smiled and drew a pale-orange scarf about her shoulders. "It is so quiet, I can hear the water in the well. Tristan is waiting out there in the night, Brangäne. Let us signal him to come to the castle."

"Yes, Tristan is waiting, but so is a spy! You do not recall, but I remember well the day we arrived here. I remember well how Melot saw more than anyone else. Even now, he is listening at the gray doors of the castle. Haven't you noticed that he never allows you or Tristan out of his sight?"

"Dear Brangäne, Melot is Tristan's most faithful friend."

"Heed my warning, my Queen, Melot is sowing seeds of evil."

Isolde grasped her lady-in-waiting's hand, begging her to extinguish the great torch that flamed near the foot of the steps—the signal that all was safe for Tristan to appear.

"I beg you to let the torch burn tonight," Brangäne said as she peered into the black forest.

"You are foolish and afraid, Brangäne. Go and watch from the top of the castle. I will put out the torch myself."

Reluctantly, Brangäne turned and slowly walked away. Isolde looked at the light and for a moment watched the orange flames, tipped with red, as they curled and flickered in the summer air. The gray smoke rising from the fiery fringe reminded her of the sea mists that left their damp sadness on all of Tintagel. She threw the torch to the ground and watched it sputter and die. She looked down the long avenue of trees for Tristan. It was quiet, very quiet. She could see nothing. Nobody. Taking her scarf from her shoulders, she ran to the stairway, and leaning over the wall, waved the long strands. The moon came out from behind the clouds, transforming Isolde's scarf into a streak of orange flame in the night. She looked up and saw Brangäne silently looking out into the darkness, her figure silhouetted against the moon. Looking down the row of trees again, Isolde saw Tristan running to her at last.

"Oh, Tristan, you have been away so long," the Queen said as the knight reached her side.

"The torch kept burning such a long time. I thought the sun had forgotten to set."

"The light has always been our enemy," Isolde said, sitting down on a stone bench beneath a massive tree. "I have loved you, Tristan, since the first day I saw you, wounded on the beach, with the early morning sun shining in your face."

Tristan sat next to her, his arm around her.

"Now we are in the safety of the night for a while." Tristan drew her to him. "I wish the night would let us forget the day."

"I would like to dream and never waken," Isolde said, rising and walking farther into the garden.

From the tower, Brangäne watched them as she listened for the sound of the huntsmen, returning from the forest. The moon disappeared and the gray fingers of dawn were appearing on the horizon. The mists were rising again and the figures of Tristan and Isolde were almost obscured from her sight.

"Let me die now," Tristan said, resting his head on Isolde's arm.

"We are bound together, Tristan, and will be freed only by death," Isolde answered. "It would be better to die this way together, than live as we must, apart.

Brangäne called down from the tower. "Take care, it will soon be daylight."

"Shall I listen to her?" Tristan asked.

Isolde smiled. "Let us listen only to the night, for the daylight will bring us more unhappiness. Let us think of the death that night will bring us. The glorious death that will release us from this life away from each other." (Duet "O sink hernieder.")

As they kissed, Brangäne screamed from the castle and Kurvenal rushed into the garden, shouting, "Tristan, save yourself!" But it was too late. King Marke and Melot had returned, and now stood before the young lovers. Isolde turned and hid her face in shame, and Tristan tried to shield her with his cape.

The old King was stunned and speechless. Melot spoke. "You see, my lord, my accusations were right."

The King raised his hand for silence. Perplexed and hurt, he leaned upon his huge sword. "Oh, Tristan," he said, "how could you betray me so? You, who have been so faithful to me. You, who won the beautiful Isolde for me. How could you wound me like this?"

Tristan looked up at the sad old monarch. "I cannot answer you, my King."

Turning to Isolde, Tristan asked, "Will you follow me into a land where there is no sun; where there is only the night we have longed for?"

"I followed you from Ireland. I will follow you anywhere."

Tristan bent down and kissed her on the forehead. Melot started forward, drawing his sword and crying, "You traitor!"

Tristan turned quickly, his sword in his hand, shouting, "Who will risk his life against me?" But as Melot thrust his sharp blade at him, Tristan let his own sword fall, leaving himself open to the full impact of the villainous Melot's blow. Isolde fell sobbing at Tristan's feet.

Brangäne led the weeping Queen into the castle and Kurvenal carried his mortally wounded master out of the garden to the harbor. As the sun rose higher and higher, the young knight and his faithful servant sailed away from the gray cliffs of Cornwall to Brittany.

ACT III

AT HOME again in the castle of his ancestors, Tristan lay dying. The fortress and its gardens gave the impression of being ownerless. Everything was dilapidated and badly kept, and gray-green roots and leaves reached out and strangled anything that lay in their path. The days came and went, endless and lonely. The wound from Melot's sword refused to heal and Tristan grew so weak that he was unable to move. Kurvenal placed him in the shade, beneath the branches of an old lime tree where, if he should waken, he could look out onto the sea, the gray sea that separated him from his beloved.

At last the melancholy wail of a shepherd's pipe awakened Tristan. He called to Kurvenal, "Where am I?"

"Where are you? You are in safety. Don't you recognize your father's castle?"

"Did I hear music?" Tristan asked, trying to raise himself.

"Yes, you heard the shepherd's pipe. He is over there on the hill, feeding your sheep."

"My sheep?" Tristan asked, rubbing his eyes.

"Your sheep, my lord."

"I have been asleep so long that I remember nothing but the name Isolde. When will she put out the torch and come to me, Kurvenal?"

His servant tried to calm Tristan by assuring him that she was on the way. "You sometimes hold me as a fool, Tristan, but today you will see that I am right. She will arrive. Days ago I sent a message to Cornwall, asking her to come. She is the only one who can heal the wound and make you well again."

The knight drew Kurvenal to him and embraced him. "Faithful friend, how can I ever thank you? You who have been my protector and have been by my side in battle, now you bring Isolde to me."

Tristan turned and stared wildly at the sea. "I see it! I see it! The flag waving from the masthead of her ship! Don't you see it, Kurvenal?"

Shading his eyes from the sun, Kurvenal looked ahead. "There is no ship in sight, Tristan."

Tristan fell back on his couch, dreaming of Isolde. He dreamed of the day they had met and of the magic potion. Visions of golden goblets and flashing swords raced through his brain. He saw the white-capped waves and Isolde's ship on the horizon. Isolde's red-orange hair blazed in the sun. He awoke crying, "Don't you see her, Kurvenal? Go to the turret of the castle. Bring her to me!"

Kurvenal ran to the watchtower, for now the shepherd was signaling that a ship had been sighted. "You are right, my lord. A ship is nearing from the north. The flag is at the masthead."

"Can you see her?"

"No, just now the ship is hidden by the rocks beyond the reef. But have no fear, one of the best of seamen is at the helm."

Tristan struggled to get up but he was too weak.

"They've passed the reef and are safely coming in to shore, and—yes, I do see Isolde!"

"Hurry, Kurvenal! Bring her to me!" Kurvenal ran down the rocky steps to the sea, and Tristan was alone. He staggered up from his bed and tore the bandage from his body. He fell to the ground sobbing, "Only Isolde can heal me now. Isolde!"

Tristan could hear Isolde's voice, and he tried vainly to crawl across the gnarled roots and the dying leaves to meet her as she ran up the crooked steps from the sea. But he had time only to speak her name before he fell dead in her arms.

Kurvenal, who had assisted Isolde up the perilous path from the shore, saw his master die, and in his anguish he mistook the sound of voices coming from the harbor for those of an enemy. Melot must be there, he thought. Calling for the shepherd to assist him, he ran down the steps to defend his master and the castle. At the foot of the cliff he saw Melot with King Marke and Brangäne, and he struck Melot down without a word.

"Kurvenal, Kurvenal, you must be mad! You mistake us all," Brangäne said, looking anxiously about for Isolde.

"Hold back!" roared King Marke. But Kurvenal paid no attention to him, and in the foray was deeply wounded by the King's guard.

Death was everywhere. Tristan was dead. Melot and Kurvenal were dead, and Brangäne looked at Isolde who appeared as dead, her face on the ground against Tristan's.

"Dear lady," Brangäne moaned, "it was I who told the King of the magic potion, and he followed you here. But only to forgive Tristan and you!"

The King touched Isolde gently, beseeching her to understand his reason for coming. "I did not mean to bring this death, Isolde. I came to give you to Tristan in marriage."

But Isolde did not hear his words, for her eyes were drawn to Tristan's and to the glow of the sun that surrounded his body.

"You see, he is smiling now. Look, my friends, his heart is beating again. Do you hear the music, Brangäne?" (Aria "Liebestod")

Brangäne could not, but from the ocean and the sky came the music of a choir of trumpets. The mist from the sea rose, softly swirling, enveloping the rocks and the castle. Isolde quietly placed her orange scarf over Tristan's body and smiled at the sun. As death overtook her, too, she fell on Tristan's body, and the King raised his hand in a blessing on the dead. She felt the warmth of the sun drawing her spirit away with Tristan's beyond the gray cliffs of Cornwall to the night behind the sun.

IL TROVATORE

THE TROUBADOUR

BY GIUSEPPE VERDI

(1813–1901)

Libretto by Salvatore Cammarano

BASED ON THE PLAY *EL TROVADOR,*

BY ANTONIO GARCIA GUTIERREZ

FERRANDO	. . . .	BASS
LEONORA	. . . .	SOPRANO
INEZ	. . . .	SOPRANO
MANRICO	. . . .	TENOR
COUNT DI LUNA	. . . . . .	BARITONE
RUIZ	. . . .	TENOR
AZUCENA	. . . .	MEZZO-SOPRANO

TIME: FIFTEENTH-CENTURY SPAIN

PLACE: BISCAY; ARAGON

FIRST PERFORMANCE: TEATRO APOLLO, ROME;
January 19, 1853

Il Trovatore is one of Verdi's most popular operas. The first night it was performed, in Rome, the Tiber River was flooding its banks, but the weather did not dim the enthusiasm of the opening-night audience.

It has been said that the libretto for *Il Trovatore* is confusing and absurd, but its beautiful melodies has kept the opera in public favor.

ACT I

THE black night hung heavily over the palace of Aliaferia. The noises of the border war between Aragon and Biscay were momentarily stilled, and only the usual sounds disturbed the palace and its gardens. No one roamed the formal paths or touched the black-green hedges that were trimmed in intricate geometrical designs. As it neared midnight, the soldiers and servants of the Count di Luna paced the hall in front of their master's room. Some of them leaned against the walls, and Ferrando, the captain of the guard, urged them not to fall asleep.

"Look sharp there! You know that the Count may return any second. And after these nightly watches at his beloved's balcony he returns in strange, jealous moods. He fears that he has a rival in the troubadour who sings every night in Leonora's garden," Ferrando said.

The men grumbled and rubbed their eyes. Several of them walked over to the captain and asked him to tell them the real story about Carzia, the Count's brother. Ferrando made sure that no one was entering the great hall before motioning to the men to gather around him.

"Well, in happier times there lived a proud father who had two sons. The second boy's faithful nurse slept next to the child's cradle every night. But one morning when she awoke she saw an ugly gypsy woman leaning over the baby. The hag was wearing the symbols of a sorceress. The nurse screamed out in terror and soon the servants rushed in and dragged the witch out."

The candles grew dimmer and the men huddled together, hanging on Ferrando's every word. "The gypsy claimed that she only wanted to chart the child's horoscope, but she was lying! She had bewitched the boy, and day by day he grew weaker and weaker." The captain leaned close to one of the younger soldiers whose eyes were wide with fear. "But the witch was pursued and captured. They burned her at the stake! The story goes that the gypsy's daughter then stole the child, and later the family found the boy's skeleton at the same spot where the witch had been burned."

"What happened to the father?" the young soldier asked.

"His remaining days were few and sorrowful. Yet he never gave up the hope that his boy was still alive and he made his oldest son, our master, Count di Luna, swear that he would never stop searching for him."

"Was there ever any news of the gypsy girl?" the soldiers asked.

"None. But it is common belief that the ghost of her mother still roams this world in many shapes." (Aria "Di due figli vivea.")

"It's true," shouted one of the men. "Sometimes she changes into a screech owl . . . or a raven. You can see her flying through the night like an arrow."

"She does, and I have seen her," Ferrando said. "It was just as midnight was striking . . ." Just as suddenly the black bell of the church began to strike the hour of twelve and a gust of cold night wind blew through the hall, extinguishing most of the candles. The soldiers and servants jumped to their feet, afraid perhaps that the witch was among them. But their curses against her were drowned out by the relentless striking of the bell.

(SCENE 2) The beautiful Leonora, so beloved of Count di Luna, was a titled lady-in-waiting to the Queen of Aragon, and, indeed, di Luna had reason for being jealous. Every night Leonora and her companion, Inez, walked in the gardens of the Aliaferia Palace, hoping to hear the troubadour's song. As she strolled down the long paths, Inez broke the silence. "Why should we stay here any longer? It's late and the Queen is asking for you."

Leonora turned and looked at her. "We must stay. I cannot bear another night without seeing him. Since that day of the tournament, when I first saw him, I have been unable to forget him. Do you remember how he was the victor in all the events, and how I placed the crown on his head?" She sighed. "The civil war broke out and I never saw him again. But then . . ."

"What happened?"

"It was a quiet night . . . like tonight. But that evening the moon came out from behind the clouds. I listened to the songs of a troubadour, and in every song I heard my name . . . *my* name. I ran out to the balcony, and it was he!"

"It frightens me," Inez said as she looked about the garden.

"I can never forget him. I'd even die for him." (Aria "Tacea la notte placida.")

Inez put her hand to Leonora's lips. "I pray that one who loves that way will never have to regret it," she said, and led Leonora into the palace.

Coming down the path, di Luna could see them clearly as they went up the marble steps to the Queen's apartment. He was determined that, as soon as the Queen was asleep, he would confront Leonora and tell her of his great love for her. As he walked toward the steps, he heard the sound of the troubadour's song. He stopped, trembling with rage. He could see Leonora, coming into the garden. Di Luna wrapped his cloak about him and waited where he stood as Leonora ran toward him.

She cried out in excitement, "It is so late. I've been counting the minutes."

But the singing stopped, and as she stood before the Count she heard only the word, "Faithless!" as it rang out from a shadowy figure standing in the dark of the trees.

The moon came out from the clouds and struck the troubadour's silver visor. The darkness had deceived her, and now she was able to recognize both the men. She threw herself at the singer's feet. "I thought that I was speaking to you. You know that I love you!"

"If you are not a coward, reveal yourself," the Count demanded.

The troubadour lifted the visor of his helmet. "I am Manrico."

"You fool!" roared di Luna, reaching for his sword. "You dare to approach these royal grounds when you are sentenced to death for treason?"

"Why delay?" asked Manrico. "Call your guards and hand your rival over to the executioner."

"No. I will be the one to draw your blood . . ."

Leonora held out her long white hand to the irate Count. "At least for a moment be reasonable. I am the cause of all your anger. I am the guilty one. Kill me; I cannot love you."

Manrico stepped between them. "His anger is useless. He is the one who will die!" Leonora heard the sound of sword against sword and saw the wings of a black raven against the moon. Then she fell to the ground and remembered no more. (Trio "Di geloso amor sprezzato.")

ACT II

DAWN broke over the mountains of Biscay, and the sun crept down into the gypsy camp. Its rays of red and orange mingled with the flames of the great fire that was still burning. The flames

seemed to hypnotize Azucena, an old gypsy, who stared into them oblivious to everyone around her—even Manrico. Lying near her, he, too, seemed hypnotized, but not by the flames. He was staring at his sword which he held tightly in his hands. Azucena was unaware of even the happy songs of the other gypsies as they awoke and went to their forges to begin the day's work. Not even the loud, rhythmic swing of their hammers and their resounding clang against the forges stirred her from her dreaming at the fire. (Anvil Chorus)

As the flames crackled and soared, she relived her life. And as her past came back to her she began to talk aloud. "The mob ran to the fire! The flames rose about her and the vengeful crowd screamed with approval." She reached out to the flames, almost touching them with her gnarled hands. "The echo of her death still repeats itself from hill to hill!" (Aria "Stride la vampa.")

"Your song is a sad one, old woman," some of the gypsies who had gathered around her said.

"Just as sad as the story that inspired it," she replied. Turning to Manrico, she whispered, "Avenge me . . . avenge me!" Manrico looked into her dark eyes and wondered why she always repeated that mysterious phrase. But Azucena said no more and quietly returned to staring into the flames as the gypsies left the camp to find some food in one of the nearby villages.

Manrico put his sword aside and moved closer to Azucena. "Now that they have gone, tell me the horrible story that brings you so much pain."

The old gypsy rested her face in her hands and began to speak.

"The story is about your grandmother's death. She was burned at the stake . . . there, where that fire is burning now. She was accused by a haughty Count of having bewitched his son. She was burned there!" Manrico stepped back in horror.

"She was led to the stake . . . I was following her, carrying my baby in my arms. . . . All I could hear were my mother's cries of 'Avenge me. . . .' "

"And did you avenge her?" Manrico asked.

Azucena did not even look up. "I managed to steal the Count's son and I dragged him to the fire. The flames were burning brightly and in a moment of madness I pushed the child in." With a shudder Azucena fell back. "But then I looked around, and the Count's son was still at my side. I had destroyed my own child!" (Aria "Condotta ell'era in ceppi.")

The fire had gone out and she sank to the ground, wailing. Then, as if her madness had returned, she hysterically pushed aside imaginary flaming logs in a futile attempt to save her child again, but now only the black earth and smoking ashes fell through her fingers.

Manrico was silent and astonished. Then, kneeling

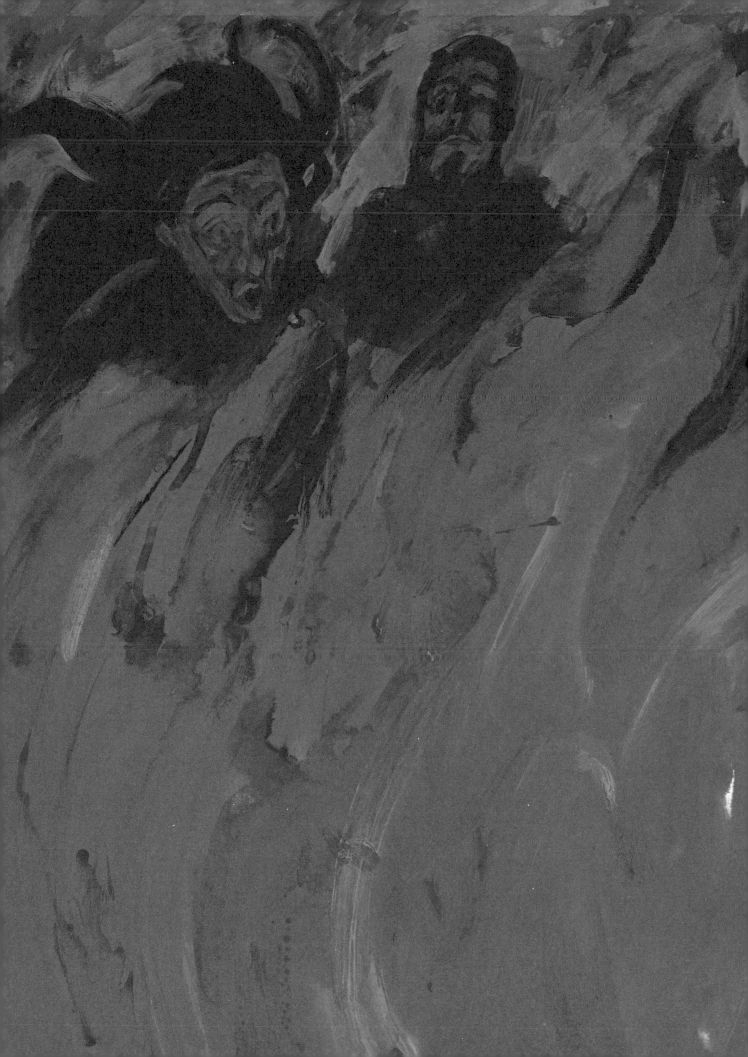

at her side, he asked, "If I am not your son, who am I?"

Azucena rubbed her eyes with her blackened hands. "You *are* my son!"

"But you said . . ."

"Perhaps I did. When the terrible memory comes back to me, foolish words come to my lips. Haven't I always been a mother to you?"

Manrico smiled. "I can never deny that."

Azucena looked deep into his eyes. "If you are alive today, you owe it to me. Didn't I come to the battlefield of Petilla to find you and nurse you back to health?"

"Yes," Manrico said with pride, "I stood before di Luna while thousands retreated. I fell before him, but I fell like a strong man."

Azucena laughed in an ugly way. "Yes, that was the thanks he gave for the pity you showed him in that duel in the gardens of Aliaferia. What ever kept you from killing him that night?"

Manrico turned away. "I cannot explain the strange pity I felt for him. There is no explanation." (Aria "Mal reggendo.")

"A strange pity . . . a strange pity," Azucena mumbled, looking back into the fire. "If you fight the evil man again, kill him. Tell me that you will do as I bid you?"

Manrico picked up his sword. "I swear it. This blade will cut into his wicked heart."

They both turned, listening to the sound of a horn that echoed down the mountainside. "It is only Ruiz, sending the usual messenger," Manrico said, and he blew his horn in answer.

Azucena was lost again in the pageant of the dead fire before her and kept murmuring, "Avenge me, avenge me."

Ruiz' messenger ran up to Manrico and waited as the troubadour read the letter he had brought. "Castellor is in our hands. You are to supervise its defense. Upon receiving this, immediately hurry here. This evening, deceived by the news of your death, Leonora is taking the veil at the Convent of the Holy Cross."

Azucena turned and saw the look of anguish on Manrico's face. "What is it?"

"Hurry down the hill and prepare a horse for me," Manrico told the messenger.

The old gypsy woman tried to block Manrico's way. "What do you want to do? You are still ill from your wounds."

"Nothing will stop me from going to Leonora," Manrico said as he put on his helmet and cloak.

He quickly embraced the old woman and ran down the hill. Azucena watched him go and turned again to the smoking embers. Some tiny flames were not dead. They still sputtered and licked at the remaining bits of wood. She watched them curling

upward in the morning sun. Pushing her dirty gray hair back under her black head scarf, she sat down and waited. The black ravens in the trees watched and waited, too.

(SCENE 2) The moon crept behind the clouds as Count di Luna and Ferrando entered the courtyard of the convent. Observing that not a single member of the cloister was about, di Luna felt more at ease.

"This is a bold and dangerous thing that we are about to do," his captain commented.

"Bold, yes," said di Luna, "but my love for Leonora demands it. I thought with Manrico dead, all obstacles were past. Now, she chooses the convent! But she is *mine,* and I will not let the church claim her!" (Aria "Il balen.") The bell in the chapel began to toll.

"The services are about to begin." Ferrando said.

The Count nodded. "Before she reaches the altar we will seize her. Go, take your men into the shadows. Hide yourselves." As they all moved into the black, cavernous shadows of the tall poplar trees, the sound of nuns' voices wafted out into the courtyard. From his hiding place the Count could see Leonora and Inez as they walked slowly in the file of nuns.

"Why are you weeping, Inez?" Leonora asked.

"Because you are leaving us forever."

"Dry your eyes, Inez. I must turn to Him now. There is no longer any hope or laughter here on earth. Manrico is dead and gone forever, but one day I may meet him in the land of the blessed. Now, lead me to the altar."

"No!" di Luna shouted as he appeared from the shadows.

Inez drew Leonora to her to try to protect her as Manrico and Ruiz with their men pushed open the great iron gates and swarmed into the courtyard.

"Can I believe this?" Leonora said. "It is surely a dream . . . or am I in heaven?"

The Count and his followers were outnumbered. But he shouted, "If you want to live, Manrico, then flee from her and from me!"

"God confounds the wicked," Manrico answered, "and God has saved me from the dead."

Ferrando turned to his master. "You're fighting against fate."

Manrico took Leonora's hand. "Come, follow me."

"You dare to try and steal her from me?" di Luna roared, drawing his sword. But he was disarmed by Ruiz and his men, and his struggling, wild fury was to no avail.

"Surrender now while fate is smiling on you," Ruiz said as the Count retreated. There was a flurry of black and white as the nuns ran into the convent. Manrico and Leonora ran from the courtyard.

ACT III

THE red and black banners of Count di Luna's military camp waved defiantly in the wind. The Count's soldiers, brave with the assurance of added reinforcements, were anxious to start the attack on Castellor. Ferrando walked among his men, spreading the word that their commander planned to storm the castle at dawn. As he watched, its dazzling walls changed color, from dust-red to a leaden hue. "There are spoils *there,*" Ferrando told the soldiers, "so win them and they will be ours!"

The Count came out of his tent and looked up at the castle, too, thinking all the while that Leonora was there and that with the dawn he would take her from Manrico.

Ferrando returned from investigating a disturbance on the outskirts of the camp. "A gypsy was roaming near here and she has been captured," he said.

"Have you seen her?" di Luna asked.

"No, but the guards are bringing her here."

"What wrong have I done?" wailed Azucena as she was dragged before the Count.

"Where have you come from?" the Count demanded.

"I don't know," the old woman answered. "It is the gypsy custom to wander without a plan. The sky is her roof and the world her country."

"Where have you come from?" di Luna repeated.

"From Biscay. The mountains there were my home."

Ferrando watched her closely, for her face seemed to be familiar.

"Were you in those mountains for a long time?" the Count asked. "Do you recall the son of a Count who was stolen from his castle?"

"Who are you?" asked Azucena, pulling away from the guards.

"The stolen boy's brother," shouted di Luna. "Did you ever hear of him?"

"Never . . . let me go now and find my own son."

"Wait!" said Ferrando, grabbing her tattered shawl. "She's the *one,* the one who committed the horrible deed . . . the one who burned the child."

"Oh, Manrico, why don't you come to save your mother?" wept Azucena.

"Manrico's mother!" laughed the Count. "What luck!"

Azucena struggled with the ropes that bound her. "You are more wicked than your wicked father. Beware, for there is a God who helps the helpless . . . that God will punish you!"

"Through me my brother's death will be avenged," snarled di Luna.

The soldiers swarmed around the old gypsy as Ferrando told her of the pyre they would build for her. "In a little while you will feel the earthly flames, Azucena, and also the flames of hell. Even your soul will suffer and burn!"

Azucena pulled herself away from the guards and spat at him, but they quickly forced her back and pulled her away. Di Luna and Ferrando looked up at Castellor and at the red and black banners still dancing in the wind. As they went into the Count's tent they failed to see the huge black bird that soared in the sky. They thought its errie sound was only another of the gypsy's cries for help.

(SCENE 2) The great black creature flew up and past the castle, but was unseen by Leonora and Manrico. Looking toward the window of the balcony, Leonora asked, "What was that sound of arms I heard a moment ago?"

"It is vain to pretend that our danger is not great," Manrico answered. "We'll be attacked before dawn tomorrow, but we will be the victors."

Leonora sighed. "What a grim light to have shining on our wedding."

"Rid yourself of such forebodings, beloved. Your love has made me stronger. But even if it is my destiny to die, my thoughts will be with you." She put her head against his shoulder and listened to the quiet strains from the organ in the castle chapel. (Aria "Ah si, ben mio.")

Ruiz rushed into the room and drew Manrico to the balcony. "Look . . . the gypsy in chains! Those barbarians have already lighted the pyre."

"Oh, dear God!" said Manrico as he leaned against the iron rail of the balcony and peered down into the valley. "My legs fail me . . . my eyes are clouding over."

"You're raving," Leonora said, putting her arm about him.

"I should!" he said. "I'm her son! Ruiz, get our men together. Hurry. Put out that fire or *I* shall with your blood," he screamed in the direction of di Luna's tent.

He heard Leonora weeping and turned to her. "Before I loved you, I was already her son. Even your suffering cannot keep me here, Leonora. I must save my mother—or at least die with her." (Aria "Di quella pira.")

"It would have been better for all of us to have died long ago," Leonora said as she walked slowly into the room. Manrico, however, could think of nothing but saving Azucena, and Leonora's sobbing was lost in the cries of "To arms! To arms!" Manrico and Ruiz dashed from the room, as from the courtyard below the sounds of war rumbled and clanged. In the valley a raven was circling and circling the curling smoke from the flaming pyre that waited for Azucena.

ACT IV

AS FERRANDO had told his men, Castellor would and did fall to Count di Luna. Manrico was captured, but Leonora and Ruiz were not to be found. The Count never suspected that either of them had the daring or the courage to return to Aliaferia in an attempt to save Manrico. But they did.

Leonora looked up at the tower of the prison with its iron bars, and drew her black mantilla around her. "Leave me now, Ruiz. And do not fear for me. I can save him and I am protected." Her eyes were fixed on the onyx and gold ring on her right hand. When Ruiz had gone, she leaned against the cold stones of the wall and called upon the winds of night to carry her words of love to Manrico. (Aria "D'amor sull' ali rosee.") She started up in panic as the sound of some monks praying for Manrico interrupted her thoughts.

"I can hardly breathe," she said aloud. "Is my heart beating?" She moved back into the shadows, hoping that her terror would subside.

High in the tower she could now hear Manrico's voice calling her name. "Do not forget me, Leonora. Farewell." (Aria "Ah! che la morte ognora.")

"Forget," she breathed; "I will save your life with mine!" She remained hidden in the blackness as a door opened and she saw di Luna just a few steps away from her.

"At dawn the son goes to the block and the mother to the stake," he ordered his retainers as they walked into the tower. He looked into the night and wondered aloud, "Where could Leonora

be? All our searching has been in vain. Where are you?" he said, shaking his fist at some imaginary being.

"I am here before you."

"You? Why have you come here?"

Leonora moved out of the darkness. "His last hour is approaching and you ask me that? I have come to ask for mercy."

"Mercy for him? You're mad!" Di Luna was enraged. "The more you love him, the more I shall torture him. No price will save him." He pushed her aside.

Leonora let the black lace fall away from her face, and held out her hand sadly. "If he goes free, I will stay with you. Let him see me and hear me. Let him escape and I will marry you."

"Swear to it!" di Luna said, holding her face in his hands.

"I swear it before God."

Di Luna called to a guard, and as he whispered to him Leonora put the black ring to her lips and drained its contents.

Turning to her he said, "He shall live!"

Leonora looked up at him with tears of joy in her eyes. "My heart gives thanks to you. Now, fearless with joy, I can await the end."

"Do not whisper, Leonora. Tell me again that you will be mine. Remember that you have sworn."

"My word is sacred," she answered. "Let us go."

She shuddered as di Luna put his arm around her and opened the door to the tower. Looking back, she saw the moon fading away, and a sudden cold wind on her shoulders made her draw her black mantilla tight about her. Together they groped their way up the dark stairs to Manrico's cell.

(SCENE 2) In the prison cell, Azucena reclined on a pile of straw and stared empty-eyed at a dim light that hung from the vaulted ceiling. Manrico turned his gaze away from the barred window to look at her. "Can't you sleep, Mother?"

"No. Sleep flees from my eyes. I am praying."

Manrico wrung his hands. "If we could only escape!"

"Do not worry. The barbarians cannot torture me . . . the finger of death is already on my forehead. They'll find a corpse. No," she said fiercely, "they'll find a skeleton!"

"Stop, Mother," the troubadour said, trying to quiet her.

"They're coming," the old gypsy said, rising to her knees. "They want to drag me to the stake!"

"There's no one coming, Mother. No one."

"Look at the terrible flames! Look at her eyes. Who will save me?" she raved, falling into Manrico's arms.

"If you love me still, Mother, sleep . . . rest and be calm."

She looked at him and smiled. "We'll go back to our mountains and enjoy our former life. You'll sing and I will rest . . . rest." (Duet "Ai nostri monti.")

Manrico stayed at his mother's side until her breathing assured him that she was at last asleep. The feeble light from the door behind him fell on her face, and he turned.

"It is I, Manrico," Leonora said. "You will not die. I have come to save you."

"To save me?"

Leonora pointed to the door. "Yes. You must hurry. Leave!"

"Without you?" Manrico asked, taking her in his arms. But Leonora tore away from him.

"Leave! Leave!" she pleaded.

"Look into my eyes, Leonora. I can see it now. You sold your love to di Luna!"

"That's unjust, Manrico. Give in to me and not your anger. You're lost if you do not go now!"

Manrico pushed her away. He heard his mother, dreaming aloud. He watched as her lips formed the words, "We'll go back to our mountains."

Leonora fell at Manrico's feet. "Can't you see that my strength is failing? Do not curse me now."

"Go away, Leonora. I detest you for having given your love to di Luna!"

The young girl reached out for his hand, but he withdrew it in anger and she fell on the stones of the floor, calling out, "Death is in me now, Manrico. I had not expected the poison to work so fast . . . Inez's ring . . ."

Manrico picked her up in his arms. The Count stopped on the threshold of the door, watching the two figures. Leonora's hand slipped away from Manrico's lips and grew cold in the folds of black lace that lay about her on the floor.

"Take him to the block!" di Luna roared at the soldiers who followed him into the cell.

Azucena awoke to see Manrico being dragged away. His cries of "Mother, Mother, farewell," rang in her sleep-drugged mind.

"Manrico!" she screamed as di Luna pushed her toward the window.

"Do you see it, woman? He's dead!"

Azucena wildly pushed his hands from her shoulder and struck out at him in wild fury. "*He* was your brother!" she screamed. Di Luna stared at her in bewilderment.

"Mother, you are avenged!" she cried with a howl of triumph, and fell dead to the floor. Di Luna was alone with his horror now. The gypsy's spirit soared out of the prison cell into the smoke-filled sky. Far off the cry of an owl joined the other sounds of night as it fell on Aliaferia.

169   IL TROVATORE

TURANDOT

by Giacomo Puccini

(1858–1924)

LIBRETTO BY GIUSEPPE ADAMI AND RENATO SIMONI

BASED ON SCHILLER'S VERSION OF THE PLAY

CHARACTERS

Ping Baritone	Liù . . Soprano	The Emperor . Tenor
Pang . Tenor	King Timur Bass	Turandot . Soprano
Pong . Tenor	Calaf . . Tenor	A Mandarin Baritone

TIME: **Legendary**   PLACE: **Peking**

FIRST PERFORMANCE: **Teatro La Scala, Milan;**

April 25, 1926

Turandot was Puccini's last opera, and the composer died before he had completed the final act. Puccini's friend, Franco Alfano, finished the opera, using sketches for the music that Puccini had left.

Arturo Toscanini conducted the première of *Turandot*. When he reached the point in the opera where Puccini had left off, he put down his baton, stopped the music, and said to the audience, "Here the Maestro laid down his pen."

ACT I

PING! Pang! Pong! Pong! Ping! Pang! The tiny glass cylinders tinkled against each other in the windows of the Imperial Palace as the evening breezes rustled through the city. The Princess Turandot, glancing through the yellow, silken curtains, could see the crowd below her, swarming at the Imperial gates. The massive, silent door, with its figures of winged phoenixes and terrifying monsters, blazed like molten gold in the light of the setting sun. So did the enormous bronze gong, hanging between the arches of the wall. She stared coldly at the grisly heads fixed to poles on the wall. These had once been Royal Princes! All had failed to answer her three riddles. And so it would continue to be with every new suitor, she thought.

Turandot's subjects at the gate looked up silently. They were listening to a fierce and frightening-looking Mandarin as he read the Emperor's latest decree. "The Prince of Persia has failed to answer the Princess Turandot's three riddles. He must die when the silver moon rises."

The Mandarin looked at the empty sky and walked away.

"Death! Death to the Prince," screamed the populace, rushing at the great gold doors. But the guards beat the people back. The crowd cried out in terror as the ivory handled whips cut into faces and shoulders and arms. The people drew back, falling over each other in an attempt to escape the sting of the leather strips.

Liù, a young slave girl, crouched close to her old master, bravely trying to shield him from the hysteria of the mob.

Answering her cries for help, a young man rushed to her side. "Liù! Father!" he exclaimed, suddenly recognizing them. "What are you doing here?"

So it was that father and son, both in exile, found each other in Peking. Liù, who had been in love with the young man for a long time, smiled at him. Calaf embraced his father, the old King Timur, and said, "I am called the Unknown Prince here, so please do not speak my name."

Liù looked into Calaf's eyes and he smiled at her. "I have remained at your father's side since the day of his defeat," the girl said, "because I have never forgotten the first day you favored me with that same smile."

The citizens of Peking, returning to the square, were enthralled by the sight of the executioners sharpening their great swords again. They watched as the sparks from the wheel spattered the air. "This sword," the executioners growled, "has been bathed in blood. It will never be out of work while Turandot reigns. Come! Make the gong ring! Hear Turandot's three enigmas, you foolish lovers!"

The crowd became nervous and anxious. They called upon the moon to rise so that they might witness the newest execution. The moon, silver and cold, answered their pleading song. Coolly, it shone down on a funeral procession as it entered the city, children, priests, officials, and after them, alone, a handsome young nobleman, the Prince of Persia. He raised his head when he heard the cries of the fickle crowd, so recently crying for his death, now wailing, "Mercy for the Prince! Mercy!"

Calaf, stunned and angered by the horror of the scene, spoke up loudly, "Where is this heartless Princess Turandot? Let me see her face so I may curse her!"

He had no sooner spoken than the Princess of Ice appeared, shimmering in the moonlight. There was gold all about her. The gold threads of her gown dazzled the eyes. Gold ornaments dripped from her magnificent headdress. Even the diabolical designs of gold paint on her eyelids somehow enhanced her strange beauty.

The Unknown Prince shielded his eyes with his white fur gloves, as if he feared being blinded by the mysterious light surrounding her. Silence hung over everything. But then Turandot's slender hand, tipped with its long fingernails, made a commanding gesture. The sign of the death sentence! Then, slowly, she re-entered the palace. The hungry crowd, eager to participate in the gory proceedings, pushed through the great gate and was gone.

"Turandot! Turandot!" cried Calaf, "Turandot!" and he rushed toward the great gong. Trying to restrain him, Liù and her master, King Timur, were pushed aside.

Calaf's voice was echoed by the death cry of the Prince of Persia, "Turandot!"

Now Calaf was hypnotized by a desire to see Turandot again, and would have flung himself upon the gong bodily, had three masked figures not stopped him from summoning the Princess. One of these, addressing the others, said, "As Imperial Ministers, Most High Pong and Most High Pang, I think this brash young man should be informed of what lies ahead of him."

"You are right, Most High Ping," replied the other two, in unison. "Go back to your country, Unknown Prince, if you wish to save your head. The graveyards of Peking are full of lunatics like you!"

Calaf paid little attention to them, and once again tried to force his way toward the gong. The excited conversation between him and Ping, Pang, and Pong soon brought Turandot's serving maids to the edge of the wall, and they ordered everyone to be silent, for the Princess was sleeping.

"How dare you order us, the Royal Ministers, to be silent?" blustered the three men. "Be off!"

"Turandot. Turandot," murmured Calaf as his father moaned, "My son, you have lost your senses," and the Ministers continued repeating their often proved belief that Turandot's three riddles could never be solved, for they were as indefinite as the deepest night and more unyielding than iron or gold.

"I *will* win Princess Turandot," boasted Calaf.

The Ministers pointed to the top of the wall where the executioners were placing the head of the Prince of Persia on a spike. "Her love is there," they laughed scornfully.

Little Liù, who had remained in the background, came forward, pleading, "It was you I thought of, dear Prince, during all the days of our exile. Your name has been on my lips always. If you insist upon trying to win Turandot's love, your father will lose a son and I will lose this last shadow of a smile. I will have nothing left." She began to weep. (Aria "Signore, ascolta.")

"Do not weep, Liù," Calaf said, touching her cheek tenderly. "If long ago I smiled at you, remember that day. You can show me how grateful you are by staying with my father. You can make his loneliness easier. I can smile no more, so I ask this of you." (Aria "Non piangere, Liù.")

He turned away, only to be confronted by Ping, Pang, and Pong again, urging him to get out of Peking and to forget Turandot.

"Do not leave Liù and me alone," begged old Timur. "Come away with us."

"I will listen to none of you!" shouted Calaf. "I hear no one but Turandot calling me! I must go and meet my fate." Wildly, he rushed to the gong and seized the hammer. He struck the gong three times, each time calling the golden Princess' name: "Turandot! Turandot! Turandot!"

Liù and Timur trembled in fear, and the three Ministers ran away, muttering over the uselessness of reasoning with this new madman. "Death is always happy when the gong sounds," they laughed. Their voices echoed in the night, but their words fell dead at Calaf's feet. He stood motionless, staring at the gold Palace.

ACT II

THE next morning the Royal Ministers discussed the events of the night before. "Well, the gong has been struck again," said Pong. "Start the preparations for a new burial . . . or a possible wedding!"

"Holiday lights or mourning lanterns?" asked Pang.

"Funeral biers or shimmering palanquins?" cackled Ping.

"Singing priests or moaning ones," they remarked together, "they are all the same."

"China was so peaceful until Turandot was born," lamented Pang.

"Already there have been twelve executions this year," sighed Ping.

"These dreadful executions keep us from our lovely homes in Honan and Tsiang," complained Pang and Pong.

"And from my fragrant garden at Kui!" added Ping.

"This world is full of madmen obsessed with Turandot," groaned Pang, listing the unending names of Royal Princes who had already met their death because of the Princess of Ice.

"Perhaps," prayed Ping, "the time will come when the evil Princess will give way to love."

"Perhaps," sighed Pong, "her heart will then be warmed."

"It will herald a new era when her heart of ice is thawed," commented Pang and Pong. They sniffed the incense, daydreaming of that new world. The sound of the trumpets summoning everyone to the trial brought them back to reality. It was time for Turandot to present her unanswerable riddles again, and the Royal Ministers must be there.

(SCENE 2) A gigantic staircase seemed to reach up into the clouds. On each of its three landings, servants were setting fragile lanterns of every color. Curling clouds of incense floated up from their golden braziers, casting an aromatic mist over everything.

The square at the foot of the steps seemed to be holding all the people of Peking. They were awestruck by the brilliant gathering of Ministers and officials, and especially impressed by the eight Wise

Men who stood at the top, holding their scrolls of silk, emblazoned with jewels. The people knew that the answers to Turandot's three riddles were written on these scrolls. Just as the sun swept into full view, Ping, Pang, and Pong signaled the restless crowd to pay homage to their Emperor.

The old Emperor sat silently until he saw the Unknown Prince, followed by Liù and Timur, walking to the staircase. Then he began to speak in a high-pitched, whistling voice. "Unknown Prince, I am bound by a ghastly oath. I entreat you to leave and save your life."

"I will undergo the trial," answered Calaf, and the Emperor made a helpless little gesture. The ceremony began.

As the trumpets blared, Turandot walked slowly toward her father. Looking at Calaf with eyes of ice, she pulled her golden cape around her. The silence of a few seconds seemed like an eternity. She began to speak. "Many hundreds of years ago, my pure and noble ancestor, Princess Lo-u-ling, ruled this country in beauty and peace. She was murdered by the King of Tartary." Turandot glared at Calaf. "She lives in me! For this terrible crime, I shall have my revenge on the Princes from every corner of the world! (Aria "In questa Reggia.") Now, I shall give you the three riddles. One is Death!"

"The riddles are three," shouted Calaf, "but one is Life!"

Turandot smiled coldly before speaking again. "At night an iridescent phantom flies over all humanity, dying as the sun rises. Night brings it rebirth."

"The answer," said Calaf, "is Hope!" The Wise Men hurriedly consulted their glittering scrolls. Calaf was right!

Turandot looked witheringly at the Prince as she slowly walked down the golden staircase to announce the second riddle. "It is like a fire, burning and feverish, growing cooler only at the arrival of death. Dreams of winning make it glow more brightly and it is the color of a blazing sunset!"

Calaf hesitated for a moment, glancing at Timur and Liù. Then he looked up at Turandot and cried, "It is Blood!"

The Wise Men nodded their heads in affirmation. He was right again!

The crowd screamed their approval. Turandot was furious. "Beat those wretches! Make them be silent!" she ordered, moving down the stairs. The young Prince fell on his knees. She was close to him as she spat out the third riddle.

"She is ice that sets you afire. Her freedom makes you a slave, and to be her slave makes you a king!"

Momentarily terrified, Calaf covered his face in his hands, then suddenly he drew himself up trium-phantly. "The victory is mine," he cried. "The answer is . . . TURANDOT!"

When the Wise Men and the crowd acclaimed the Prince again, Turandot fell back as though she had been struck down by a golden arrow. Pulling her jeweled cape around her, she drew herself up the marble steps and threw herself before the Emperor. "Dear Father, I beg you not to give me to this stranger."

"Remember the oath, the sacred oath," reminded her father. "Remember the oath."

Turandot turned to Calaf. "Do you want me with my heart full of hatred and loathing?"

"No, I want you only if your heart is full of love," Calaf said. "Now that I have solved the three riddles, I propose a single one for you. If you can tell me my name before the sun rises tomorrow, I will die."

Turandot nodded, and walked away.

"You are to be commended on your courage, young Prince," said the Emperor. "I welcome you to my palace. Perhaps," he chuckled, "I will call you 'Son' tomorrow." Calaf proudly followed the Emperor into the golden palace, with the joyous praise of the people ringing in his ears.

ACT III

THAT evening in the gardens of the palace, Calaf roamed among the green-tinged bronze statues. He leaned against one of them, listening to the distant voices of Turandot's royal heralds. Their words of warning to the people of Peking rose and fell on the cool, night air. No one was allowed to sleep and everyone would die if the name of the royal stranger was not brought to the Princess of Ice before the rising of the sun.

"The Princess is awake tonight, too," Calaf thought to himself, looking at the golden dots of stars in the sky. "She, too, is worried about the mystery of my name." (Aria "Nessun dorma.")

The shadowy arms of the royal fruit trees opened wide, and from their darkness Ping, Pang, and Pong appeared. They begged him to tell them his name. If he did, the Ministers and all of Peking would be saved from horrible tortures.

"We will help you escape from Peking," urged Pong, offering the Prince great chests of gold and jewels. Calaf was unimpressed.

"We will give you the most beautiful girls in the city," Pang said.

"No, I will have none of your offers," Calaf replied. "I am the Prince who is going to conquer Turandot. Even if the world collapses around me, I want Turandot! I wish that the dawn would come. I'm tired of all your coaxing."

A sound of excited but relieved voices surged over the garden wall. "The Prince's name is known!"

Calaf looked up in surprise to see Timur and Liù, their bodies battered and dripping blood, being dragged into the once-peaceful garden.

"Let them go!" Calaf shouted, running to them. "They don't know my name!"

Ping knew differently, for he had seen them and remembered them both from the day before. He smiled to himself as Turandot entered the garden. "Golden Princess, these prisoners know the stranger's name. However, we may need special instruments to make them tell their secret."

Calaf's efforts to protect Timur and Liù were in vain. Turandot looked through him with her eyes of ice, ordering them to speak. The shocked old man could not utter a word.

"I, alone, know the secret name you're seeking," Liù cried, rushing to Turandot. "And I shall keep it for myself forever."

Turandot's bloodthirsty soldiers seized Liù.

"Tell us his name. Tell us his name!" Ping said, peering into her frightened eyes.

After a few moments Turandot surprised everyone by commanding Liù's torturers to release her. The Princess of Ice looked at her. A strange tinge of warmth colored her voice when she spoke. "Who has given you the strength to display such courage?"

"Love has," Liù whispered. Her eyes were filled with tears. "Love for my master, the Unknown Prince." Turandot could not believe what she was hearing. "Tonight, by my refusing to speak, I give this gift to you," Liù continued. (Aria "Principessa, l'amore!")

"Go on with the torture!" Turandot screamed.

Trying to escape, but finding herself hemmed in by the guards, Liù rushed at the Princess, crying out, "One day you will be conquered by love, Golden Princess." The slave girl seized a dagger from a soldier's belt and stabbed herself. Stumbling toward Calaf, she reached out to touch him. Smiling, she felt the cold sting of the blade as it touched her heart. She was dead.

Turandot shattered the terrible silence that followed by taking a whip from one of the guards and brutally striking the soldier from whom Liù had taken the dagger. Timur began to weep softly, calling, "Liù, little Liù, your sweet spirit and your kindness will have their revenge." The old King held her hand as the soldiers lifted her body and carried her away. Fearful of the possible consequences, the superstitious crowd silently followed. Wailing and lamenting filled the black night as the ghostly entourage disappeared. Even Ping, Pang, and Pong seemed touched by Liù's act of devotion.

Left alone with Turandot, Calaf ordered her to raise her silken veil. "Look *there,*" he said sadly. "Look at the pure blood that stains the white pebbles of your garden. It was shed because of you!"

Turandot stood motionless. Calaf ripped the filmy scarf with its golden threads from her face. The Princess' golden eyes glittered like burnished coins. "Do not dare to touch me," she warned. "I am a goddess! It is sacrilegious to touch me." The gold dragons on her gown shivered as she recoiled in anger.

Calaf seized her and kissed her. "I love you, Turandot." His words floated like music on the incense, joining the golden bells and mysterious, faraway voices as they sang of a new life that would awaken with the dawn.

Turandot could not speak. She was listening to the bells whispering in the wind. She felt tears forming in her eyes. "I am lost and I am conquered," she said, confessing. "The first sight of you made me shudder, for I knew that I would be vanquished by you. Leave me forever and take your mystery with you."

"I have no mystery," Calaf answered, "because I *give* you my name. With it goes my life. I am Calaf, the son of Timur!"

The Princess looked at him. A tear rolled down her cheek and she said, "The trumpets are calling. You will appear with me before my people, as my conqueror!" The Princess of Ice turned and walked into her palace.

(SCENE 2) The sun rose, and as the Princess mounted the great staircase, its rays cast brilliant shafts everywhere. The crowd behind Calaf blinked, as the sparkling reflections flitted across everyone's eyes.

"Father," Turandot announced, "today, I know the stranger's name."

The people of Peking waited. The Princess' next words fell upon their ears like the most glorious music they had ever heard.

"His name is Love!"

Calaf rushed up the marble steps to Turandot and kissed her. The crowd went wild with joy. They knew that at long last, peace and happiness would reign in Peking. Their beautiful Princess was no longer a creature of death and ice. She had been made human by the power of love. As they scattered golden flowers in the streets, the sun rose high above the walls. Its rays struck the golden gong, the golden dragons, the spears of the soldiers, Turandot's shimmering headdress, and her long golden fingernails. Its warmth engulfed everything and everyone in a feeling of happiness. It was really golden Peking once again.

INDEX TO CHARACTERS AND OPERAS

BIBLIOGRAPHY

The Concise Oxford Dictionary of Opera by HAROLD D. ROSENTHAL and J. WARRACK (Oxford University Press, Inc.)

The Golden Encyclopedia of Music by NORMAN LLOYD (Golden Press)

The Golden Horseshoe by THE EDITORS OF *Opera News* and F. MERKLING (Viking Press, Inc.)

Great Singers of Today by HAROLD ROSENTHAL (Hillary House Publishers, Ltd.)

The Metropolitan Opera by IRVING KOLODIN (Alfred A. Knopf, Inc.)

Opera News, published weekly by the Metropolitan Opera Guild

Prima Donnas and Other Wild Beasts by ALAN WAGNER (P. F. Collier, Inc.)

Essays on Music by ROMAIN ROLLAND; edited by DAVID EWEN (Dover Publications, Inc.; Smith, Peter)

The World of Opera by WALLACE BROCKWAY and HERBERT WEINSTOCK (Modern Library; Pantheon Books, Inc.)